AQA
Science
for GCSE
HIGHER

Ben Clyde
Bev Cox
Keith Hirst
Mike Hiscock
Martin Stirrup

Series Editor: **Keith Hirst**

www.heinemann.co.uk
✓ Free online support
✓ Useful weblinks
✓ 24 hour online ordering

01865 888058

Heinemann
Inspiring generations

Heinemann Educational Publishers
Halley Court, Jordan Hill, Oxford OX2 8EJ
Part of Harcourt Education

Heinemann is the registered trademark of Harcourt Education Limited

© Harcourt Education Limited 2006

First published 2006

10 09 08 07 06
10 9 8 7 6 5 4 3 2 1

10-digit ISBN: 0 435 586009
13-digit ISBN: 978 0 435 58600 3

Edited by Anne Trevillion
Designed by Lorraine Inglis
Typeset by Ken Vail Graphic Design

Original illustrations © Harcourt Education Limited, 2006

Illustrated by Beehive Illustration (Martin Sanders, Mark Turner), Nick Hawken, NB Illustration (Ben Hasler, Ruth Thomlevold), Sylvie Poggio Artists Agency (Rory Walker).

Printed by Bath Colourbooks

Cover photo: © Superstock

Index compiled by Indexing Specialists (UK) Ltd

Picture research by Zooid Pictures Ltd

Acknowledgements
The authors and publisher would like to thank the following individuals and organisations for permission to reproduce photographs:

Keith/Custom Medical Stock Photo/Science Photo Library p iv R; Peter Gould/Harcourt Education p iv L; Corbis UK Ltd. p 2 TR, TL; Trl Ltd./Science Photo Library p 2 B; Bsip/Photolibrary.com p 3 TR; Richard Young/REX FEATURES/Rex Features p 3 TL; Burke/Triolo Productions/Foodpix/Photolibrary.com p 3 B; Jack Sullivan/Alamy p 4 T; Mike Egerton/Empics p 4 B; Robert Harding Picture Library Ltd/Alamy p 6; Saturn Stills/Science Photo Library p 9; Liba Taylor/Corbis UK Ltd. p 14; EMPICS Sports Photo Agency/Empics p 20; Ian Hooton/Science Photo Library p 21; GettyImages/PhotoDisc p 22; Michael Donne/Science Photo Library p 23; Nick Sinclair/Science Photo Library p 25; Plainpicture/Photolibrary.com p 28; Zooid Pictures p 32 R; Cnri/Science Photo Library p 32 L; Ian Hooton/Science Photo Library p 34; Rex Features p 36; TORTEL SYGMA/Corbis UK Ltd. p 42 T; Keren Su/Corbis UK Ltd. p 42 B; C. N. R. I./Phototake Inc/Photolibrary.com p 43; Niall Benvie/Photolibrary.com p 44 TR; Brandon D. Cole/Corbis UK Ltd. p 44 TL; Index Stock Imagery/Photolibrary.com p 44 B; Ifa-Bilderteam Gmbh/Photolibrary.com p 45; Doug Allan/Photolibrary.com p 46 L; Jonathan Blair/Corbis UK Ltd. p 46 R; David Tipling/Photolibrary.com p 47 TR; Frank Lane Picture Agency/Corbis UK Ltd. p 47 BR; Corbis p 47 L; Getty Images/PhotoDisc p 48 TR; Bildhuset Ab/Photolibrary.com p 48 L; Phototake Inc/Photolibrary.com p 48 BR; Terry W. Eggers/Corbis UK Ltd. p 49 TR; Martin B. Withers; Frank Lane Picture Agency/Corbis UK Ltd. p 49 M; Ken Wilson; Papilio/Corbis UK Ltd. p 49 L; Botanica/Photolibrary.com p 49 BR; Nigel Cattlin/Alamy p 50; Densey Clyne/Photolibrary.com p 51; DR Jeremy Burgess/Science Photo Library p 53; David M Dennis/Photolibrary.com p 54; Holt Studios International Ltd/Alamy p 56; GettyImages/PhotoDisc p 57; David Hoffman Photo Library/Alamy p 58 L; Nick Cobbing/David Hoffman Photo Library/Alamy p 58 R; Phototake Inc/Photolibrary.com p 59; Corbis p 60; David Fox/Photolibrary p 63; John Reader/Science Photo Library p 65; Getty Images/Photodisc p 66 L; NASA Goddard Space Flight Center (NASA-GSFC) p 66 R; Dobson agency/Rex Features p 67 L; Danny Lehman/Corbis UK Ltd. p 67 R; W.T. Sullivan III & Hansen Planetarium/Science Photo Library p 68 T; Photodisc/Photolink/Harcourt Education p 68 B; Getty Images/Photodisc/ pp 69 T & B; Peter Adams/Index Stock Imagery/Photolibrary.com p 71; GettyImages/PhotoDisc p 72; Corbis p 73; SIMONPIETRI CHRISTIAN SYGMA/Corbis UK Ltd. p 74; Reuters/Corbis UK Ltd. p 74; Victor De Schwanberg/Science Photo Library p 75; Harcourt Education p 76; Tim Ayers/Alamy p 82 T; Getty Images/PhotoDisc/ p 82 BR; Carol Dixon/Alamy p 82 BL; Jason Hawkes/Corbis UK Ltd. p 83 R; Getty Images/PhotoDisc/ p 83 L; Leslie Garland Picture Library/Alamy p 84; Chris Howes/Wild Places Photography/Alamy p 86 T; Josè Manuel Sanchis Calvete/Corbis UK Ltd. p 86 B; Getty Images/PhotoDisc p 88 TR; Gillian Darley; Edifice/Corbis UK Ltd. p 88; Alistair Berg/Alamy p 88 TL; Paul Hardy/Corbis UK Ltd. p 89; Nick Gregory/Alamy p 90 T; Martin Stirrup p 90 B; Chris Henderson/Construction Photography p 91 T; Corbis p 91 B; Index Stock Imagery /Photolibrary.com pp 92, 93 B; Lee Pengelly/Alamy p 93 T; Biophoto Associates/Science Photo Library p 94 TR; Vaughan Fleming/Science Photo Library p 94 TL; Charles Bowman/Photolibrary.com p 94 B; Corbis p 95 T; Marie-Louise Avery/Alamy p 95 B; Getty Images/Brand X

Pictures/ p 96 T; Jesper Jensen/Alamy p 96 B; Paul Thompson; Eye Ubiquitous/Corbis UK Ltd. p 97; Dan Sinclair/Zooid Pictures p 99; Tony Waltham/Robert Harding Picture Library Ltd /Photolibrary.com p 100 B; Charles D. Winters/Science Photo Library p 100 T; Michael Barnett/Science Photo Library p 101; Getty Images/PhotoDisc p 102 T; Harmon Maurice/Images.Com/Photolibrary.com p 102 M; James L. Amos/Corbis UK Ltd. p 102 B; Science Photo Library/Science Photo Library p 103 T; Paul Seheult/Eye Ubiquitous/Corbis UK Ltd. p 103 B; NASA/Photolibrary.com p 104 B; Joel Stettenheim/Corbis UK Ltd. p 104 T; Alan Novelli/Alamy p 106 TL; Peter Turnley/Corbis UK Ltd. p 106 TR; Reuters/Corbis UK Ltd. p 106 B; Corbis p 110; POPPERFOTO/Alamy p 112; Paul Glendell/Alamy p 113; Pablo Corral Vega/Corbis UK Ltd. p 114; Getty Images/PhotoDisc p 115; Martin Bond/Science Photo Library p 116; Botanica/Photolibrary.com p 117; Index Stock Imagery/Photolibrary.com p 122 B; Cordelia Molloy/Science Photo Library p 122 T; Visual Arts Library (London)/Alamy p 126; NOGUES ALAIN SYGMA/Corbis UK Ltd. p 128; AJ Photo/Science Photo Library p 130; Zooid Pictures p 132; TH Foto-Werbung/Photolibrary.com p 134 T; Sheffer Visual Israel/Photolibrary.com p 134 B; Gerry Johansson/Bildhuset Ab/Photolibrary.com p 135; IPS Photo Index/Ips Co Ltd/Photolibrary.com p 136 L; Frank Wieder/Photolibrary.com p 136 R; Bryan & Cherry Alexander Photography/Alamy p 137; David R. Frazier Photolibrary Inc/Alamy p 137; Getty Images/PhotoDisc p 138; Garry Gay/Alamy p 138; Getty Images/PhotoDisc p 140; Michael Carter Photography/Photolibrary.com p 141; Peter Sapper/Photolibrary.com p 142; Tomas del Amo/Phototake Inc/Photolibrary.com p 143; Jon Arnold Images/Photolibrary.com p 145; Getty Images/PhotoDisc p 146; AP Photo/Eric Skitzi/Empics p 147 T; Corbis UK Ltd. p 147 B; Corbis p 149; Gali Danielle/Jon Arnold Images /Photolibrary.com p 150; Corbis UK Ltd. p 151; Illustrated London News p 153; Centre for Alternative Technology p 163 T; Chinch Gryniewicz; Ecoscene/Corbis UK Ltd. p 163 M; Frances M. Roberts/Alamy p 163 B; Foodpix/Photolibrary.com p 164; Martin Palm/Bildhuset Ab/Photolibrary.com p 166; NASA p 167; Pasieka/Science Photo Library p 168 T; Eyal Bartov/Photolibrary.com p 168 M; Doug Allan /Photolibrary.com p 169 B; Jeff Morgan/Alamy p 171; John T. Fowler/Alamy p 172 T; Martyn Chillmaid/Photolibrary.com p 172 B; Colin Garratt; Milepost 92 /Corbis UK Ltd. p 173; Peter Turnley/Corbis UK Ltd. p 174; Nonstock Inc./Photolibrary.com p 176 T; Index Stock Imagery/Photolibrary.com p 176 B; Milepost 92 /Corbis UK Ltd. p 177; Jon Hicks/Corbis UK Ltd. p 178; Corbis UK Ltd. p 179; Nasa/Science Photo Library p 179 T; Diaphor La Phototheque/Reso E.E.I.G/Photolibrary.com p 179 B; Justin Kase/Alamy p 180; Gehl Company/Corbis UK Ltd. p 181 T; Sheila Terry/Science Photo Library p 181 B; Robert Ho/Fotolibra p 182 R; Glen Dimplex UK Limited p 182 L; Sheila Terry/Science Photo Library p 183; Rosenfeld Images Ltd/Science Photo Library p 184 T; Robert Landau/Corbis UK Ltd. p 184; Igor Kostin/Corbis UK Ltd. p 185; Chris Laurens/Alamy p 186 T; Martin Bond/Science Photo Library p 186 B; A ROOM WITH VIEWS/Alamy p 187; Cordelia Molloy/Science Photo Library p 188 T; Courtesy of Dulas Solar/Dulas Limited p 188 M; Action Press/Rex Features p 188 B; TH Foto/Alamy p 189; Stock4b Gmbh /Photolibrary.com p 196; Roger Coulam/Alamy p 198 T; Zooid Pictures p 198 B; David M Dennis/Photolibrary.com p 199; Diego Lezama Orezzoli/Corbis UK Ltd. p 200; Morton Beebe/Corbis UK Ltd. p 202; Jason Lindsey/Alamy p 203; Martyn F. Chillmaid p 204 TL; Rex Features p 204 R; Anthony Cooper/Ecoscene/Corbis UK Ltd. p 204 BL; Paul Kay/Photolibrary.com p 205; Martin Bond/Science Photo Library p 206 T; Mauro Fermariello/Science Photo Library p 206 B; Shout/Rex Features p 207 T; Antonia Reeve/Science Photo Library p 207 B; Tracy Pompe p 209; geogphotos/Alamy p 210; Charles D. Winters/Science Photo Library p 212 T; Radon Centres Ltd. p 212 B; Novosti Photo Library/Science Photo Library p 213; Cordelia Malloy/Science Photo Library p 217 T; Phototake Inc /Photolibrary.com p 217 B; European Southern Observatory/Science Photo Library/Science Photo Library p 222 T; Todd Haiman/Images.com/Photolibrary.com p 222 B; European Southern Observatory HQ p 223 TL; NASA/Index Stock Imagery/Photolibrary.com p 223 BL; J.P.Harrington/K.J.Borkowski/University of Maryland/NASA p 223 R; Getty Images/PhotoDisc p 224 T; John k. Davies/Science Photo Library p 224 B; NASA/ESA/P. Feldman (Johns Hopkins University)/H. Weaver (Johns Hopkins University Applied Physics Lab)/NASA p 225 R; Harvard College Observatory/Science Photo Library p 228 T; Margaret Bourke-White/Time Life Pictures/Getty Images p 228 B; PhotoDisc/StockTrek p 229;

The authors and publisher would like to thank the following individuals and organisations for permission to reproduce copyright material:

British Heart Foundation Coronary heart disease statistics, p 13 M, p 15 T, p 17 M; Smokenders Program, p 24 B; Pittet D. et al *Effectiveness of a hospital-wide programme to improve compliance with hand hygiene* The Lancet 356 (9238), p 37 B; Blackburn T. and Hawkins B. *Bergmann's rule and the mammal fauna of northern North America* Ecography 27 (6) Blackwell Publishing, p 46 T; NASA Earth Observatory, p 72 T; National Research Council of Canada, from Canadian Building Digest 60, December 1964, p 203 B; Andy Darvill, p 212 B; Department of Biology, Lancaster University, p 206 B. All Crown Copyright material is reproduced with the permission of the Controller of HMSO and the Queen's Printer for Scotland.

Every effort has been made to contact copyright holders of material reproduced in this book. Any omissions will be rectified in subsequent printings if notice is given to the publishers.

Tel: 01865 888058   www.heinemann.co.uk

How to use this book

This book has been designed to cover the new AQA GCSE Science curriculum in an exciting and engaging manner and is divided into six units: B1a, B1b, C1a, C1b, P1a and P1b.

The book starts with two double page spreads focusing on 'How science works', which show you how scientists investigate scientific issues, including those in our everyday lives.

Each unit in the book is broken down into separate sections, for example unit B1a consists of sections 1 and 2. Each section is introduced by a double page introductory spread which raises questions about what is covered in the section, acts as an introduction to the section, and includes a box encouraging you to think about what you are going to learn in the section.

The introductory spread is followed by double page content spreads which cover what you need to learn, but which also cover 'How science works' and the procedures you need to be familiar with to enable you to produce your internally assessed work: the Practical Skills Assessment and the Investigative Skills Assignment.

Each section includes at least one 'ideas, evidence and issues' spread which either focuses on interpreting data and evidence or on evaluating the role of science in society and the issues that affect all our lives.

Throughout the content pages there are in-text questions to test your understanding of what you have just learnt and to further your appreciation of how science can be used and what the issues are surrounding the development of science and technology.

At the end of each unit there are two double page spreads of questions to test your knowledge and understanding of the unit. They will also prepare you for the kinds of questions you will meet in exams.

The words displayed in bold in the text also appear in the glossary at the end of the book, together with a definition.

Contents

C1b Oils, Earth and Atmosphere

P1a Energy and Electricity

P1b Radiation and the Universe

How science works

Why study science?

Even if you are not going to become a scientist, it is important that you know how scientists work. Science affects almost every aspect of our lives – sometimes in very obvious ways, like the development of new technology or new drugs that can be used to treat us, and sometimes in less obvious ways, like additives in our food that we may be unaware of.

We need to know what scientists are up to, so that they cannot 'pull the wool over our eyes' or 'blind us with science'. We need to be able to understand the way in which scientific experiments are carried out and the way in which information is collected. We need to be able to tell the difference between facts and opinions and to judge whether the information, or the people providing it, are biased in any way. Then we can make our own judgements based on an understanding of the facts.

Scientists frequently use a number of technical terms, and often these have meanings that are slightly different from the meanings in everyday speech. These terms have been printed in **bold** and are explained in the text and in the Glossary.

General principles

Many scientific investigations start with **observations**. These need to be made carefully and should be unbiased. They are often the basis for investigations or classification of things.

One of the skills that you need to learn is the ability to distinguish between scientific fact and opinion.

Local residents noticed that large numbers of fish seemed to be dying in the river. The river flows past several factories but then flows through farmland. They suspected a detergent factory was the cause of the pollution.

▲ Not all scientists work in laboratories.

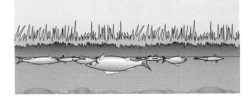

▲ Observing the fish dying in this river started a local investigation.

▲ This factory discharges waste into the river.

River pollution blamed on detergents factory

Local residents have become alarmed at the number of fish dying in the River Sabrina, and have blamed the detergents factory of Lees & Co. Local farmer Fred Guest, who has lived by the river for 30 years, said, 'I've never seen anything like it. I know it's caused by Lees because they use chemicals that contain cyanide, and I've seen them discharging waste into the river.'

A spokesperson at Lees & Co. said, 'It's nothing to do with us. The cause of the problem is all the nitrates that local farmers are putting on the land in fertilisers. They get washed down into the river. There was never any problem until recently – they used to use natural manure.'

Question

a Are the statements made by
(i) Farmer Fred Guest, and
(ii) the spokesperson for Lees & Co. giving facts or opinions? Give a reason for your answer.

As a result of protests, a team of scientists was called in to carry out an investigation. They decided to sample the water in the river at different places.

Question

b What do you think that the scientists should be measuring in the water?

Designing an investigation

When you are designing an investigation you need to plan carefully to make sure that you are measuring the correct **variables** at suitable **intervals** (length of time between measurements) and over a suitable **range**. You need to be ready to measure values between the upper and lower ones that will occur, for example daytime temperature.

The **independent variable** is the one that you deliberately alter. The **dependent variable** is the one that changes as a result of this. Other variables may also affect the outcome, and these need to be controlled or monitored. These are called **control variables**.

You also need to think about whether you need to repeat any of the measurements to improve **reliability**. A value becomes more reliable the more times it is measured, for example taking a reading five times and working out an average.

It is important your results and conclusions are **valid**. Valid results are ones that answer the original question. A valid result can be matched by other scientists following your method. They should get the same result, which validates your result.

The scientists sampled the water at four different points.

The scientists also needed to choose their measuring instruments carefully. In any investigation, it is important to make measurements using the most suitable instruments. Different instruments measure to different levels of **precision**. A tape measure measures to the nearest 1 centimetre and a ruler to the nearest 1 millimetre. You also need to use instruments effectively to get **accurate** results. An accurate reading is one that is nearest to the true result.

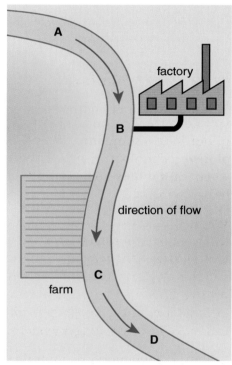

▲ Map showing section of the river and four sampling points.

Questions

c For each letter on the map, A, B, C and D, say why you think that the scientists chose this particular point.
d What variables do you think that the scientists should have controlled or monitored to make sure that it was a fair test?

Presenting the data

The scientists presented their **data** in a table.

The table only shows the average of the measurements. It is often important to see all of the original data in order to see whether there was a wide variation and whether there were any **anomalous** results.

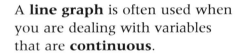

Part of river	Average concentration of nitrates	Average concentration of cyanide
A	2.0	0.02
B	2.5	10.45
C	3.5	8.32
D	2.2	4.78

Questions

a In this investigation, what was (i) the independent variable, and (ii) the dependent variable?

b What is meant by the term 'anomalous results'?

c What should be done with anomalous results before calculating the average?

d What other important information is missing from the table of results?

Displaying the data

Often it is useful to display the data in a graphical form. There are several ways of doing this, and you need to know which is the best one to use. If you choose the wrong one, it can be very unhelpful and at worst misleading.

Three of the most common methods are shown below.

A **pie chart** is often used when you want to show the percentage or fractional contribution of several parts to the whole.

A **bar chart** is often used when you are dealing with variables that are **discrete**, **ordered** or **categoric.**

A **line graph** is often used when you are dealing with variables that are **continuous**.

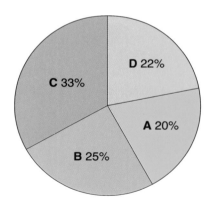

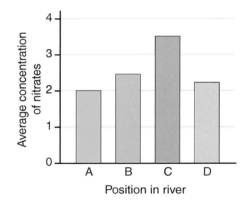

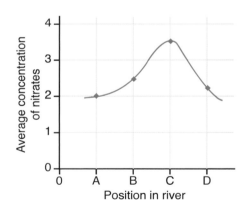

Question

e Which of the three methods of displaying data in graphical form do you think the scientists should have used in this case? Explain your answer.

A **discrete variable** is a variable whose value is restricted to whole numbers.

An **ordered variable** is a variable that can be ranked, e.g. first, second, third, etc.

A **categoric variable** is a variable that can be described by labels, for example by colour or size.

A **continuous variable** is one that can have any numerical value, for example time, speed or length.

Analysing results and drawing conclusions

The scientists issued the following statement:

> Although both pollutants are present in above average quantities, we cannot yet determine which, if either of them, is responsible for killing the fish. This would require more data.

If it were clear that cyanide or nitrates caused the fish to die there would be a **causal** link between one variable causing a change in the second.

Science and society

The managers of the detergent factory looked at the data and made the following statement: 'This has proved that it is not our factory that has caused the problem: it is the nitrates in the water. There is a significant increase in nitrate levels just after the river has passed the farmland.'

Farmer Fred Guest's response to this was: 'Rubbish! The increase in cyanide is far greater than the increase in nitrates. It is the factory's pollution that is killing the fish.'

Sometimes the conclusions that people come to may be influenced by other things and not just the scientific evidence. For example, for many years tobacco companies were accused of misleading the public about the effects of smoking. They might have wanted to do this so that they did not lose sales of their products.

Question

f Which of the following additional data do you think would be most useful to the scientists? Give a reason for your answer.
- A chemical analysis of the dead fish
- Sampling at different points in the river
- More samples at the same points in the river
- More samples over a longer period of time

Questions

g Do you think that either of these claims is reasonable? Explain you answer.
h Suggest one way in which it might be possible to prove that one of the claims is correct.

Question

i Can you think of any reasons why the company operating the detergents factory might have been biased in coming to their conclusion?

Your work as a scientist

These are the sorts of problems and questions that you will have to deal with in your science course. In your practical work you will need to think carefully about all of these points:
- observing
- designing an investigation
- making measurements
- presenting data
- looking for patterns and relationships
- coming to conclusions
- considering the relationship between science and society.

Finally, remember that sometimes it is difficult to collect enough evidence to be able to answer a question properly. There are also questions that cannot be answered by science alone, but need moral or social judgements to be made.

The human body can perform amazing feats.

▲ To do this, dozens of muscles in the rider's body must contract in exactly the right sequence. These muscles are coordinated by the nervous system.

▲ These players are very skilful. The actions of their arms and upper bodies are perfectly coordinated.

Passing on information

Injuries have damaged the spinal cords of these athletes. The spinal cord acts like a telephone cable – it carries information. Damage to the spinal cord, which connects the legs to the brain, means that information in the legs can't reach the brain – the person has no feeling in his legs. It also means that information can't get from the brain to the leg muscles, so the legs are paralysed.

Our nervous system allows us to collect information about the world around us. Some people are born with **sense organs** that do not work correctly. The other senses may become much keener to compensate. For example, many blind people are able to judge the direction and distance of a sound source much better than a sighted person.

▶ The dog is this blind man's eyes.

Where would we be without hormones?

Many of our body processes are controlled by chemicals called **hormones.** These are produced by organs called **glands.** The hormones pass from glands into the bloodstream, which transports them around the body. Each hormone affects one or more organs, known as the target organs.

How different would our lives be if scientists had not discovered how hormones worked?

▶ Without insulin treatment, people with type 1 diabetes would die soon after birth.

◀ Patrick Steptoe – the pioneer of IVF. Without his work thousands of 'test-tube' babies would not have been born.

Making decisions

Every day you make decisions that affect your health. For example, choosing what to eat and drink is a decision you make several times each day. These decisions may be influenced by what you read in newspapers and magazines and see on TV.

Good food, bad food

A recent survey monitored more than 200 TV adverts and found that 95% of the food products advertised during children's programmes contained high levels of sugar, fat or salt. Junk foods are also advertised using interactive websites and toys or games. This advertising encourages young children to eat more and more unhealthy foods.

A parents' campaign group is trying to get a ban on food advertising aimed at children. They say, 'A car can't run on bad petrol, and our kids can't run on bad food'. Recently PepsiCo, the company that makes products such as Pepsi and Walkers crisps, announced it is to restrict advertising to children.

Many people say they need more advice on how to find out if a food is healthy. Information on food labels helps people to compare foods and make healthy choices. However, a recent survey of 70 food products found that the information on some labels was inaccurate. One 'kid's pizza' contained 47% more sugar than stated on the label.

Think about what you will find out in this section

How does the nervous system help us to respond to external and internal changes?	What are the pros and cons of using hormones to control human fertility?
How to evaluate the effects of food and exercise on health.	Can we trust the information in food advertisements and on labels?
How is the female menstrual cycle controlled?	

When we exercise

During a marathon, runners top up with 'sports drinks' several times. Why do they need to do this?

The graph compares the rate of heat production and the body temperature of a marathon runner during a race with those of the same athlete at rest.

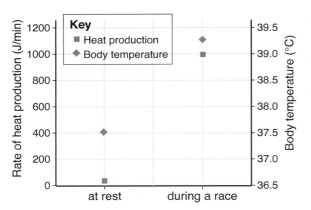

Key
- ■ Heat production
- ◆ Body temperature

▲ Refuelling during a marathon.

The marathon runner's body is cooled by sweating. For every 2.5 MJ of heat produced by the muscles, about 1 litre of sweat is evaporated. A marathon runner loses about 5 litres of sweat during a race.

Athletes drink sports drinks to replace the fluid they lose as sweat when they are running. If you have ever tasted sweat you will know that it is a bit salty. The saltiness is due to ions – salt consists of sodium ions and chloride ions.

> **Question**
>
> a   (i)   By how much does body temperature rise during a marathon?
> (ii) Calculate the percentage increase in heat production by a marathon runner during a race.

Replacing salt and sugar

When we sweat we lose a lot of water, but not quite as many **ions**. This leaves us with more ions in our blood than normal. If the balance of ions and water changes in our bodies, cells do not work so well. Sports drinks help to replace both the water and the ions.

Sports drinks also contain glucose. This helps to top up the athlete's blood sugar levels during the marathon. To work properly, body cells need a constant supply of glucose for their energy needs. This glucose is supplied by the blood.

▼ Sales of sports drinks are rocketing.

> **Question**
>
> b   Why does the athlete's blood sugar level fall during the race?

Posters for a sports drink say that it is the 'water designed for exercise'. The eye-catching television advert for this drink shows an athlete made of water running, doing cartwheels and back flips, diving into a large pool and swimming away. A voice says, 'Imagine water redesigned for exercise and for better hydration than water alone.'

The drink contains 2 g carbohydrate and 35 mg sodium per 100 ml – and provided 10 calories. The ingredients are: water, glucose syrup, citric acid, acidity regulators, flavouring, sweeteners and vitamins.

Why is our body temperature kept at 37°C?

Enzymes control most of the chemical reactions in our bodies. Enzymes work best at a particular temperature. When we are healthy our internal body temperature is 37°C. This is the temperature at which the enzymes found in human cells work best.

The graph shows how temperature affects the rate of a reaction involving an enzyme.

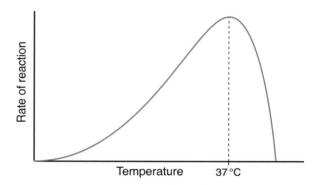

▲ This graph shows the effect of temperature on the rate of an enzyme-controlled reaction. If our bodies were cooler than 37°C, the chemical reactions in our cells would be much slower. If we heat enzymes above 45°C their structure changes and they stop working.

Balancing the water budget

To stay healthy the body needs to balance the gain and loss of both water and ions. Besides losing water when we sweat, we lose water in the air we breathe out. This is why a mirror becomes misty if we breathe on it.

The kidneys control the balance of water and ions in the body. They do this by producing fluid called urine. Urine contains the excess salts and water that the body does not need. It also contains other waste materials.

The amount of water entering the body should balance the amount of water leaving the body.

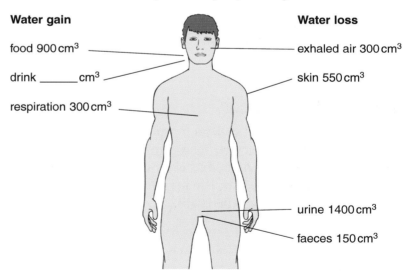

Water gain
food 900 cm³
drink _____ cm³
respiration 300 cm³

Water loss
exhaled air 300 cm³
skin 550 cm³
urine 1400 cm³
faeces 150 cm³

Detectors and sensors

Most houses have fire alarms that contain a smoke detector. Detectors are sensitive to changes in the environment – in this case smoke. Our bodies have detectors to alert us to internal and external changes. These sense organs have specialised cells called **receptors**. A change in the environment that can be detected by a receptor cell is called a stimulus.

The human body has receptors that are sensitive to:

- light
- sound
- touch and pressure
- chemicals
- changes in temperature
- changes in position.

The receptors that are sensitive to changes in position are found in the ears. These receptors help us to keep our balance.

▲ Smoke detectors in the alarm keep you safe.

Question

a Where in the human body are the other types of receptor found?

The nervous system

The brain and the spinal cord consist of millions of **neurones**, grouped into fibres called **nerves**. They carry information to the brain. Nerves from parts of the body below the head enter or leave the spinal cord, rather than the brain itself. The spinal cord carries information to or from the brain.

The central nervous system collects information from body receptors, makes sense of it and then sends messages back via the nerves to the organs that need to respond. Information passes along neurones as electrical **impulses**. For example, if temperature receptors in your fingers tell the central nervous system that they have touched something extremely hot, a message is sent to the muscles in your hand. The muscles respond by contracting, moving your hand away from the heat. A quick, automatic response like this is called a **reflex action**. We do not need to learn how to do it, or think about doing it.

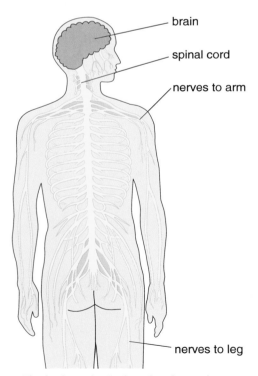

brain

spinal cord

nerves to arm

nerves to leg

▲ The brain and spinal cord make up the **central nervous system**.

Reflex actions

Three types of neurone are involved in this type of reflex action. A **sensory neurone** carries impulses from the receptor to the central nervous system. A **relay neurone** then carries impulses between the sensory neurone and a **motor neurone**. The motor neurone carries impulses to the organ that will allow the body to respond to the stimulus. This organ is called an **effector**.

Information is passed from one neurone to another at junctions called **synapses**. When an electrical impulse reaches the end of one neurone, it releases a chemical transmitter. This chemical passes across the synapse to the next neurone and causes an impulse to be sent along it.

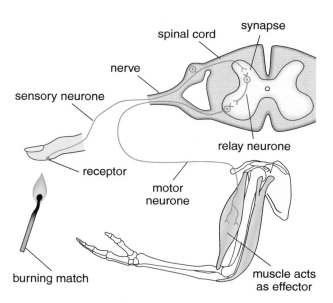

▲ How your nervous system stops you from getting burned.

Question

b (i) What type of receptor is involved in this reflex action?
(ii) In which organ is the receptor found?

The effector that moves our hand away from a hot object is a muscle. Not all our reflexes depend on muscle movement. Other reflexes help the body to work properly. When you smell food that you like, your mouth will automatically begin to water. In this case it is not a muscle that brings about the reaction, but the salivary glands in the mouth. This is the mouth-watering reflex.

Question

c What is the effector in the mouth-watering reflex?

Pupil in bright light

Pupil in dim light

The width of your pupils depends on light intensity. The iris of your eye controls the width of the pupil. The width can vary between 1.5 and 8 mm. The pupil gets narrower in bright light. This is a reflex action.

Question

d Design an experiment to measure the width of the pupil under different light intensities. Remember you must not touch the surface of the eye. Explain what you will do to make sure your experiment produces reliable results.

Key points

- The central nervous system coordinates the body's reactions to stimuli. Receptors detect stimuli and send information along neurones to the brain or spinal cord, which makes effectors react.
- Information from receptors is taken to the central nervous system by sensory neurones. Information is carried from the central nervous system to effectors by motor neurones. Relay neurones carry information within the central nervous system.

Changing methods of birth control

Women began taking substances to prevent pregnancy 4000 years ago, when Chinese women drank mercury. Methods of preventing pregnancy are called contraceptives. In the centuries that followed:

- Greek women drank diluted copper ore.
- Italian women drank tea made from willow leaves and mules' hooves.
- African women drank gunpowder mixed with camel foam.
- Canadian Indian women drank alcohol brewed with dried beaver testicles.

Until the twentieth century, contraceptive methods were often based on 'old wives' tales' rather than science.

A scientific approach to designing contraception began in 1937, when scientists discovered that a hormone could prevent the release of eggs in female rabbits. By the 1950s scientists had worked out how hormones controlled human fertility. They were able to use this knowledge to produce birth control pills.

> **Question**
>
> **a** Which one of the old wives' tales could possibly be linked to hormones? Give the reason for your answer.

The menstrual cycle

Every month, an egg develops inside a female ovary. At the same time, the lining of the womb becomes thicker, ready to receive a growing embryo. If the egg is not fertilised, the womb lining breaks down, causing bleeding. The monthly cycle of changes that take place in the ovaries and womb is called the **menstrual cycle**. The menstrual cycle is controlled by several hormones. The action of the hormones involved is summarised in the diagram.

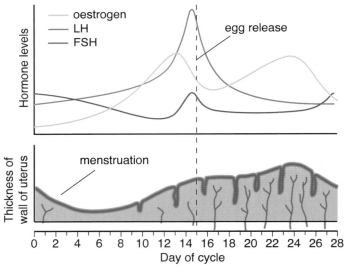

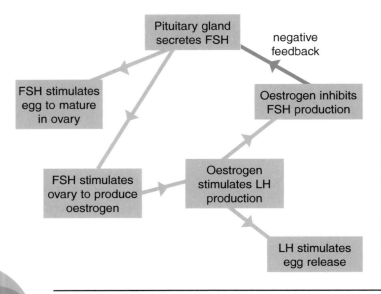

> **Questions**
>
> **b** During the menstrual cycle, which hormone is (i) the first to be secreted; (ii) the last to be secreted?
> **c** What is the relationship between oestrogen concentration in the blood and the thickness of the lining of the uterus?
> **d** What effects does oestrogen have on the pituitary gland?
> **e** Which hormone do you think causes egg release?

The pill

A woman can take the **contraceptive pill** to stop her from becoming pregnant. The pill contains a hormone that has the same effect on the pituitary gland as oestrogen. It stops the pituitary gland making FSH. This means that no eggs will mature in the ovaries.

Benefits and problems

The pill decreases the chance of getting cancer of the womb by 50% and of cancer of the ovaries by 40%. However, there is an increased risk that women will develop blood clots. The table shows some data about this risk. There are two types of contraceptive pill available – 'old type' and 'new type'.

Situation	Risk in cases per 100 000
women not on the pill	5
women taking 'old type' pill	15
women taking 'new type' pill	25
women who smoke	100
pregnant women	60

Question

f *Imagine you are a doctor. Using the data in the table, what would you say to a woman who wanted to go on the pill and was worried about side effects?*

Fertility drugs

If a woman's own level of FSH is too low, her ovaries will not release eggs and she cannot become pregnant. Infertility can be treated by injecting FSH into the blood. FSH acts as a fertility drug by stimulating the ovaries to produce mature eggs.

Unfortunately, the treatment does not always work. Or sometimes it may cause more than one egg to be released. This can result in twins, triplets, quadruplets or even more!

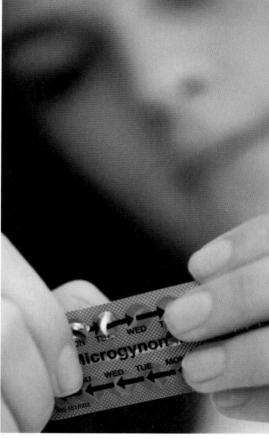

▲ A daily task for many women who don't want to get pregnant.

Key points

- Hormones are chemicals which control many processes in the body such as the menstrual cycle.
- In the menstrual cycle:
  - FSH stimulates eggs to mature in the ovary
  - LH causes egg release
  - oestrogen causes the lining of the womb to increase in thickness.
- Artificially produced hormones (contraceptives) can be given orally to women to help control fertility.
- FSH is also called the fertility drug because it can be given to women to stimulate egg release and help them get pregnant.

Interfering with nature?

> **Sixty-six-year-old Adriana Iliescu became the world's oldest mother when she gave birth to a daughter following fertility treatment.**
>
> Ms Iliescu is a retired professor who lives alone. She said she had delayed having a child so she could concentrate on her academic career. Ms Iliescu became pregnant through IVF, using donated sperm and eggs, and this was her third attempt at having at baby.

Question

a Should Ms Iliescu have been given fertility treatment? Give arguments for and against.

Test-tube babies

Many women are infertile because of blocked oviducts. This means that eggs cannot travel down to the uterus. Nor can sperm travel upwards to meet an egg. This type of infertility can be treated by using **IVF – *in vitro* fertilisation**. This literally means fertilisation in a test tube, which led to the term 'test-tube baby'.

The first stage is to obtain eggs from the woman. She is given injections of LH. Eggs are then collected just before they are released.

The eggs are mixed with sperm from the father outside the body and the fertilised eggs are allowed to divide to form embryos. At the stage when the embryos are still just a ball of cells, they are inserted into the woman's womb.

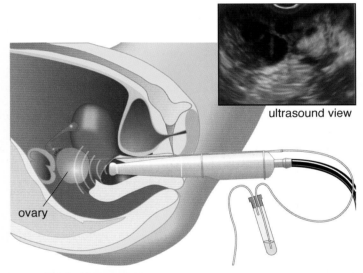

ultrasound view

ovary

▲ Using ultrasound to view the ovary, the doctor inserts the needle through the wall of the vagina into the ovary and removes the eggs for use in IVF.

Questions

b (i) Explain why LH is used in IVF treatment.
(ii) Three embryos are usually inserted into the mother, even if she only wants one child. Suggest why.
c (i) Explain why FSH can be used as a fertility drug.
(ii) A drug called clomiphine is often used instead of FSH. This drug blocks the effect of oestrogen on the pituitary gland. Explain how clomiphine works as a fertility drug.
(iii) Explain why hormones similar in their effect to oestrogen can be used as contraceptive drugs.

What are the statistics?

The average success rate for IVF treatment using fresh eggs in the UK is shown right.

A typical cost of a cycle of IVF treatment is approximately £3000. On top of this, the couple will have to pay for the costs of consultation, drugs and tests. The single biggest risk from IVF treatment is multiple births, and particularly triplet births. Many women decide to abort one of these triplets. Multiple births carry potential health risks for both the mother and the unborn child:

1 Multiple birth babies are more likely to be premature and the babies below normal birth mass.

2 The risk of death before birth or within the first week is more than four times greater for twins and almost seven times greater for triplets than for single births.

3 The incidence of cerebral palsy – a form of brain damage – is approximately five times higher for twins and approximately 18 times higher for triplets than for single births.

Women aged	Success rate (%)
under 35	27.6
35–37	22.3
38–39	18.3
40–42	10

Question

d How is the success of IVF treatment affected by age? Suggest an explanation for this.

Questions

e Currently 0.5% of IVF births are triplets – down from almost 4% in the early 1990s. 20% of IVF births are twins. Use the information above to explain this trend.
f Imagine that you are a doctor. What advice would you give to a couple who were considering IVF treatment? Use the information above in your answer.

Thirsty work

The table gives the composition of some sports drinks. Osmolarity is a measure of the effect of glucose and ions on cells. Blood plasma and body cells both have an osmolarity of about 290 units. Solutions with osmolarity higher than 290 will cause water to leave cells. Solutions with an osmolarity of less than 290 units will cause cells to swell.

Sports drink	Carbohydrate (g/l)	Sodium ions (mmol/l)	Chloride ions (mmol/l)	Osmolarity units
Coca Cola	105	3	1	650
Dioralyte	16	60	60	240
Gatorade	62	23	14	349
Isostar	73	24	12	296
Lucozade	180	0	0	658
Lucozade Sport	64	23	14	280

Question

g Which drink would be: (i) best for a marathon runner; (ii) worst for a marathon runner? Explain the reasons for your answers.

Key points

- There are benefits and problems arising from the use of hormones to control fertility which need to be considered carefully before use.
- We can evaluate the claims of manufacturers for their sports drinks by considering what the body needs and whether the drink supplies it.

Changing lifestyles

This article shows how worried medical experts are about the effect of poor diet and lack of exercise on young people. Experts are warning that many children are overweight and therefore have more chance of developing serious health problems in later life, including heart disease, diabetes and high blood pressure. The risk of health problems increases the more overweight a person becomes.

Each year a national survey is carried out to measure the health of adults and children. The survey involves an interview with a health professional and a visit by a nurse. Over 16 000 adults and 4000 children were involved in the 2004 survey. The graphs show the trend in the number of adults who are very overweight. People are described as being **obese** when they are so overweight that their health is seriously damaged.

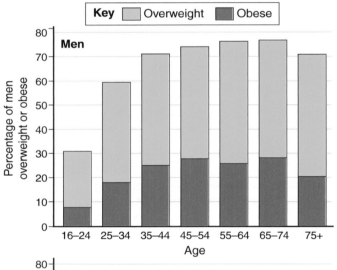

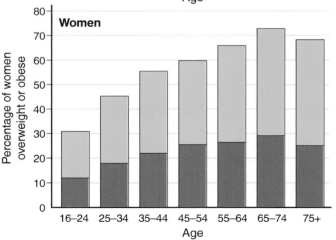

BRITISH CHILDREN TOP LEAGUE FOR UNHEALTHY LIVING

From our health correspondent.

The largest study of youth health reveals that British children live on sugary snacks and almost no fruit and vegetables.

The World Health Organisation report, based on surveys of more than 160 000 children in 35 countries, found that the dietary habits of Britain's young were among the worst.

Doctors recommend at least five portions of vegetables daily for a healthy diet. More than two-thirds of children aged 11–15 admitted that they did not eat even a single portion of vegetables a day. A third of 11-year-olds drank at least one sugary drink a day, as well as eating sweets and chocolate every day. Snacks and sugary drinks are high energy foods.

Poor diet and increasingly inactive lifestyles are blamed for a massive increase in the number of people who are overweight.

Questions

a Use the information in the newspaper article to explain why poor diet and inactive lifestyles are blamed for the increase in obesity.
b In the 25–34 age group: (i) what percentage of men are obese; (ii) what percentage of women are overweight?
c Suggest why obesity increases with age.

You are what you eat

The amount and type of food that you eat has a major effect on your health. Food provides the energy you need to stay alive and be active. It also provides the proteins, vitamins and minerals your body uses to grow and to replace damaged cells and tissues. By eating a varied diet you are more likely to get everything you need to keep your body healthy. Deficiency diseases can occur when the body doesn't get enough of a certain vitamin or mineral. These diseases are avoided by eating the right kinds of food. For example, you need vitamin C to develop resistance to disease. Eating fresh fruit provides your body with the vitamin C it needs. The diagram opposite shows the types and proportions of different foods that make up a healthy balanced diet.

The energy balance

You need to eat enough food each day to provide the energy your body needs. A diet may provide all the vitamins and minerals a person needs, but it can still be unbalanced by providing too much or too little energy. If you take in more energy than you use, your body stores the extra energy as fat and you put on weight. The key to maintaining a healthy weight is to balance your energy intake with your energy output.

High and low metabolisms

Your body converts the energy in food into a form it can use by **respiration**. The rate at which reactions are carried out in the cells of your body is called the **metabolic rate**. Your metabolic rate is affected by:
- the amount of exercise you do
- the proportion of muscle to fat in your body
- the genes you have inherited.

Lifestyle trends

Too much food and a lack of exercise can make a person put on weight. The less exercise you take and the warmer the climate, the less food you need. It is much easier now than ever before for people in the developed world to become overweight. In the developed world, social and technological changes mean that many people have very inactive lifestyles. Sitting in front of the television or computer rather than playing sports, and travelling by car rather than walking for short distances, mean that people need to eat less. But at the same time, high-calorie foods, such as snacks and processed meals, are more common than ever.

People who are active and exercise regularly are usually fitter and healthier than people who take little exercise. Your metabolic rate increases during exercise and remains high for some time afterwards, so fitter people generally have a healthy weight.

The graph shows the results of a survey of over 6000 young people from all over the UK. Each person was asked to complete a questionnaire about the amount of exercise they carried out during a typical week.

▲ These are the proportions of different foods that make up a healthy **balanced diet**. Does this match your diet?

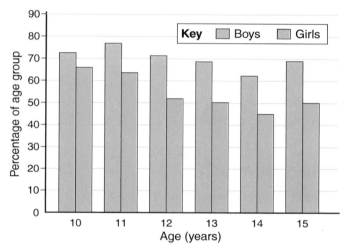

▲ Percentage of young people taking part in at least 60 minutes of physical activity a day (national survey 2002).

Questions

d Medical experts recommend that young people carry out at least 60 minutes of moderate exercise every day. What percentage of 15-year-old boys achieves this recommendation?

e Suggest a reason for the change in activity levels among girls as they get older.

Key points

- A balanced diet supplies the correct amount of energy and nutrients for a healthy body.
- The metabolic rate is the rate at which the chemical reactions in the body happen. This depends on how much you exercise, the proportion of muscle to fat in the body and inherited factors.
- People who exercise regularly are usually fitter than those who don't.

Eating too little

In some developing countries people are suffering from health problems linked to a lack of food. People become **malnourished** if their diet does not provide the energy, protein, vitamins and minerals their bodies need. The photograph shows the effects of famine in Africa, which has led to millions of people going without food and having to rely on international aid. As well as making people lose too much weight and feel extremely weak, a lack of food also causes:

- **deficiency** diseases
- reduced resistance to disease
- irregular periods in women.

▲ As well as dying from hunger, people are also more likely to become infected with disease as a result of malnutrition.

Eating too much

In the developed world eating too much food is a cause of malnutrition. Over-eating and taking too little exercise are leading to high levels of obesity and diseases linked to excess weight. The food you eat and the lifestyle you choose to lead will have a long-term effect on your health. Overweight people who do little exercise and have poor eating habits are more likely to develop long-term health problems such as arthritis, diabetes, high blood pressure and heart disease.

Arthritis and being overweight

Your joints move easily because the end of each bone is covered with a layer of **cartilage**. The cartilage may get worn away with use, allowing the bones to scrape against each other. This is called **arthritis** and it makes the joints feel stiff and painful.

Overweight people have more weight pressing down on their knee and hip joints. As a result, the cartilage in these joints is more likely to wear away, causing arthritis.

FAT EPIDEMIC WILL CUT LIFE EXPECTANCY

The childhood obesity epidemic caused by poor nutrition and lack of exercise is creating a health crisis. The average life expectancy is expected to drop for the first time in more than a century.

The chairman of the Food Standards Agency said obesity was a 'ticking time bomb' and was one of the most serious issues facing the nation.

Diabetes and controlling blood glucose

Diabetes is an illness where the body cannot control the amount of glucose in the blood. One form of diabetes, called type II diabetes, usually develops in people over the age of 40. The risk of developing diabetes increases as body mass increases. Diabetes is three times more common in people who have gained an extra 10 kg in mass. Type II diabetes was recently diagnosed in children for the first time. All reported cases so far have been in overweight children.

The graph shows the trends in the prevalence of diabetes and obesity.

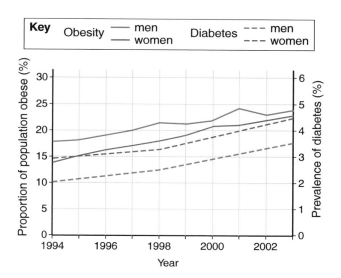

> ## Questions
>
> **a** Between 1994 and 2003 what was the percentage change of women: (i) with diabetes; (ii) who were obese?
>
> **b** Describe the evidence that shows that diabetes and obesity are linked.

Slimming programmes

People who are overweight can lose weight gradually by following a sensible slimming programme. This involves eating less energy-rich food and taking more exercise. The information on food labels can help you choose foods that are lower in fat and energy. Normal slimming programmes are unlikely to make someone to lose too much weight. But a small number of people become so worried about being fat that they start to eat too little to meet the body's basic energy needs. Their weight can drop dangerously low. There are health risks for people who lose too much weight too quickly.

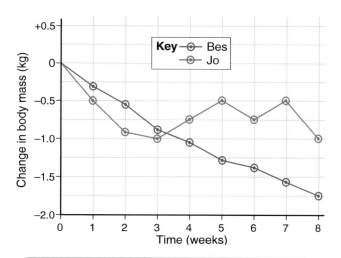

The graph shows the changes in body mass of two young women who are trying to maintain a healthy weight. Bes controls her weight by avoiding foods high in fats and sugars, and taking regular exercise. Jo is always switching from one diet to another and often goes for days eating very little.

> ## Questions
>
> **c** How much weight did (i) Bes and (ii) Jo lose over the 8 weeks?
>
> **d** Calculate the mean mass lost per week by the two women.
>
> **e** Why is Jo's crash dieting referred to as 'yo-yo' dieting?
>
> **f** Suggest reasons why Bes's methods to control her weight are healthier than Jo's.

Key points

- In the developed world, eating too much and exercising too little are leading to obesity and related diseases including arthritis and diabetes.
- In the developing world, famine leads to infection due to reduced resistance to disease, and to irregular periods in women.
- Data can be used to evaluate slimming programmes.

Heart disease

It is important to have a healthy heart. A poor diet and lack of exercise can lead to heart disease. If you are aware of the risks, you can try to avoid them.

Your heart is a powerful muscular pump working throughout your life to get blood to every tissue in your body. Heart muscles also need a blood supply to keep working. Blood flows to the heart muscles along coronary arteries. In a healthy heart, the walls in these arteries are smooth and blood flows easily. When fat deposits build up within the walls of the arteries their diameter is reduced. Blood flow is more difficult and the heart muscle receives less oxygen. This weakens the heart. If an artery becomes completely blocked, blood carrying oxygen doesn't get to some of the heart muscle. This causes a heart attack.

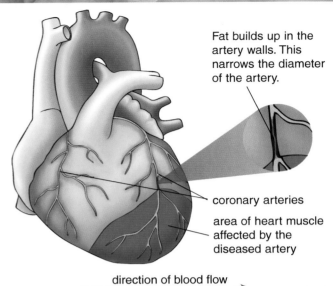

Fat builds up in the artery walls. This narrows the diameter of the artery.

coronary arteries

area of heart muscle affected by the diseased artery

direction of blood flow

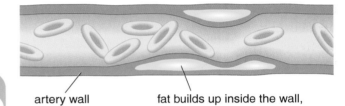

artery wall

fat builds up inside the wall, reducing the diameter of the artery

▲ Artery in a diseased heart.

Question

a *Explain how the heart muscle in the shaded area on the diagram will be affected by the narrowing of the artery.*

Cholesterol

Cholesterol is a fatty substance that is mainly made in your liver. Your liver makes cholesterol from the saturated fats in your food. Cholesterol plays a vital role in how every cell works. Too much cholesterol in the blood can increase your risk of getting heart disease.

Cholesterol is transported in the bloodstream attached to proteins. The combination of protein and cholesterol is called **lipoprotein**. There are two types of lipoprotein:

- low-density lipoprotein (**LDLs**), which carry cholesterol from your liver to your cells

- high-density lipoproteins (**HDLs**), which carry the extra cholesterol that your cells don't need back to your liver.

Your risk of heart disease is increased if you have a high level of LDL (called 'bad' cholesterol). A high level of LDL causes fat to build up on the artery walls, causing heart disease. HDL helps to prevent cholesterol building up in arteries. HDLs are 'good' cholesterol. A high level of HDLs and a low level of LDLs is good for heart health.

The amount of cholesterol your liver produces depends on a combination of diet and inherited characteristics. The amount and type of fat you eat can change the amount of cholesterol in your blood. Saturated fats, found in animal fat, increase blood cholesterol levels. Unsaturated fats (called monounsaturated and polyunsaturated fats), found in fish and vegetable oils, may help to reduce blood cholesterol levels. Processed foods often have a high proportion of fat. Consuming too many processed foods can contribute to high cholesterol levels.

Question

b *Explain why a high level of HDLs and a low level of LDLs is good for heart health.*

Different populations around the world have diets containing different amounts of cholesterol. This graph shows the dietary cholesterol levels and the incidence of heart disease in different countries.

Questions

c Describe the evidence that shows that high levels of cholesterol increase the risk of heart disease.
d Describe the evidence that shows that other factors as well as cholesterol levels may lead to heart disease.

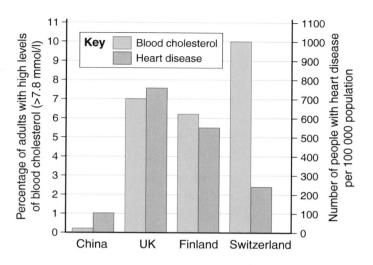

Fighting high blood pressure

People with **high blood pressure** have a greater risk of developing heart disease. Blood pressure is measured in the arteries. A certain pressure is needed to keep our blood flowing. Blood pressure in the arteries changes as your heart beats and then relaxes. The highest pressure occurs at the moment the heart contracts and forces blood into the arteries. The lowest pressure occurs as the heart relaxes between beats.

The bar chart shows how blood pressure varies with age. The data was obtained using people with similar weight and taking readings under similar conditions, for example while resting.

Questions

e In which age group does the percentage of males with high blood pressure become higher than in females?
f At which age group does the percentage with high blood pressure exceed 50%?
g This survey looks at the effect of age on blood pressure. Give two features of the people used in the survey that should be kept as similar as possible. Explain why these features should be similar.

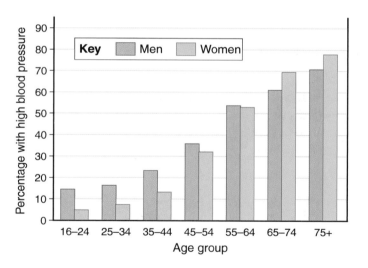

Too much salt

Too much salt in your diet can lead to increased blood pressure. Health experts recommend that adults consume less than 6 g of salt a day. Currently, the average daily intake in the UK is far too high, with the vast majority of adults consuming more than 9 g of salt each day. About 75% of the salt people consume comes from processed foods such as canned soups, take-aways and ready prepared meals.

Key points

- High cholesterol levels in the blood increase the risk of heart disease and blocked arteries.
- There are two types of cholesterol. Low-density lipoproteins (LDLs) are bad and can cause heart disease. High-density lipoproteins (HDLs) are important for a healthy heart.
- Saturated fats increase bad cholesterol. Monounsaturated and polyunsaturated fats reduce levels of bad cholesterol.

Do you believe what you read?

The latest trends in slimming diets and slimming products appear regularly on TV and in magazines, claiming that they can help people lose weight effortlessly. Some adverts use 'evidence' and scientific jargon to try to convince people that a diet really works.

The advert below shows how one company tries to get people to buy their slimming pills as a way of losing weight. The advert refers to 'proof' to try to convince you that this product works. Many companies use adverts like this. Most of the 'evidence' is based on reports from just one or two people showing dramatic weight loss in a short time. Having an understanding of how evidence is used to provide reliable results enables you to question what you read and to make informed decisions.

Medical experts say that there is only one way to lose weight – eat healthy foods and keep energy intake below energy expenditure, and aim to lose a sensible amount of weight.

Question

a Adverts showing photographs of a person 'before and after' losing weight by using a slimming product used to be common. This type of advertising has now been banned. Suggest reasons why the evidence in this kind of advert should be regarded as unreliable.

Slimming drugs warning

SLIMMING DRUGS WARNING

A warning against 'miracle' slimming drugs has been issued after a survey by trading standards officials.

Officials investigated a variety of slimming products offered for sale over the internet. They found that three-quarters of the products tested made false claims. Most companies could not provide reliable evidence to back up their weight-loss claims. These are some of the claims that companies are making about their products:

- tablets that enable the body to burn fat before food is digested
- pills that allow people to lose weight without dieting or exercising
- a product that burns fat while people are asleep.

Health experts warn that if a product or a diet programme sounds too good to be true, it probably isn't good for you and isn't true.

A scientific evaluation

Meal replacements are widely used as a way of losing weight. Meal replacements, such as Slim·Fast, are energy-reduced products that contain added vitamins and minerals.

Three hundred people were interviewed to take part in a study to compare a meal-replacement diet with a conventional low-calorie diet. Sixty-six people were chosen to take part in the study. All these had a similar level of health and fitness. Those chosen to take part were divided at random into two groups. One group received the meal replacement and the other group, the control group, received a conventional low-calorie diet. This method of comparison is called a randomised control trial.

Weight change was measured after 3 months and after 6 months. The results are shown in the table.

Time interval	Mean weight loss (kg)	
	Meal replacement group	Control group
after 3 months	6.0 ± 4.2	6.6 ± 3.4
after 6 months	9.0 ± 6.9	9.2 ± 5.1

The scientists concluded that there was no significant difference between the two groups. The meal replacement is as effective as conventional low-calorie dieting in achieving weight loss.

Questions

b Suggest why the data is presented using figures such as 6.0 ± 4.2.

c Do you agree with the scientists' conclusions from the survey? Support your answer using information from the survey.

Key points

- Data can be used to evaluate claims about slimming products and slimming programmes.
- It is necessary to distinguish between opinion based on valid and reliable evidence and opinion based on non-scientific ideas.

Drugs and disease

Drugs are chemicals that affect the processes in our bodies. Most medical drugs are beneficial in treating illness if they are used in the right way. But misusing recreational or medical drugs can harm our bodies.

Alcohol

Many drugs are extracted from natural substances. They have been used by people around the world as part of different cultures for medicines and recreation for thousands of years. Alcohol has been fermented from fruit and grain since at least ancient Greek times.

Alcohol is the oldest known drug. It is a drug that affects the nervous system. People drink it because it can cause an excited mood and lack of inhibitions. But even small amounts slow down the body's reactions. This is why it is illegal to drive a car after drinking a certain amount of alcohol. Larger amounts of alcohol can lead to a loss of self-control. People behave in ways that they wouldn't when sober. Drinking more alcohol than your body can process can make you lose consciousness and even fall into a coma.

MAY DAY CELEBRATIONS END IN TRAGEDY

Hundreds of students followed a centuries-old tradition and jumped off Magdalen Bridge at dawn on May Day into the River Cherwell at Oxford. But most of them were drunk after all-night parties and they ignored police warnings that the river was too low this year. The result was at least ten students with serious injuries to spines, legs and ankles.

▲ Would the students do this if they were sober?

Worrying reports

You are probably protected against measles, mumps and rubella. The MMR **vaccination** is given to young babies to provide life-long protection against these three diseases. Deciding whether to have a young child vaccinated can be a very worrying decision for parents when they read reports saying that the MMR vaccination may harm their child. The following reports appeared in recent newspapers.

WHY I WOULDN'T GIVE MY BABY THE MMR JAB

No one said being a parent is easy. The most difficult problem I have faced so far is the question of MMR – the measles, mumps and rubella vaccine.

Over the past six months it has become the most hotly debated subject among the mothers I know. Before my daughter was born I ignored this issue. Now she is one year old and I have to make a decision. But what shall I do?

When I see my daughter running around I feel sick at the thought that I could do her harm. All the information about the dangers of MMR has left me very confused. Only one of my friends is getting her child vaccinated with MMR. The information provided for parents doesn't convince us that the vaccine is safe. I can't take the risk of letting my child have the vaccine.

WE WISH WE'D HAD THE MMR

Cases of measles are soaring as parents reject the MMR vaccination amid fears that it may be harmful.

One parent whose daughter, Clara, almost died from the complications of measles said,

'Even now it hasn't sunk in that my daughter almost died of measles. As she lay in intensive care the doctors said it was touch and go. I thought measles was just a harmless childhood illness. I'd had it as a girl with no problems. Now it could rob me of my daughter.

All my other children had the MMR jab. But when Clara was due for her jab she had a bad cold so I delayed the injection. That delay almost cost me my daughter.'

Who to believe?

The safety of the MMR vaccination has often been reported on TV and in newspapers. Following these reports, many parents chose not to have their child vaccinated using MMR. The main issues about the safety of MMR are:

- parents have the responsibility to decide
- nearly all the evidence gathered from several countries showed that MMR was safe
- the research of one doctor raised concerns about health risks
- some reports presented information carefully, but some reports emphasised parents' worries and fears
- recent evidence shows that the research findings about health risks were not reliable.

Think about what you will find out in this section

What are the dangers of using common drugs such as alcohol and tobacco?	Is there enough evidence to suggest a link between taking cannabis and developing mental illness?
The advantages and disadvantages of being vaccinated against diseases.	How scientists ensure that new medicines are safe to use.
How scientists ensure the reliability of their evidence.	How the treatment of disease has changed.
How the credibility of science suffers as the result of any bias in research.	

Why do people use drugs?

Some drugs are so dangerous that they are illegal in Britain. An example is highly addictive heroin, which leads to severe health problems in many users, including mental health problems. But it isn't only illegal drugs that are dangerous. Science has shown that tobacco and alcohol cause thousands of deaths in Britain every year. People continue to use these drugs from habit, or to change their mood. Even though smoking and drinking are legal for adults, people need to know what these drugs do to their bodies in order to understand the risks they are taking.

The NHS has to spend far more money on treating the effects of legal drugs than illegal drugs, because far more people use them. Many people would argue that these drugs should be made illegal. Many cities are now banning smoking in public places. Some councils think that a much higher tax should be put on alcohol to discourage binge drinking.

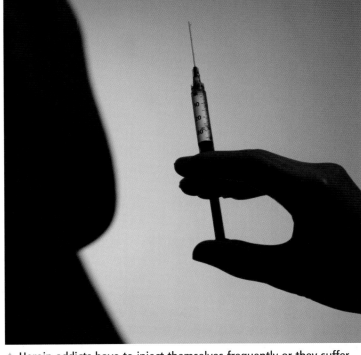

▲ Heroin addicts have to inject themselves frequently or they suffer severe withdrawal symptoms.

More than a quarter of 15- and 16-year-old European girls admitted binge drinking says survey of 100 000 students

Nearly 2000 English children aged 14 and under are admitted to hospital each year because of drunkenness, a rise of 13.5% over 6 years

38% of teenagers in Britain – 42% of boys and 35% of girls – admit trying illegal drugs

How do people get addicted to drugs?

Drugs are chemicals that change the way the body works. Most medical drugs have been developed by scientists to help cure or relieve the symptoms of illness. They are prescribed by doctors or sold in pharmacies. Recreational drugs, such as alcohol and nicotine (a drug in tobacco), are used to change the way a person feels and even thinks.

All drugs change the chemical processes in our bodies. When your body gets used to the change, it may become dependent on the drug. People become **addicted** to drugs when their whole body chemistry changes. Some people using sleeping tablets or tranquillisers as medicines can get addicted to them too.

Hard drugs like heroin and cocaine are very addictive. If an addict stops taking the drug, their body loses its natural balance and they suffer **withdrawal symptoms**. This can make them very ill. Even people drinking a lot of coffee can suffer very mild withdrawal symptoms if they stop drinking it.

Questions

a (i) Explain what is meant by addiction.
(ii) Many smokers are now trying to give up the habit. How does stopping smoking affect them?
b Explain why drugs can alter the way we behave.
c What are the possible effects of drug damage: (i) to the lungs; (ii) to the liver?

▲ Breathalysers are used to deter people from drinking and driving.

Alcohol

Drinking too much alcohol in the long term can lead to alcohol addiction, known as alcoholism. Many alcoholics die young because of damage to their liver or brain. It is important that people understand the risk of long-term health problems, so they can make an informed decision about how much and how often to drink. The table shows estimates of the cost of drinking alcohol to the UK.

Question

d (i) The population of the UK is approximately 60 000 000. How much do the effects of drinking alcohol cost per head of population?
(ii) The costs are divided into four groups. Which is the highest group of costs? Suggest a reason for this.

The tables give data about trends in drinking alcohol in Britain. There is one unit of alcohol in half a pint of beer or one glass of wine.

Questions

e How is alcohol consumption related to age?
f How did alcohol consumption change between 1988 and 2004?

Key points

- Drugs change the chemical processes in the body so people may become addicted to them and suffer withdrawal symptoms.
- People use legal and illegal drugs recreationally. The impact of legal drugs on health is much greater than that of illegal drugs as more people use them.
- Alcohol slows down the reactions of the nervous system, helping people to relax, but too much can lead to unconsciousness or coma and liver and brain damage.

Cost group	Cost (£ millions)
Health care costs	1500
Workplace and wider economy costs	
• lost output due to absenteeism	1800
• lost output due to reduced employment	2100
• lost output due to premature death	2500
Crime costs	
• alcohol-related offences	1750
• property/health and victim services	2500
• costs in anticipation of crime (alarms, etc.)	1500
• emotional impact costs for victims of crime	4600
Drink driving	
• Criminal Justice System costs	77
• cost of drink-driving casualties	430

▲ Estimated overall costs of alcohol misuse.

Weekly alcohol consumption by age	1988	1992	1996	2000	2004
More than 14 units					
16–24	15	17	22	33	33
25–44	14	14	16	19	19
45–64	9	11	13	14	14
65 and over	4	5	7	7	7
More than 35 units					
16–24	3	4	5	9	10
25–44	2	2	2	3	3
45–64	1	1	2	2	2
65 and over	0	0	1	1	1

▲ Females: trend in percentage of females drinking more than 14 and more than 35 units of alcohol per week.

Weekly alcohol consumption by age	1988	1992	1996	2000	2004
More than 21 units					
16–24	31	32	35	41	37
25–44	34	31	30	30	29
45–64	24	25	26	28	28
65 and over	13	15	18	17	15
More than 50 units					
16–24	10	9	10	14	12
25–44	9	8	6	7	8
45–64	6	6	5	7	8
65 and over	2	2	3	3	3

▲ Males: trend in percentage of males drinking more than 21 and more than 50 units of alcohol per week.

Tobacco

Tobacco smoke is a mixture of hundreds of different chemicals. Many of these chemicals harm the human body. Some of these are known as **carcinogens**. They stimulate cells to divide rapidly, which can lead to cancer of the mouth or lungs. Tobacco affects the lungs in other ways as well.

Evaluating ways to stop smoking

The NHS is very keen to reduce the number of smokers. It provides money for each local health authority to fund helplines.

There are two common methods of stopping smoking:

- *cold turkey*. This is stopping without any kind of aid. Withdrawal symptoms are very severe in the initial few days. But they fade away within the first two or three weeks. Most people give up smoking using this method.

- *nicotine replacement therapy* (NRT). NRT is clinically proven to be twice as effective as the cold turkey method. NRT eases withdrawal symptoms while the smoker gets used to not smoking and the dose is gradually reduced. NRT methods include gum, skin patches and lozenges.

Most 'stop smoking' courses involve counselling and NRT. Even so these methods have a low success rate.

for free help and advice call
0800 328 8537

> **Question**
>
> **a** (i) Suggest one reason why NRT is twice as effective as 'cold turkey'.
> (ii) Suggest one reason why most people giving up smoking do so by 'cold turkey' rather than by NRT.

The table gives the results of an evaluation of one 'stop smoking' course.

> **Questions**
>
> **b** How many people took part in the course?
> **c** What is the relationship between failure to stop smoking and age?
> **d** What is the relationship between stopping smoking completely and income? Suggest one explanation for this relationship.
> **e** One person running the course said, 'The data proves that the course was more successful in stopping women smoking than men.' Was he correct to say this?

	% who did not stop smoking (number = 46)	% who stopped smoking for a time (number = 107)	% who stopped smoking completely (number = 93)
Total	18.7	43.5	37.8
Gender			
Male	18.0	44.0	38.0
Female	15.0	45.9	39.1
Age			
18–39	19.5	45.5	35.1
40–49	15.9	46.3	37.8
50+	12.5	41.6	45.8
Income			
less than £20 000	31.3	46.8	32.9
£20 000–£30 000	6.9	55.2	37.9
£30 000–£40 000	11.4	45.7	42.9
£40 000–£50 000	20.4	34.7	44.9
more than £50 000	13.3	49.3	37.3

The man who saved lives

Sir Richard Doll began his study of lung cancer in 1948. Deaths from lung cancer had risen 50-fold in the previous few years. Many scientists blamed pollution, while others, including Sir Richard, thought the tar being used on Britain's new roads was responsible.

Sir Richard visited 2000 people with suspected lung cancer. He found that nearly all these were heavy smokers. He came to the conclusion that there was probably a link between smoking and lung cancer. But most cancer workers did not accept his findings. They said that smoking could not be the cause of lung cancer because they knew that some non-smokers develop lung cancer. People didn't realise that lung cancer could have several causes. Smoking is only one cause of lung cancer.

To convince them, Sir Richard decided to look at people's smoking habits and see whether that could predict who would contract lung cancer. He chose doctors for his sample. Within two and a half years, he found 37 doctors who had died from lung cancer. All were smokers and a high proportion smoked heavily. Sir Richard had found that smoking was the most important cause. The association between cancer and lung cancer was now very clear.

Underweight babies

One of the most poisonous substances in tobacco smoke is **carbon monoxide**. This stops red blood cells from binding with oxygen, so a smoker's blood carries less oxygen around the body.

The graph shows the relationship between birth mass and the number of cigarettes smoked by the mother.

▲ Sir Richard Doll, the scientist who discovered the link between smoking and cancer. From *Cancer World*, 31 December 2004.

Question

f (i) Explain, as fully as you can, why doctors were reluctant to accept the conclusions of the first survey.
(ii) Explain why the second survey gave powerful evidence of the link between lung cancer and smoking.

Questions

g (i) From this data, what is the relationship between birth mass and the number of cigarettes smoked by the mother?
(ii) How valid and reliable is this data?
h Give one factor, other than smoking, which could also affect the birth mass of the babies. Explain how this factor could be related to the smoking habits of the mother.

Key points

- Nicotine is the addictive substance in tobacco smoke. Tobacco also contains carcinogens and carbon monoxide. Carbon monoxide in the blood reduces the oxygen in the blood so that pregnant women who smoke may give birth to underweight babies.
- There are a number of different ways people can be helped to give up smoking.

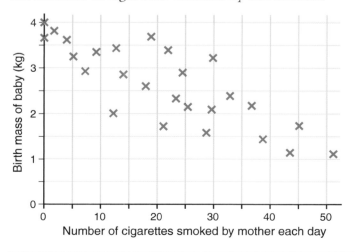

Developing new medicines

The treatment of disease is always being improved by the development of new drugs. Before a new drug can be used, it is put through several tests and has to pass each stage. The first stage is to test the drug in laboratories to find out if it is toxic. People who are being treated for a medical condition may then be asked if they would like to be part of a **clinical trial**. This is a research project to find out if a new drug works better than an existing one or if it has any side effects. A drug can only be used after it has been thoroughly tested and trialled to make sure that it is safe.

An unsafe drug

Thalidomide is a drug that was first used in Britain in 1958. It was thought to be a safe drug because it had been tested and trialled. However, the drug was not approved for use in the US because medical experts there thought there was insufficient proof of the drug's safety.

Thalidomide was given to women in the first few months of pregnancy for use as a sleeping pill and to overcome the morning sickness women feel at the start of pregnancy. Many women who took the drug gave birth to babies with limbs that weren't properly formed. The drug was banned worldwide in 1961 after it was discovered that it caused tragic birth defects. The total number of babies damaged by thalidomide throughout the world was about 10 000.

The newspaper article shows that thalidomide is being used again to treat leprosy. This is a disease which affects the skin and nerves in the hands and feet. In severe cases of leprosy the skin dies, causing hands and feet to become deformed.

In 1964 a critically ill leprosy patient was in such pain that he hadn't slept for weeks. He was given thalidomide and slept soundly for 20 hours. After receiving more thalidomide his pain disappeared. Six other patients were then treated and showed similar results. Following randomised trials on 173 leprosy patients, 92% were relieved of their symptoms. A follow-up study by the World Health Organization involving 4552 leprosy patients showed improvement in 99% of patients.

THALIDOMIDE – should we risk another tragedy?

Thalidomide, the drug banned 30 years ago, has been given approval for use again. It will be given to leprosy sufferers but with strict restrictions to minimise any risks.

Question

a Before a female leprosy patient can be given thalidomide she must first be tested for pregnancy and then use birth control while taking the drug. Explain why these restrictions are necessary.

Testing a new drug

The Heart Protection Study was carried out to test the effectiveness of a drug called simvostatin. This drug is taken by people who are at risk of having a heart attack.

To assess the long-term effects of taking statins, a study was carried out by a team of heart specialists at a leading UK hospital. The study involved 20 536 patients with heart disease, aged between 40 and 80. The health of these patients was monitored closely over a 5-year period.

A total of 10 269 of the patients took a simvostatin tablet daily, whilst 10 267 received a placebo every day. The placebo was a tablet that had no effect on cholesterol levels. Patients were randomly placed into the 'statin' group or the 'placebo' group and were not told which tablets they were receiving during the trial.

At the end of the study the researchers concluded that taking statins over 5 years would prevent major circulation problems occurring in:

- 100 of every 1000 patients who have already had a heart attack
- 80 of every 1000 patients with heart disease
- 70 of every 1000 patients with diabetes.

The main conclusion for the study is that simvostatin is safe and it reduces the risk of people having a heart attack or a stroke.

Heart drug could save lives

The Heart Protection Study provided proof that thousands of lives could be saved each year by using drugs called **statins** to lower the amount of cholesterol in the blood. This eight-year research project was carried out by the British Heart Foundation and the Medical Research Council.

▲ Statins are so valuable in preventing heart disease and are so safe that they can now be bought without a doctor's prescription.

Questions

b This type of study is called a randomised control trial.
  (i) What feature of the study was randomised?
  (ii) How was a control used in the study?
c A heart disease patient has a 1% chance of having a heart attack. How would this risk change after treatment with statins?
d It is important that studies to assess drugs are highly reliable. What features of this study show that the findings are reliable?

Key points

- New drugs are tested to see if they are toxic and then trialled in chemical trials with people to check if they are effective and whether they have any side effects.
- Thalidomide is an example of a new drug that was tested and trialled and thought to be safe. It was given to pregnant women, resulting in terrible defects and the banning of the drug.
- Statins are a new drug being developed and tested which lower the cholesterol level in the blood and so treat and prevent heart disease.

A harmless joint

Many people smoke cannabis as a recreational drug – it helps them to 'chill out'. Most of these people think that cannabis is harmless. But the mother of the young man described in this article would not agree with them. Many scientists believe that cannabis can cause psychological problems. But other scientists are uncertain whether cannabis actually causes these problems.

The active ingredient in cannabis is a chemical called THC. Enthusiasts have bred cannabis plants which contain 20 times more THC than the wild variety. People who smoke this cannabis are much more likely to develop psychological problems than those who smoke the wild variety.

Does cannabis cause mental illness?

Patients with mental illness may lose contact with reality or suffer from delusions. Here are some results of research into cannabis and mental illness.

New Zealand scientists followed 1000 people born in 1977 for the next 25 years. They interviewed people about their use of cannabis at the ages of 18, 21 and 25. The questions were about their mental health. The researchers took into account factors such as family history, current mental disorders, and illicit substance abuse.

The scientists' findings were:

- Mental illness was more common amongst cannabis users.

- People with mental illness did not have a greater wish to smoke cannabis.

- Cannabis probably increased the chances of developing mental illness by causing chemical changes to the brain.

- There was an increase in the rate of mental illness symptoms after the start of regular use of cannabis.

My son sat with me on a hospital bench outside the hospital canteen. Suddenly, he looked up and said,

'Oh, mother, you don't know how terrible it is to be Hitler.'

'You're not Hitler,' I said. 'Your voices are only your own thoughts.' He looked up.

'You really believe that?'

'I do,' I said.

He was in better form than he had been. At this moment he was not complaining that the nurses were plotting to kill him. He had told me that cannabis was the most dangerous of the many drugs he had taken, because it was the cannabis which had triggered the paranoia, and it was the drug he feared most. He died of heroin poisoning in a dealer's flat in 2000.

▲ Many people think that smoking a joint is harmless – but is it?

Scientists studied 45 000 Swedish male conscripts (men called up for army service). This was 97% of the male population aged 18–20 at that time. They followed these men for the next 15 years. They found the men who smoked cannabis heavily at the age of 18 were six times more likely to develop schizophrenia in later life than those who did not smoke cannabis.

Question

a *(i) What type of scientific research was this?*
(ii) What were the control variables in the investigation?
(iii) What did the investigation show about the link between cannabis and psychosis?

Question

b *Why do many scientists think that this study gives powerful evidence for a link between cannabis use and schizophrenia?*

A study in 2004 looked at 600 same-sex twins, one of whom was dependent on cannabis and one of whom was not. Scientists found that the twin who was dependent on cannabis was three times more likely to think about suicide than their co-twin who was not cannabis-dependent.

Question

c *Why is data from twin studies regarded as powerful evidence of a link between cannabis use and mental illness?*

Many people think that cannabis should be legalised. Here are some of their views.

Cannabis is a safer drug than alcohol. It leads to fewer deaths, both direct and indirect, suppresses the violent tendencies that alcohol releases, and has fewer long-term effects on health.

Four million people in the UK have used cannabis in the last month. Society is not disintegrating as a result. Are you saying that each and every one of these 4 million is a desperate loser, a waster, a drop-out? Most of them will be people you know, holding down good jobs, good lives, good families.

Let's look at the empirical facts – cannabis use exists, and is not doing the UK any harm. (Nor is Holland sinking into a pit of cannabis-inspired debauchery, and they decriminalised it nearly 25 years ago!)

Key points

- It is important to evaluate the claims made about the effect of cannabis on health, and to look at the link between cannabis and addiction to hard drugs before legalising it.
- The link between smoking tobacco and lung cancer only gradually became accepted.

The 'evil dealer' is another myth. Most people buy from friends. Cut out the dealers that do exist by decriminalising cannabis and encouraging people to grow their own.

Question

d *Some people say that there is enough evidence to ban the use of cannabis. Others say that its use should be legalised. Discuss this in groups then report back to the whole class.*

Pathogens

Bacteria and **viruses** are types of **microorganism**. Microorganisms that cause disease are called pathogens. Many diseases are caused by viruses and bacteria getting into the body. Once bacteria or viruses are inside the body they may reproduce very quickly. Some bacteria release poisons called **toxins** which make you feel ill.

Viruses can only reproduce inside living cells. When a virus gets into a body cell it uses it to make thousands of new viruses. The new viruses burst out of the cell ready to invade other body cells. This damages or even destroys the cell.

The table shows some common diseases caused by viruses and bacteria.

Diseases caused by bacteria	Disease caused by viruses
tonsillitis	colds
whooping cough	flu (influenza)
typhoid	measles
tuberculosis	mumps

Question

a When people cough and sneeze they release tiny droplets of moisture into the air. Pathogens can stick to the droplets and get into your body when you breathe in. Name two diseases from the table which can be spread in this way.

Spreading disease

Bacteria and viruses can pass from one person and infect another. This is how some diseases spread and affect many people. You can become infected by pathogens in the air you breathe, the food you eat and liquids you drink, and by touching someone. By making sure that your environment is clean you lessen the chance that you will become infected.

Cells to fight pathogens

Your body has different ways of protecting itself against pathogens. White blood cells are specialised cells that defend your body against pathogens.

There are several different types of white blood cell. Some **ingest** (take into the cell) any pathogens that they come across in your body. Once the pathogen is inside, the white blood cell releases enzymes to digest and destroy it.

Other white blood cells release chemicals called **antibodies** which destroy pathogens. Antibodies can only destroy a particular bacteria or virus, so white blood cells learn to make many different types. For example, when a flu virus enters the body antibodies are made which destroy the flu virus. After the virus has been destroyed, flu antibodies remain in the blood and act quickly if the same pathogen enters in the future. White blood cells also produce **antitoxins**. These are chemicals that prevent the toxins made by pathogens from poisoning your body.

Question

b Describe the ways that white blood cells prevent pathogens causing disease.

membrane folds around the bacteria

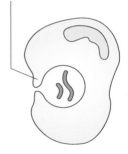

white blood cells can change their shape and wrap around bacteria

cell releases enzyme

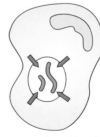

once inside the white blood cell, enzymes are released to digest the bacteria

▲ Some white blood cells ingest and destroy pathogens.

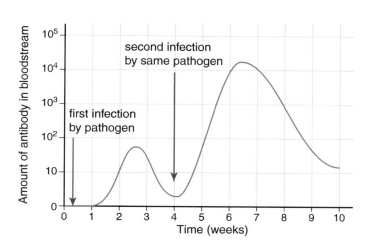

microbes come into contact with white blood cell · microbes

white blood cell releases antibodies · antibodies

antibodies react with microbes and destroy them

▲ Some white blood cells release antibodies which destroy pathogens.

Life-long protection

Once your white blood cells have destroyed a type of pathogen you are unlikely to develop the same disease again. This is because your white blood cells will recognise the pathogen the next time it invades your body and produce the right antibodies very quickly to kill the pathogen before it can affect you. This makes you **immune** to the disease.

Question

c Some pathogens, such as the virus that causes the common cold, keep changing (mutating). Other viruses, such as the virus that causes chicken pox, tend not to change. Use this information to explain why people keep catching colds but usually only get chicken pox once.

The graph shows what happens when someone is infected by a particular pathogen. The graph also shows what happens when the person is infected a second time by the same pathogen.

Questions

d How long did it take to start producing antibodies: (i) after the first infection; (ii) after the second infection?
e Explain why antibodies were produced more quickly after the second infection.
f Suggest why the person did not become ill after the second infection.

A global threat

Flu is a viral disease that affects many people every year. Most people recover within 1–2 weeks, but flu can cause serious illness and death, especially in very young children and old people. When an outbreak of flu affects thousands of people in a country it is called a flu **epidemic**. Sometimes flu spreads very rapidly around the world, affecting people in many countries. This is called **pandemic** flu. These alarming headlines show the concern about a possible pandemic outbreak of flu.

BIRD FLU BIGGER THREAT THAN TERRORISM

Is your country ready for bird flu?

New flu strain could kill millions around the world

Key points

● Microorganisms such as bacteria and viruses which cause disease are called pathogens. They produce toxins which make us feel ill.
● White blood cells protect the body against pathogens by ingesting them, producing antibodies to destroy them or producing antitoxins which counteract the toxins produced by pathogens.

Feeling ill

If all your defence systems fail and a pathogen gets inside your body, it starts to reproduce rapidly. You will eventually start to feel ill and show the **symptoms** of disease. The symptoms are the effects that the disease has on your body, such as a high temperature and headaches.

Some medicines relieve the symptoms of disease. For example, people take **painkillers** to ease aches and pains. Painkillers do not kill the pathogens that cause the disease. They just make you feel better while your body fights the pathogens.

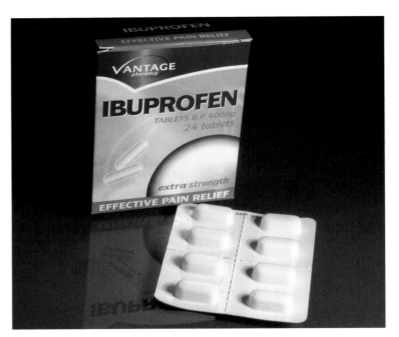

Killing bacteria

Antibiotics are medicines that help to cure diseases caused by bacteria. You take antibiotics to kill bacteria that get inside your body. Doctors use many different antibiotics to treat people. **Penicillin** was the first antibiotic to be discovered.

Antibiotics can't kill viruses. Because viruses live and reproduce inside body cells, it is difficult to develop medicines that kill viruses without damaging body cells and tissues.

The effect of antibiotics on bacteria can be measured in the laboratory. This is done by using small discs of paper containing antibiotic. The discs are placed in a dish containing bacteria growing on a gel. The photograph shows the effect of the antibiotic. The clear zone that forms around the disc is where bacteria have been killed. A more effective antibiotic will leave a wider clear zone.

The diagram shows the results of testing different antibiotics.

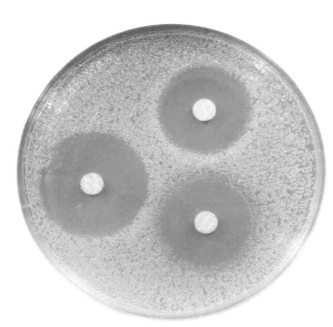

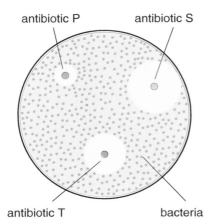

antibiotic P   antibiotic S

antibiotic T   bacteria

▲ Finding out which antibiotic works best.

a Which antibiotic kills the most bacteria? What evidence supports your answer?

b To which antibiotic do the bacteria show resistance? Use evidence from the diagram to explain your answer.

Resistance to antibiotics

Many types of bacteria have developed **resistance** to antibiotics (they are no longer killed by antibiotics). When an antibiotic is used, the non-resistant bacteria are killed but a small number of resistant bacteria remain. The resistant bacteria survive and reproduce. Continued use of the antibiotic causes the number of resistant bacteria to increase. This is an example of natural selection. To prevent more and more types of bacteria becoming resistant, it is important to avoid overusing antibiotics. This is why antibiotics are not used to treat non-serious infections like a sore throat. Doctors should only prescribe an antibiotic to treat a serious disease. By avoiding overusing antibiotics, you increase the likelihood that they will work when you really do need them.

Question

c *Explain how natural selection could lead to an increase in the number of antibiotic-resistant bacteria when patients fail to complete their treatment.*

Changing viruses

Flu viruses are always changing (mutating) to produce new strains. Pandemic flu occurs when a new flu virus is produced that is very different from previous strains. Because the new strain is so different people will have no immunity to it. This allows the new strain to cause more serious illness and to spread quickly from person to person.

A number of Asian countries have recently been affected by bird flu. The virus that causes bird flu has also infected a small number of people. Scientists are worried that the virus could eventually combine with a human flu virus. This could produce a new virus that could cause a deadly pandemic.

Question

d *Explain why the bird flu virus combined with a human flu virus would spread very rapidly and cause a pandemic.*

Key points

- Painkillers relieve the symptoms of diseases but do not kill the pathogens.
- Antibiotics such as penicillin can cure bacterial diseases by killing the bacteria. They do not work on viruses.
- Many bacteria have become resistant to antibiotics due to natural selection.
- Due to an increased understanding of antibiotics and immunity, the way we treat disease has changed.

A quick jab

It is not always necessary to suffer from a disease once before you become immune to it. When you were a young child you were probably **immunised** to protect you from very harmful diseases, such as whooping cough, measles and polio. **Immunisation** usually involves injecting or swallowing a **vaccine** containing small amounts of a dead or weak form of the pathogen. Because the pathogen is weak or inactive, the vaccine does not make you ill but your white blood cells still produce antibodies to destroy the pathogen. This makes you immune to future infection by the pathogen. Your white blood cells will quickly recognise the pathogen if it gets into your body and respond by producing antibodies. The pathogen does not get a chance to reproduce enough to make you ill.

The level of antibody in the blood after some vaccinations does not get high enough to give protection. In this case a second, or booster, injection of vaccine a few weeks later is needed. The graph shows the level of antibodies in a person's blood following a first and second injection of a vaccine.

Immunisation programmes

Immunisation provides protection against several diseases that used to be very common in children. An example is the use of MMR vaccine – a combined vaccine that makes your body develop **immunity** to measles, mumps and rubella. Each of these diseases is caused by a virus that is easily spread from someone with the disease to someone who is not immune.

Vaccines such as MMR have saved millions of children from illness and even death. Before a measles vaccine was available, an average of 250 000 children developed measles and 85 children died every year. The graph shows the effectiveness of the immunisation programme against measles.

Question

a   Explain why being given a vaccine protects you against a disease but does not cause you to develop the disease.

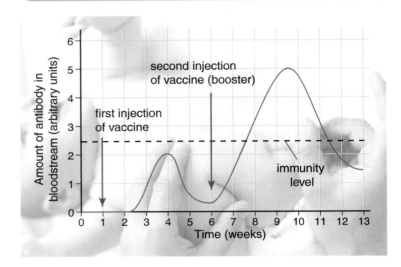

Questions

b   What was the difference in arbitrary units in the level of antibody between the first and second injection?

c   Explain why the person became immune after the second injection but not the first.

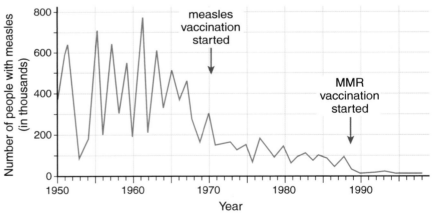

Question

d   (i) What was the maximum number of cases of measles in any one year before a vaccine against the disease was introduced?

(ii) What was the maximum number of cases of measles in any one year after the introduction of the measles vaccine?

Concern about vaccines

Children who are not vaccinated are much more likely to develop serious illnesses. Whooping cough is a disease that can cause long bouts of coughing and choking, making it hard to breathe. The disease can be very serious and can kill babies under 1 year old. More than half the babies under 1 year old with whooping cough need to be admitted to hospital and many need intensive care.

In the 1970s parents were concerned about possible side effects of the whooping cough vaccine, and fewer children were vaccinated against whooping cough. As a result major outbreaks of whooping cough occurred, with thousands of children being taken into hospital.

Recent concerns about side effects of the MMR vaccine have led to a decrease in the number of babies receiving the vaccine. In a measles outbreak in 2002, 18 out of 20 patients had not received the MMR jab.

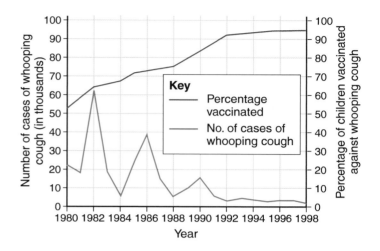

Question

e (i) Explain why two major outbreaks of whooping cough occurred in 1982 and 1986.
(ii) Describe the relationship between the percentage of children being vaccinated and the number of whooping cough cases since 1990.

Protecting against flu

Elderly people could become seriously ill if they caught flu. Doctors recommend that the elderly are vaccinated against flu each winter. The bar chart shows the number of people in the UK aged 65 and over and the percentage of those who were vaccinated against flu.

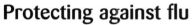

Questions

f (i) Explain why doctors advise people to be vaccinated against flu every year.
(ii) What evidence in the bar chart shows that the campaign to encourage the elderly to get vaccinated is working?
g Calculate the total number of people aged 65 and over who were vaccinated against flu in (i) 1999/2000 and (ii) 2002/03.

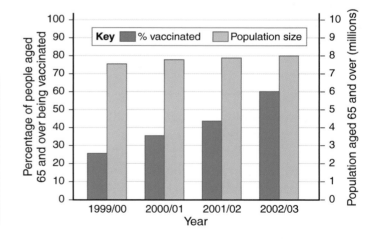

Key points

● People can be immunised using dead or inactive forms of a pathogen in a vaccination. This stimulates the white blood cells to produce antibodies and makes the body immune.

● MMR is an example of a vaccine. Some vaccinations may appear to have side effects and so it is necessary to weigh up the advantages and disadvantages of being vaccinated against a particular disease.

MRSA

MRSA stands for methicillin-resistant *Staphylococcus aureus*. *Staphylococcus aureus* (*S. aureus* for short) is a common type of bacterium often found on the skin of healthy people causing no harm at all. Sometimes *S. aureus* invades the skin and gets into the bloodstream causing serious infections. These serious infections need to be treated with antibiotics. Serious infections are more likely to occur in people who are already unwell.

HOSPITAL SUPERBUG KILLS BABY

A one-day-old baby boy was killed by the hospital superbug MRSA.
Baby Luke was only 36 hours old when he died.
Luke was born showing no signs of bad health.

Antibiotic resistance

Methicillin is a powerful antibiotic drug. Antibiotics have been used to kill bacteria very successfully for many years. Bacteria that are not killed by antibiotics continue to multiply. This is why you are always advised to complete a course of antibiotics, even if you start to feel better. If you do not complete a course of antibiotics, it is likely that some bacteria will survive. The bacteria that survive will be more resistant to the antibiotic.

> **Questions**
>
> **a** Explain why patients are advised to complete a course of antibiotics.
> **b** Explain why the overuse of antibiotics has led to the development of so-called 'superbugs'.

Antibiotics can still be used against MRSA. The infection may require a higher dose over a longer period of time to kill the more resistant bacteria. Alternatively a different antibiotic can be used to which the bacteria have less resistance.

> **Questions**
>
> **c** What was the percentage increase in antibiotic-resistant types of S. aureus *between 1995 and 2000?*
> **d** To test if a patient is infected with MRSA used to take 3 days. A test was developed in 2005 which can be completed in 2 hours. Explain why a test that can be carried out quickly is an advantage.

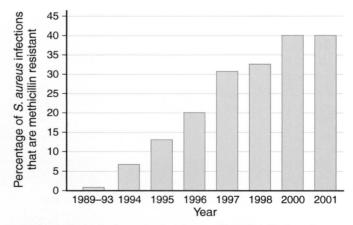

▲ This graph shows how the incidence of MRSA infections has increased over recent years.

the bug stops here

Contaminated hands spread infections.
Improvement begins with you.
Clean your hands.

Cleaner hospitals

Hand washing is an important way to prevent pathogens passing from one hospital patient to another. The first person to recognise the importance of hand washing was a Hungarian doctor called Semmelweiss. He worked in hospitals in the 1840s. At that time doctors had little knowledge of the cause of disease, so no attempt was made to prevent the spread of pathogens. Even though he did not know about bacteria and viruses, Semmelweiss argued that as doctors went from one patient to another they could be spreading life-threatening diseases. He made all the doctors working with him wash their hands after an operation and before visiting a new patient. Deaths on the hospital wards where Semmelweiss was in charge fell from 12% to just 1%.

Hand hygiene

A study of the importance of washing hands as a method of preventing the spread of MRSA was carried out in the 1990s. Trained staff observed doctors and nurses at timed periods to monitor if they washed their hands and how thoroughly this was done. They also measured the amount of hand-washing solution that was used. The results of this study are shown in the table.

Year	Amount of hand-washing solution used (litres per 1000 patient days)	MRSA infections per 100 admissions
1993	3.5	0.50
1994	4.1	0.60
1995	6.9	0.48
1996	9.5	0.32
1997	10.9	0.25
1998	15.4	0.26

Questions

e Which method of measuring hand washing used in the study is the most reliable? Explain your answer.

f Explain the relationship between the amount of hand-washing solution used and the number of new MRSA cases.

Key point

● The mutation and resistance of bacteria and viruses makes treatment of illnesses difficult and can lead to epidemics and pandemics, for example bird flu or MRSA.

1   The table is about the functions of parts of the body.

Match words from the list with each of the numbers **1–4** in the table.

A blood   **B** gland
C kidney   **D** skin

	Function
1	produces a fluid that helps to regulate body temperature
2	produces hormones
3	transports hormones
4	produces urine

2   This is part of the report of an investigation done by a student.

The purpose of this experiment was to determine the effect of light intensity on visual acuity. My hypothesis was that the best amount of light to see in would be a medium-bright light, about 245 lux, because I find it easiest to see when a light isn't too dim, but it's not so bright that I can't work very well.

To measure the responding variable each subject read the letters on a visual acuity wall chart.

K7FL6QV4
5FX3NG7P
RK3J2SN6
U6BK7PS2
HM9QG5J

I did the experiment in a windowless room.

I put a chair 6.1 metres away from the wall chart.

I set up a rheostat to dim the lights.

I used a light intensity meter to measure the amount of light reflected off the wall chart in each light level.

I got 20 classmates to volunteer.

I adjusted the light so it reflected from the chart at 780 lux.

A student sat in the chair and read the letters on the wall chart as far as possible.

The experiment was repeated at 260 lux, 90 lux, 30 lux and 10 lux.

The experiment was then repeated for all remaining students.

My results are shown in the table.

Student	Number of errors made by each student at each light intensity				
	759 lux	243 lux	81 lux	27 lux	9 lux
1	2	1	2	5	5
2	3	3	7	7	8
3	0	0	1	2	7
4	3	4	2	6	7
5	0	1	3	5	12
6	3	2	1	6	10
7	1	2	1	2	3
8	7	7	8	8	15
9	5	4	3	5	8
10	2	0	1	1	3
11	3	3	4	7	8
12	0	1	0	0	4
13	4	4	5	6	13
14	3	2	2	3	2
15	3	4	5	4	13
16	2	1	3	3	4
17	2	4	1	5	10
18	4	5	6	6	12
19	0	1	0	0	3
20	0	1	4	4	5

a   What kind of variable is
   i reflected light intensity?   *(1 mark)*
   ii number of errors?   *(1 mark)*

b   **i** Name **one** factor that the student controlled.   *(1 mark)*
   ii Name **one** factor that the student did not control.   *(1 mark)*

c   The student used 20 volunteers. Why was this better than using five volunteers? *(1 mark)*

d   Work out the average number of errors at each light intensity. Write your results in a table.   *(2 marks)*

e   Describe **one** pattern you can see in the results.   *(1 mark)*

f   Describe **one** way of showing these results graphically. Say whether you would use a bar chart or a line graph, and say what you would plot on each axis.   *(3 marks)*

g   Is there any evidence to suggest that the student's hypothesis is correct, that the best amount of light to see in would be a medium-bright light, about 245 lux? Explain your answer.   *(2 marks)*

3 The passage contains information about the 'morning after' pill.

> **What does the pill do?**
> The 'morning after pill' stops you from becoming pregnant. It's not 100% effective, but the failure rate is quite low – probably about 10%, and rather better than that if you take it as early as possible.
>
> The pill is believed to work principally by preventing your ovaries from releasing an egg, and by affecting the womb lining so that a fertilised egg can't 'embed' itself there.
>
> In Britain and many other western countries, it is not legally regarded as an abortion-causing drug, but as a contraceptive.
>
> **Who is the pill for?**
> It's now very widely used by women (especially young women) who have had unprotected sex. And in particular, it has proved of value to rape victims, couples who have had a condom break and women who have been lured into having sex while under the influence of drink or drugs.
>
> **Is it dangerous to use?**
> You might feel a little bit sick after taking it, but only about 1 woman in every 60 actually throws up. Uncommon side effects are headache, tummy ache and breast tenderness.
>
> **If the pill didn't work, and I went on and had a baby, could the tablet damage it?**
> We simply don't know the answer to this question. At present, no one has shown any increase in abnormalities among babies who have been exposed to the morning after pill. But past experience does show that other hormones taken in early pregnancy have harmed children.

a Some people regard this pill as an abortion-causing drug. Explain why. *(2 marks)*

b **i** Some people think that this pill should only be available on prescription. Suggest why they think this. *(1 mark)*

ii Others say it should be freely available 'over the counter'. What do you think? Give reasons for your answer. *(2 marks)*

c Scientists are uncertain whether the pill might cause abnormalities among unborn children. Suggest why. *(2 marks)*

4 A laboratory technician was cleaning out a cupboard. Dust from the cupboard made her sneeze.

a In this response dust is
A the coordinator   B the effector
C the receptor   D the stimulus.

b In this response the receptor is in
A the brain   B the eye
C the nose   D the spinal cord.

c In this response the coordinator is
A the brain   B the nose
C the spinal cord   D a synapse.

d Chemical transmitters are involved in
A sending impulses along sensory neurones
B sending impulses across the gap between a sensory neurone and a relay neurone
C sending impulses from one end of a relay neurone to the other
D sending impulses from a motor neurone to a relay neurone.

5 The graphs show how the concentrations of the hormones that control the menstrual cycle vary over 28 days.

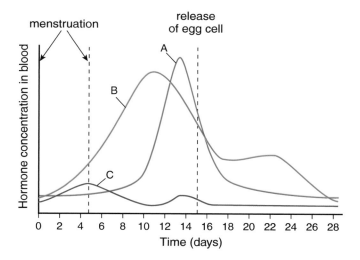

a Name
i   hormone **A**   *(1 mark)*
ii hormone **B**   *(1 mark)*
iii hormone **C**.   *(1 mark)*

b Explain why hormone **C** can be used as a fertility drug. *(2 marks)*

c Hormones similar in their effect to hormone **B** can be used as contraceptive drugs. Explain why. *(2 marks)*

6 The graph shows the average amount of cholesterol in the blood of people at different ages.

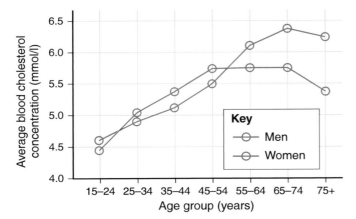

a The average blood cholesterol level for a 60-year-old woman is
  A 5.5   **B** 5.7   **C** 6.2   **D** 6.6

b Using the data from the graph, which of the following has the highest risk of developing heart disease?
  A 30-year-old men
  B 50-year-old women
  C 65-year-old men
  D 60-year-old women

c The cholesterol in the blood is
  A absorbed from the gut
  B made in arteries
  C made in the heart
  D made in the liver.

d The amount of cholesterol in the blood increases when people eat
  A salt   **B** saturated fats
  C starch   **D** unsaturated fats.

7 Adults should eat no more than 6 g of salt a day. You can work out how much salt and fat there is in foods by reading the label. The amount of salt is usually given as the amount of sodium.

Amount of salt = amount of sodium × 2.5

The label on a take-away meal has the following information:

	100g provides
Fat	8.0 g
of which saturates	6.7 g
polyunsaturates	0.3 g
Sodium	0.6 g

The mass of the whole meal is 300 g.

a Calculate the total amount of
  i saturated fats   *(1 mark)*
  ii salt in this meal.   *(1 mark)*

b Why is eating a lot of salt is bad for your health?   *(1 mark)*

c Explain why eating too much saturated fat increases the risk of heart attack.   *(1 mark)*

8 The table is about the effects some chemicals have on the body.

Match words from the list with each of the numbers **1–4** in the table.
  A alcohol   **B** carbon monoxide
  C nicotine   **D** a solvent

Chemical	Effect on body
1	affects behaviour when inhaled
2	combines irreversibly with haemoglobin
3	makes it difficult to give up smoking
4	slows down the transmission of nerve impulses

9 New drugs must be tested before use. A form of ultrasound is being used by scientists to test the effectiveness of drugs designed to break down potentially life-threatening blood clots. Scientists from King's College of Medicine in London claim the technique provides a more reliable measure of the effectiveness of drugs than was previously available, and could remove the need to test new drugs on animals.

They have used the technique to test the effectiveness of a new drug – GSNQ – which dissolves blood clots. This reduces the risk of strokes. GSNQ was compared with the standard treatment of aspirin and heparin in a group of 24 patients who underwent surgery to clean a major blood vessel in the neck. Patients treated with GSNQ were found to have significantly lower numbers of clots during a 3-hour period after the operation.

A member of the research team said: 'Before this technique assessing a drug meant either doing animal tests, or taking blood from people and studying it under the microscope. Neither was a very good measure of what would actually happen when the drug was used in people.'

New drugs will still have to be thoroughly assessed in large-scale clinical trials, but the new technique will help scientists to decide which products should go to a full trial.

a Explain why new drugs have to be tested before they go on sale. *(1 mark)*

b How did the scientists measure the effectiveness of GSNQ? *(1 mark)*

c Give **three** advantages of the above method of testing GSNQ over traditional drug-testing methods. *(3 marks)*

d Explain why GSNQ will still need to be assessed in large-scale clinical trials before it is approved. *(2 marks)*

10 The graph shows the percentage of infections caused by MRSA in a hospital intensive care unit, between 1989 and 2003.

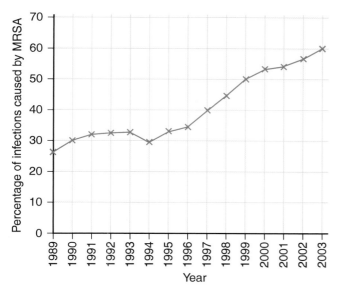

a The percentage of infections caused by MRSA became greater than 50% in
   A 1998   B 1999   C 2000   D 2001

b MRSA stands for methicillin-resistant *Staphylococcus aureus*. Methicillin is an antibiotic. Antibiotics are used
   A to kill viruses
   B to kill bacteria
   C to develop immunity
   D as painkillers.

c Some pathogens are resistant to methicillin. This means
   A a lower strength of methicillin is needed
   B methicillin kills more pathogens
   C no type of antibiotic will kill the pathogens
   D some pathogens are not killed by methicillin.

d Which of the following would be the least effective in stopping the spread of MRSA in hospitals?
   A keeping patients with MRSA infections away from other patients
   B washing hands after visiting each patient
   C wearing a fresh pair of clean gloves when treating patients
   D testing patients for MRSA

11 The bar chart shows the number of cases of influenza in a large city in the UK.

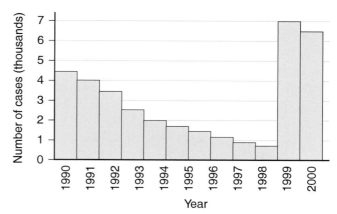

a The decrease in the number of cases of influenza between 1990 and 1999 occurred because more people
   A became immune to the flu virus
   B died from flu
   C received antibiotics
   D became infected with other diseases.

b The large number of cases in 2000 was likely to have occurred because
   A a different type of flu virus was produced by mutation
   B more people became immune to the flu virus
   C more people were vaccinated against flu
   D there were more old people.

c Most people who get flu recover in a few weeks. This is because their white blood cells destroy the virus by producing
   A antibodies   B antitoxins
   C enzymes   D vaccines.

d When people are vaccinated against flu they receive a vaccine which contains
   A antibiotics   B antibodies
   C inactive viruses   D resistant bacteria.

Variation and evolution

We often read about people trekking across freezing arctic environments. But humans still find it difficult to survive in extreme cold without special clothing. Clothes like these keep the trekker warm and dry in places where the temperature can drop to −30 °C.

Survival kits

Many animals live in arctic areas all year round – they are adapted to cold surroundings. Other animals are adapted for survival in very hot, dry environments. **Adaptations** are ways in which organisms have become specialised to survive in a particular habitat. These adaptations result from changes in genes. Competition is another factor that affects survival. Some adaptations enable an organism to compete more successfully. The genes for successful adaptations are passed on to future generations. This is how organisms evolve.

▲ Essential kit for Arctic explorers.

Changing genes

Genetic engineering, or genetic modification, techniques enable scientists to change the genetic make-up of organisms. This may involve removing faulty genes and adding healthy genes, or even developing new varieties of plants and animals with genes transferred from a completely different species. Genetically modified bacteria are used in the manufacture of drugs, such as insulin which is used to treat diabetes. Genetically modified crops (GM crops) are grown to increase food production.

Most scientists believe that foods produced from GM crops is a way of increasing food production, especially in developing countries. However, many people believe that GM food is unsafe and that it is wrong to alter the genetic make-up of organisms.

PUBLIC OPINION AGAINST GM FOODS

The public has hardened its stance against genetically modified foods. In a survey of almost 1000 people, carried out on behalf of the consumer magazine *Which?*, 61% were concerned about the use of GM material in food production.

Malcolm Coles, editor of *Which?*, said, 'Consumers clearly don't want GM foods and are hardening their stance against it.' Around a quarter support the growing of GM crops in the UK. Two years ago this figure was 32%.

◀ Growing rice plants containing an added gene to make them resistant to insect pests has led to a 10% increase in yield.

Preventing inherited disease

In future it may be possible to use genetic engineering to prevent babies being born with inherited diseases. This would involve replacing faulty genes in sperm, eggs or in newly fertilised eggs. Many people believe that using genetics this way is too dangerous and could lead to people choosing other characteristics of their children – creating 'designer babies'. Deciding whether something is right or wrong is an ethical question. Genetic engineering is controversial because it raises many ethical questions.

▶ Genes can be changed in sperm cells and fertilised eggs so that organisms develop with desired characteristics.

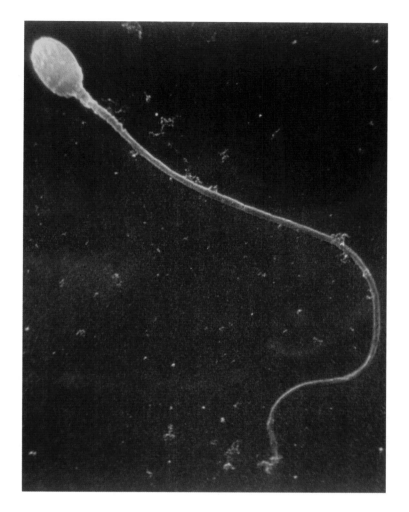

Creating the stuff of life

The tragic case of the Hashmi family has fuelled the debate over what is meant by 'designer babies'. Raj and Shahana Hashmi want to have a baby by in vitro fertilisation (IVF or test-tube baby). They want the baby to be free of inherited disease, and they want the baby's tissues to match the tissues of their 6-year-old son Zain, who suffers from a very rare blood disorder. By having a tissue match Zain would be able to have cells transplanted to save his life. The family's case is being considered by the House of Lords.

Think about what you will find out in this section

How are organisms adapted to their surroundings?	How are characteristics are inherited?
How can we produce plants and animals with the characteristics we prefer?	How can the genetic make-up of plants and animals be changed?
Why have some species of plants and animals died out, and new species developed?	What are the advantages of cloning tissues and embryos?
What are the arguments for and against genetic modification?	Why are there different theories to explain evolution?

Competing for food

Sable Island is a remote island about 300 kilometres off the coast of Canada. The island is an attractive breeding ground for Gray and Harbour seals.

The Gray seals of Sable Island have been thriving, but Harbour seal populations have plummeted in recent years. Sharks like to eat both species of seal. Harbour seal pups and adults are smaller than Gray seal pups and adults. Gray seals and Harbour seals both eat sand lances, tiny fish that live just off the shores of Sable Island. To catch these fish, Gray seals swim close to the ocean floor and dig their snouts into the sand to find hiding fish. Harbour seals follow schools of sand lances and catch fish that wander from the school.

▲ Harbour seal.

▲ Gray seal.

Question

a Suggest reasons why the Harbour seal is being out-competed by the Gray seal on Sable Island.

Competing for territory

The jaguar is a solitary animal and will avoid face-to-face confrontation by marking out territory boundaries. It does this by leaving 'scats', which are small piles of **faeces**, and by patrolling the boundaries and 'calling', which can be heard up to 1.6 km away. The size of a jaguar's territory depends on food availability. In an area where food is plentiful, such as a forest, a jaguar can survive in a circular area of about 5 km in diameter. Where food is scarce, it may need to roam over an area of 500 km².

Question

b What is the advantage to a jaguar of marking and patrolling a territory?

Competing for mates

A population of red deer live on the Scottish Isle of Rhum. Males spend much of the year living amicably in large bachelor groups. In late summer the males move to traditional mating areas. These are areas of rich grassland which support a large number of females. The males have grown new antlers and they use these to fight for the prime spots in the mating areas. The females will only mate with the males who can defend the prime sites. After the mating season the males shed their antlers and return to their bachelor herds.

▲ Fighting for mates.

Question

c *Suggest the advantage to the deer population of males fighting for mates.*

Planting crop seeds

Farmers who grow crops from seeds need to know how close together they can grow crop plants to get the best results. Automated seed planters can be programmed to sow a set number of seeds per square metre.

Cereal crops are grown to produce seeds. The graph shows the results of an investigation to find the optimum number of cereal seeds to sow.

Plants produce their own food by photosynthesis. They use energy from light to convert carbon dioxide and water into carbohydrates. They need other nutrients from the soil to make proteins.

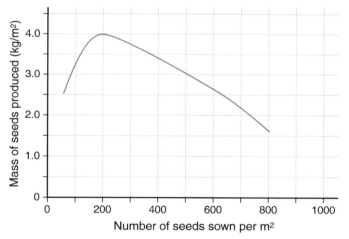
▲ The seed yield of a crop depends on the number of plants grown per square metre.

Question

d (i) *Copy and extend the graph to estimate the seed yield if 1000 seeds are planted per square metre.*
(ii) *How many plants would you advise the farmer to plant per square metre?*
(iii) *What do cereal plants compete with each other for?*

Key points

- Animals compete with each other for food, territory and mates.
- Plants compete with each other for light, water and nutrients.

The bigger the better

Animals lose heat at the surface of their bodies. The larger an animal, the smaller is its surface area compared to its volume. This means that if two animals are shaped identically, the larger one will maintain its body temperature more easily.

This explains why there are no small birds in Antarctica. Even the smallest penguin, the Rockhopper, has a mass of 2.5 kg and Emperor penguins can grow to the size of a 10-year-old child.

The nineteenth century biologist Carl Bergmann observed that birds and mammals of the same species tended to be larger and heavier when they lived in colder climates. These observations led to 'Bergmann's rule' – that there is a correlation between body mass and average annual temperature.

Since then biologists have made many observations to test Bergmann's rule. The graph shows some of their results.

> **Question**
>
> **a** Do these data support Bergmann's rule? Explain the reasons for your answer.

Body shape

Joel Allen was a scientist who gathered data relating climate to variation in animals. Allen suggested that the ratio between body weight and surface area of warm-blooded organisms increases in colder climates in order to minimise heat loss. The extremities of organisms (limbs, tails and ears) are longer in warm climates than in cold climates because they act as heat-radiating organs.

The photographs show the Kit fox and the Arctic fox. The Arctic fox lives in cold conditions; the Kit fox lives in hot conditions.

▲ Kit fox.

▶ Arctic fox.

> **Question**
>
> **b** Do these animals comply with Allen's rule? Explain the reasons for your answer.

Insulation

Penguins have a thick layer of fat called blubber under the skin. Blubber is a very good insulator. Penguins don't use their feathers for flight; they use them to keep warm. Their feathers are short and consist of fine woolly hairs. The hairs trap air next to the body. When it gets very cold the penguins puff their feathers out to trap even more air. Air is a poor **conductor** of heat. That is why double glazing works – the two panes of glass trap an insulating layer of air. Feathers from birds like geese and ducks can be used to fill duvets to keep us warm at night.

Huddling

In winter the Antarctic temperature drops to −30 °C and the wind speed can reach 200 km per hour. In these conditions, penguins huddle together in large groups. Most of the penguins are then sheltered by a layer of penguins. They all take a turn on the outside! The penguins keep warm because the surface area of the whole group is reduced – it is like having one very large penguin.

▲ Penguins huddle together for protection against the wind.

Caribou

Caribou have two layers of fur covering their bodies. They have fine, crinkly underfur and a thick coat of guard hairs on top. The guard hairs are hollow and filled with air.

▲ Well insulated against the cold.

Question

c *Explain how guard hairs help the caribou to survive in the Arctic.*

The polar bear

▲ Polar bears are well adapted to life in the Arctic.

Question

d *Look at the photograph of the polar bear. Suggest four ways in which polar bears are adapted to life in the Arctic.*

Key points

- Animals may be adapted for living in cold places by reducing heat loss by:
  - reducing their surface area, e.g. smaller ears and shorter limbs
  - insulation, e.g. long hair or a thick layer of fat
  - behaviour, e.g. huddling to reduce the total surface area of all the animals.

Death Valley

Death Valley in California, USA, is one of the hottest and driest places on the Earth. The temperature can rise to 55 °C. There is rarely more than 2 cm of rain per year. Death Valley got its name from the number of gold prospectors who died there – mainly from thirst. But many species of animals and plants live and breed there. These organisms are adapted to survive in the dry environment.

▶ One of the most inhospitable places on Earth.

▲ The Joshua tree is one of the few tree species able to live in Death Valley.

The Joshua tree

The main problem facing desert plants is dehydration. Heat from the Sun evaporates water from their surfaces. The key to surviving in the desert is to collect as much water as possible when it rains and store it. To do this the Joshua tree has two sets of root systems. One set is a shallow root system; the shallow roots only reach down to 50 cm, but they spread out over a wide area to catch rainwater. The other set of roots stores any surplus water in undergound bulbs. The bulbs are buried up to 10 m under the soil. A bulb can reach 1 m in diameter and have a mass of 20 kg.

> **Question**
>
> **a** Suggest two advantages of the bulbs growing up to 10 m underground.

The creosote bush

The creosote bush has several adaptations for surviving in the desert:

- its small leaves are covered by a waxy substance
- the leaflets fold together to decrease surface area
- during extremely dry periods, the leaves are shed.

> **Question**
>
> **b** Explain how each of these adaptations helps the plant to survive in the desert.

Spring leaves and summer leaves

Some plants produce different types of leaves in the wet season and the dry season. The table shows the dimensions of the leaves in one of these plant species.

Leaf dimension	Spring leaf (wet season)	Summer leaf (dry season)
length (mm)	30	50
maximum width (mm)	10	1
surface area (mm²)	300	150
volume (mm³)	60	60

> **Question**
>
> **c** (i)   Calculate the ratio of the surface area to the volume of the two types of leaf.
> (ii)   Explain the advantage to the plant of producing summer leaves.
> (iii)   Give one disadvantage to the plant of producing summer leaves.

The jack rabbit

We cool ourselves down by sweating. But sweating uses up precious water. The jack rabbit uses its big ears to cool down. Its ears act like the radiator of a car. A car radiator receives hot water from the car engine, gives out heat to the environment and returns cooled water to the engine. In the same way, the jack rabbit's ears receive warm blood from the body and radiate heat to the environment. The cooled blood then returns to the body. This method of cooling conserves water.

▲ Ears are not just for hearing.

Defence mechanisms

Plants have many ways of deterring animals from eating them. These include structural adaptations and chemical adaptations.

▲ Honey locust tree.

> ▶ Danger signal.

Question

d How is the honey locust adapted to protect itself from hungry herbivores?

Hemlock is a poison produced by hemlock plants. The plant produces the poison to deter animals from grazing on it. To warn animals off, the plant smells like rotting vegetables.

The bright stripes on the monarch butterfly larva advertise its presence. The larva feeds on milkweed. Milkweed contains chemicals that are poisonous to birds, but not to the larva. Any bird that eats a larva will find it very unpleasant and will not eat another larva.

▲ Hemlock.

Key points

- Plants may be adapted for surviving in hot places by having a thick, waterproof covering to reduce water loss, reducing the area of their leaves to reduce water loss, storing water and having long roots to collect water.
- Animals may be adapted for surviving in hot places by increasing their surface to increase heat loss, e.g. having large ears.
- Animals and plants may be adapted to cope with specific features of their environment, e.g. thorns, poisons and warning colours to deter predators.

How many woodlice live in a wood?

A quick look at the photograph will tell you that the woodlice are not distributed evenly across their habitat. Because of this it is not easy to find how many woodlice there are in this part of the wood. Instead of trying to count all the woodlice, we can use sampling. We count the numbers in a small area, then use this number to estimate the total number.

Question

a *What assumption do we make when calculating the total population size in this way?*

▶ Woodlice live on the floor of a wood.

Quadrats

The most common method of sampling animals and plants is using the quadrat. This is a square frame, usually of side either 50 cm or 1 m. Quadrats are often subdivided into 10 cm squares.

▶ A 1 m quadrat divided into 10 cm squares.

A group of four students each placed a 10 cm quadrat on the floor of the wood. The diagram shows their quadrats.

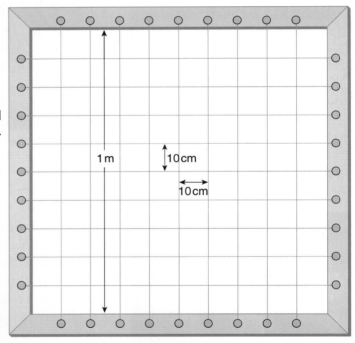

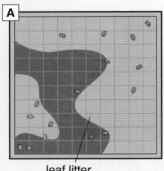

A

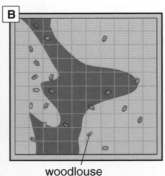

B

leaf litter   woodlouse

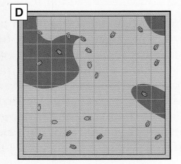

C

D

Question

b *(i) Count the number of woodlice in quadrat A. Use this number to estimate the number of woodlice in 1 m² of woodland.*
(ii) Now calculate the average number of woodlice in quadrats A, B, C and D. Use this number to estimate the number of woodlice in 1 m² of woodland. Compare your answer with that in part (i). What does this tell you about using quadrats to estimate population size?

Uneven distribution

The woodlice are not evenly distributed on the floor of the wood.

> ## Question
>
> **c** (i) Where are most of the woodlice found?
> (ii) Suggest a hypothesis to explain this distribution.
> (iii) Design an investigation to test your hypothesis. You should include: the independent variable, the dependent variable, how you intend to measure the dependent variable, the control variables.

← 50 cm →

Area covered with clover

▲ Clover growing amongst grass.

Estimating cover

Clover grows in clumps amongst grass. A student wanted to find out the area of a lawn that was covered by clover. She placed a 50 cm quadrat on the lawn as shown in the diagram.

> ## Question
>
> **d** (i) To estimate the area of lawn covered by clover, count any square more than half covered by clover as a clover square. Use your answer to calculate the percentage of the quadrat covered by clover.
> (ii) How could you modify this method to get a more accurate estimate of the area of the quadrat covered by clover?

Moorland plants

Bracken and bilberries both grow on moorland. A group of students wanted to find out if the distribution of bracken and bilberries was affected by the pH of the soil. Using a large number of quadrats, they calculated the percentage area covered by each species in soils with different pH. The table shows their results.

pH	Average percentage cover	
	Bilberry	**Bracken**
4.8	82	0
5.0	78	12
5.2	66	26
5.4	55	39
5.6	38	56
5.8	16	65
6.0	8	71

> ## Question
>
> **e** (i) Plot the results on **one** bar chart to show how pH affects the distribution of the two species.
> (ii) Use the bar chart to describe patterns in the data.
> (iii) Suggest an explanation for the distribution of the two species.

> ## Key points
>
> ● We can use quadrats to sample the distribution of organisms in a habitat.
> ● The larger the number of quadrats, the more reliable the results.
> ● The distribution of organisms in a habitat is affected by many factors including light, shade, temperature, water, ions and pH.

There's no-one like you!

There may be many people in your school but it is easy to tell them apart. Even though there are millions of people in the world, no two are exactly the same. Your height, eye colour and the shape of your earlobes are just three **characteristics** that vary from person to person – and distinguish you from everyone else.

The similarity between parents and their offspring is because some characteristics are **inherited** – they are passed from parents to their offspring. Other characteristics are affected by environmental factors. For example, your strength and speed are not just inherited characteristics – they are also affected by many environmental factors including diet and training. Similarly, the size of leaves on a plant is affected by light, temperature and nutrients.

A group of students recorded some of the different characteristics in their class. The results are shown in these graphs.

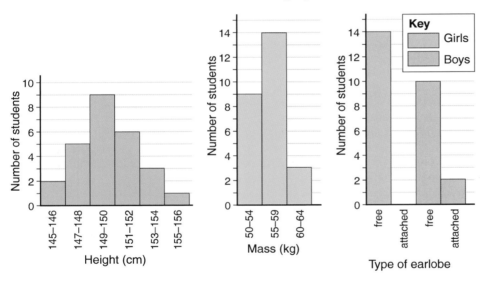

Key
- Girls
- Boys

Questions

a   *Suggest which of the characteristics surveyed are the results of (i) inherited factors only and (ii) the results of both inherited and environmental factors. Explain your answer in each case.*

b   *All of the girls had free earlobes. The students concluded that girls do not have attached earlobes. Explain why this conclusion is not justified.*

c   *Explain how the height bar chart could be modified to show variation in height more accurately.*

Passing on genes

Inherited information is passed on by **genes**. Different genes control different characteristics. The genes that control characteristics are carried on the **chromosomes** contained in the nucleus of a cell.

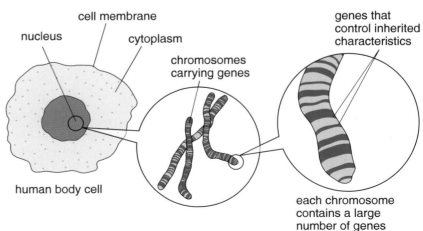

cell membrane

nucleus

cytoplasm

chromosomes carrying genes

genes that control inherited characteristics

human body cell

each chromosome contains a large number of genes

The start of life

Your life started when a **sperm** cell from your father fertilised an **egg** cell from your mother. This is why you have inherited half of your genes from your father and half from your mother.

Sperm and egg cells are sex cells called **gametes**. The joining or fusion of male and female gametes is called **sexual reproduction**. This type of reproduction produces individuals who have a mixture of genetic information from two parents.

Question

d Plant seeds are formed by sexual reproduction. Explain why a plant grown from a seed will have characteristics of both parent plants.

Reproducing from one parent

Some plants and animals can also reproduce by **asexual reproduction**. In this type of reproduction there is no fusion of cells and only a single parent is needed. The diagram shows couch grass – a common weed found in gardens. This grass spreads by producing new plants from an underground stem. The plants growing from the underground stem are produced by asexual reproduction. Individuals produced by asexual reproduction have exactly the same genes as the parent. Organisms with identical genetic information are known as **clones**.

The photograph shows bean aphids feeding on broad bean plants. In the autumn male and female aphids mate and produce eggs. The aphids that hatch from these eggs in spring are all wingless females, known as 'stem mothers'. These stem mothers produce offspring of both sexes without needing any males.

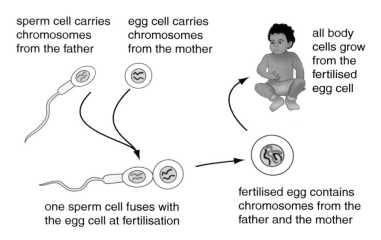

sperm cell carries chromosomes from the father

egg cell carries chromosomes from the mother

all body cells grow from the fertilised egg cell

one sperm cell fuses with the egg cell at fertilisation

fertilised egg contains chromosomes from the father and the mother

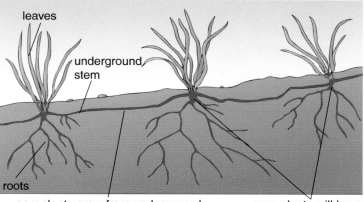

leaves

underground stem

roots

new plants grow from underground stems by asexual reproduction

new plants will have identical genes

Questions

e (i) Name the type of reproduction that produces aphid eggs in autumn.
(ii) Explain why the females that develop from these eggs are not identical.
f (i) Name the type of reproduction that produces all-female aphids in spring.
(ii) The offspring produced by the 'stem mothers' have wings. What is the advantage of producing aphids that are able to fly?

Key points

- Information is carried from parents to offspring in genes.
- Genes are carried on chromosomes found in the nucleus of cells.
- Sexual reproduction produces a mixture of genetic information from two parents.
- There is no mixing of genetic information in asexual reproduction.

Plants from cuttings

Young plants can be grown from older plants by taking cuttings. A new plant can be produced quickly and cheaply from each cutting. Plants grown from cuttings have identical genes to the parent plant and to each other.

Questions

a Why is taking cuttings an example of a cloning technique?

b A new variety of plant was developed by a gardener. Would the first plant of this new variety have been grown from a seed or from a cutting from another plant? Explain your answer as fully as you can.

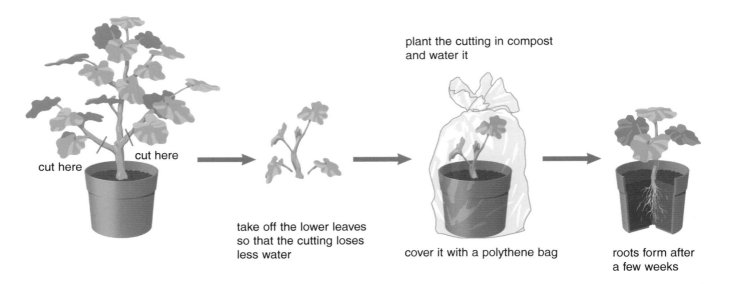

plant the cutting in compost and water it

cut here

cut here

take off the lower leaves so that the cutting loses less water

cover it with a polythene bag

roots form after a few weeks

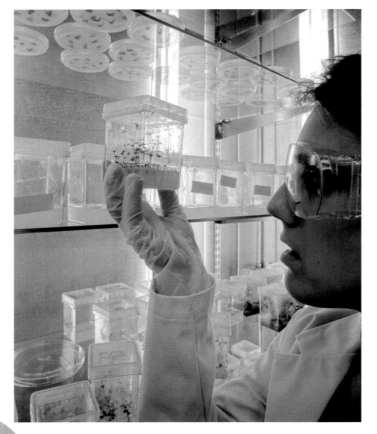

Test-tube plants

Plant **tissue culture** is a modern cloning technique. Tiny pieces of plant tissue are used to grow whole plants. The pieces of tissue are grown on a special growth medium containing nutrients and hormones. Roots, stems and leaves grow from the cells in the piece of tissue. Using tissue culture, plant breeders can grow large numbers of identical plants from just a small piece of tissue.

Tissue culture is useful when large numbers of identical plants are needed and plants cannot be produced using cuttings.

Speeding up breeding

Farmers use only animals with the most useful characteristics for breeding. For example, dairy farmers want to breed cows which produce large amounts of milk.

By using **embryo transplants** breeders can produce a large number of genetically identical calves from a single fertilised egg. This involves removing the developing embryo from a pregnant cow that has a high yield of milk. The cells of the embryo are split apart before they become specialised.

Each separated cell can then be grown in the laboratory to form multiple embryos. As the separated cells have the same genes, the embryos that are formed will also be genetically identical. Each new embryo is implanted into a host mother and continues to develop.

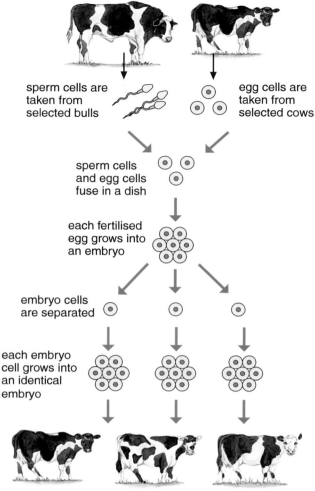

sperm cells are taken from selected bulls

egg cells are taken from selected cows

sperm cells and egg cells fuse in a dish

each fertilised egg grows into an embryo

embryo cells are separated

each embryo cell grows into an identical embryo

each embryo is implanted into a different host mother

Question

c *Breeding normally involves selecting the most suitable bull and cows and allowing them to mate. Each cow then gives birth to a single calf after a few months of pregnancy. Explain the advantages of using embryo transplants instead of normal breeding.*

Pet cloning

The diagram shows the techniques that were used to clone Snuppy.

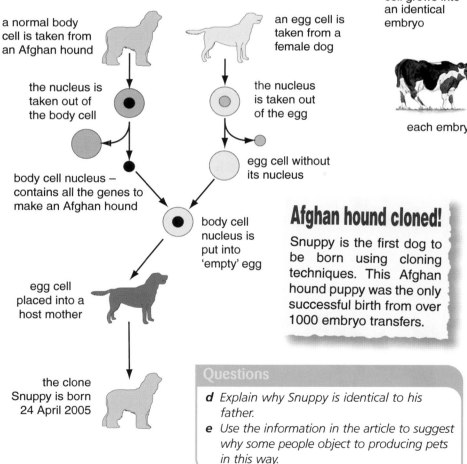

a normal body cell is taken from an Afghan hound

an egg cell is taken from a female dog

the nucleus is taken out of the body cell

the nucleus is taken out of the egg

body cell nucleus – contains all the genes to make an Afghan hound

egg cell without its nucleus

body cell nucleus is put into 'empty' egg

egg cell placed into a host mother

the clone Snuppy is born 24 April 2005

Afghan hound cloned!

Snuppy is the first dog to be born using cloning techniques. This Afghan hound puppy was the only successful birth from over 1000 embryo transfers.

Questions

d *Explain why Snuppy is identical to his father.*
e *Use the information in the article to suggest why some people object to producing pets in this way.*

Key points

- New plants can be produced quickly and cheaply from cuttings.
- Identical organisms can be produced using modern cloning techniques, including tissue culture, embryo transplants and adult cell cloning.
- Producing plants and animals using cloning techniques raises ethical issues.
- People need to be able to make informed judgements about the ethical issues concerning cloning.

Gene transfer

Scientists have recently developed ways to transfer genes from one organism to another. This process is called genetic engineering or **genetic modification** (GM for short). Genetic modification allows plants, animals and microorganisms to be produced with specific characteristics.

People have been breeding plants and animals for many hundreds of years to develop varieties with specific characteristics. Crop plants such as wheat and potatoes, and farm animals such as cattle and sheep, have been developed over many years of breeding. Traditional breeding methods involve mixing many genes over many years. Using genetic modification, the genetic make-up of an organism can be changed very quickly.

Genetic modification allows just one individual gene to be inserted into a plant or animal so that it develops a specific characteristic. When genes are inserted at an early stage in development plants and animals will grow with the chosen characteristic. Compared to traditional breeding, with GM technology new varieties can be produced much more quickly.

Using GM technology

Genetic modification is now used to manufacture foods and medicines and to produce new varieties of crop plants. One of the first applications of GM in food production was the manufacture of an enzyme called chymosin. This enzyme is used to make cheese from milk. Chymosin used to be obtained from the stomach lining of newborn calves. Calves produce chymosin to digest milk. The enzyme is now produced from genetically modified bacteria or yeast. Today about 90% of hard cheese is made using chymosin produced with GM technology.

> **Question**
>
> **a** Traditional breeding involves sexual reproduction in selected plants and animals. Explain why traditional breeding involves mixing many genes.

▲ Plant breeders have produced varieties of potato that are fast-growing and disease-resistant. This has involved selecting which plants to use for breeding over many years.

> **Questions**
>
> **b** Suggest why adult cows do not produce chymosin.
> **c** Explain why genetically engineered chymosin is popular among vegetarians.

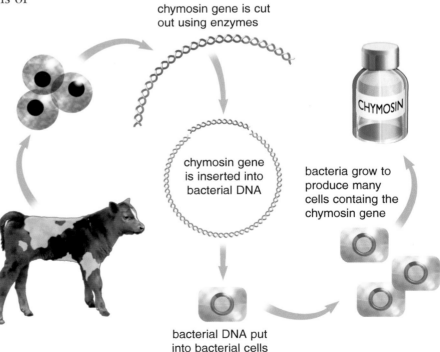

chymosin gene is cut out using enzymes

chymosin gene is inserted into bacterial DNA

bacteria grow to produce many cells containg the chymosin gene

bacterial DNA put into bacterial cells

Manufacturing medicines

GM technology is also used in medicine to manufacture substances that used to be obtained from human or animal tissues. For example, people who have haemophilia, an inherited disease, do not produce the proteins needed for their blood to clot. A bruise or a cut can result in severe bleeding. Haemophiliacs are now treated using clotting proteins which are produced by genetically modified bacteria.

GM crops

New genes can also be transferred to crop plants which are grown to produce food. Crops which have had their genes changed in this way are called genetically modified crops (**GM crops**). For example, some bacteria produce a protein that is poisonous to insects. The gene that makes this poison can be cut out of bacteria and added to crop plants. Because the GM crop plant will now produce the poisonous protein, the farmer will not need to spray the crop with **insecticide**. But other insects, such as bees, may also be killed when they feed on the GM crops.

GM crops have also been produced so that crop plants are resistant to herbicides (weedkillers). Farmers use herbicides to kill weeds which compete with the crops plants for light, water and nutrients. By inserting a gene which makes the plant resistant to herbicides, farmers can spray over an entire field, killing all plants apart from the GM crop.

Question

d *Proteins to promote blood clotting used to be extracted from human blood. Suggest the benefits of producing these proteins using GM organisms.*

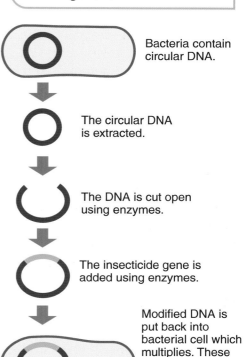

Bacteria contain circular DNA.

The circular DNA is extracted.

The DNA is cut open using enzymes.

The insecticide gene is added using enzymes.

Modified DNA is put back into bacterial cell which multiplies. These bacterial cells infect plants with insecticide genes.

Question

e *Suggest two advantages and two disadvantages of growing insect-repelling GM crops.*

Key points

- In genetic engineering, genes can be 'cut out' and inserted into other organisms.
- Plants and animals will develop with specific characteristics when genes are inserted at an early stage in their development.
- Modifying the genetic make-up of plants and animals raises ethical issues.
- People need to be able to make informed judgements about the ethical issues concerning genetic engineering.

Public concerns

Many people are concerned about the use of the use of genetically modified products. The photographs show the action some people have taken to stop GM products getting into the food we eat.

Here are some of the views of the people involved.

The protestors' views

We don't know the long-term effects. GM products could be damaging the environment and our health – but we don't know yet.

GM crops containing an insecticide could create 'superbugs' – pests which are resistant to insecticides.

GM crops could reproduce with wild plants and introduce GM genes into other plants. We don't know what effect this could have.

There is no need to increase food production in this country – we have more than enough food already.

The food scientist's view

GM products are carefully tested before being sold.

Using GM crops means that fewer harmful chemicals such as pesticides are used in the environment.

There is no evidence that GM foods have a harmful effect on the environment. It is just bad publicity from biased groups that gets people worried.

We need to increase food production on a worldwide scale to feed an ever-increasing population.

GM crops are very useful in developing countries where pests and disease are much more common than in the UK.

Question

a *Imagine that a company wants to grow GM crops near your school. The local press want people to write in with their views. Do you support GM technology or are you against it? Give as many reasons to support your view as you can.*

Designer babies

About 6000 babies are born in the UK each year as a result of *in vitro* fertilisation (IVF). A recent report states that about one in three couples have difficulty conceiving. IVF is one way of aiding conception. The technique involves taking eggs from a woman and fertilising the eggs in the laboratory – producing a 'test-tube baby'. The fertilised egg develops into a small ball of embryo cells which is then implanted into the woman.

Prior to implantation, a single cell from an embryo conceived by IVF can be removed and genetically tested before parents decide whether to implant or discard the embryo. Testing embryos using genetic screening is a major step forward in preventing inherited disease but it raises some difficult ethical questions.

The ethical issues include:

Should parents be allowed to test for other characteristics? Embryos developed from IVF treatment are tested for genetic disorders. At present tests are not carried out for characteristics such as intelligence and sporting ability. Deciding the characteristics of a child is often reported as producing a 'designer baby'.

Should embryo testing be available for all pregnant women? At present women having IVF treatment are allowed different tests from those who are pregnant, because the embryo can be tested at a very early stage in development.

Should all testing include all genetic disorders? Some people want genetic testing for genetic disorders to be offered to all parents so that they have the information. Other people say that some parents would use a result showing even a very slight disorder as a reason for abortion. This is like rejecting people with even slight disabilities.

▲ This small ball of cells is an embryo at a very early stage of development. The cells can be tested to see if they have genes that could cause an inherited disease.

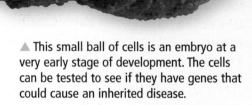

Questions

b Should parents and doctors be allowed to select any of the genetic characteristics of children? Give reasons to support your answer.

c Should genetic testing of embryos include all genetic disorders? Give reasons to support your answer.

Key points

● Applications of science in medicine and food production can raise ethical issues.
● People need to be able to make informed judgements about economic, social and ethical issues concerning cloning and genetic engineering.

Evolving organisms

There are many different types of animals and plants. Different types of organism are called **species**. There is evidence that all species have evolved from simple organisms that lived on Earth more than three billion years ago. Similar species are descended from a common ancestor by a process of gradual change.

▶ Simpler forms of life evolved to form larger and more complex organisms.

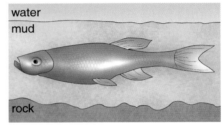

larger, more complex animals

larger, more complex plants

simple animals

simple plants

simple forms of life

Evidence from the past

Evidence of the way organisms have evolved can be seen in **fossils**. Fossils are the remains of plants and animals that are found in rocks. Fossils can be formed from:

- hard parts of animals and plants that do not decay easily such as bones, teeth, shells and the woody remains of plants
- animals and plants that have not decayed because the conditions for decay were not present (moisture, oxygen and warmth are needed for decay to happen)
- traces of animals such as footprints.

Fossils are only rarely formed. This is why there are gaps in the fossil record, and scientists can only suggest how one kind of organism evolved from another. Not enough fossils have been found to show exactly what happened to each kind of organism that lived in the past. Fossils of simple organisms, such as those made from just one cell, are extremely rare. This is one reason why scientists cannot be certain about how life began on Earth. The evidence for evolution can be interpreted in different ways. This is why evolution is a theory and not a fact, and why there are conflicting theories.

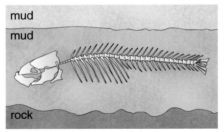

water

mud

rock

A fish dies and becomes covered by mud.

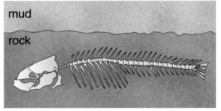

mud

mud

rock

The soft tissues of the fish decay. The only part that remains is the skeleton.

mud

rock

Mud surrounding the skeleton turns into rock.

Questions

a Whole bodies of woolly mammoths have been found in frozen soils. These mammoths were almost perfectly preserved – their stomachs were full of 30 000-year-old grass and their flesh was still attached. Explain why fossil remains usually show only the remains of hard tissues such as bone.

b Some of the mammoths were found with stone arrowheads in their bodies. Explain what this evidence tells us about how humans lived at the time that mammoth fossils were formed.

More layers of rock are formed on top of the older rock

reptile fossil

fish fossils

A record of evolution

The location of a fossil also provides evidence of its age. The deepest layers of rock are likely to contain the oldest fossils. The fossils in layers of rock provide a record that shows how plants and animals have changed over a very long period of time.

Question

c (i) Which fossil is the oldest? (ii) What is the evidence that this is the oldest fossil?

Extinct species

The **fossil record** shows that some species lived in the past but are now extinct. About 100 million years ago there were many more species of reptiles than there are today, including many dinosaur species.

Species become extinct because:
- the environment in which they live changes
- new predators or disease kill them
- they cannot compete with other species.

The 'Terror Birds' are an example of a species that is now extinct. These large, flightless birds roamed the grasslands of South America between 2 million and 62 million years ago. They were ferocious predators, able to chase their prey at speeds of 40 miles per hour. Scientists have put forward two theories to explain why these birds became extinct. One theory is that as the climate became warmer the grassland habitat was replaced with dense tropical forest. An alternative theory is that the Terror Birds could not compete with carnivorous mammals.

◀ Terror Birds are now an extinct species.

Question

d South America used to be separated from North America. At that time carnivorous mammals were only found in North America. Explain why the Terror Birds became extinct after the two continents became joined.

Similarities and differences

Comparing the features of different species provides evidence of how they may have evolved. Species that share many similar characteristics are likely to be closely related. Species that are not closely related in evolutionary history are more likely to have very different characteristics.

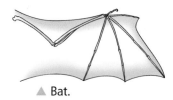

▲ Bat.

The diagram shows the bones present in the fin of a fish, the fin of a whale and the wing of a bat.

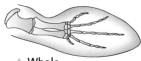

▲ Whale.

▲ Fish.

Questions

e Describe how the fins of fish and whales differ.
f Describe the evidence that suggests that whales are more closely related to bats than they are to fish.

Key points

- Fossils provide evidence of how different organisms have changed.
- Similarities and differences between species indicate their evolutionary and ecological relationships.
- Some species have become extinct.
- Scientists cannot be certain about how life began on Earth.

Changing ideas

People used to think that all species had always remained the same. They also thought that species had been created at the same time that the Earth was made. As scientists learned more and more about plants and animals they concluded that species are changing and that new species have been formed. The first explanations of how evolution occurs were put forward by Lamarck and later by Darwin.

Lamarck's theory

One of the earliest theories of how evolution takes place was proposed by a scientist called Lamarck. According to Lamarck, a species changes over a period if time because it passes on to its offspring changes it acquires during its lifetime. The diagram shows how Lamarck's theory explains how species of wading birds developed long legs.

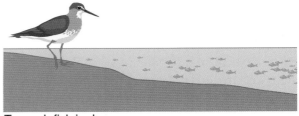

To reach fish in deeper water, wading birds stretch their legs. This makes their legs slightly longer.

Having slightly longer legs is passed on to the next generation. Birds in this generation also stretch their legs.

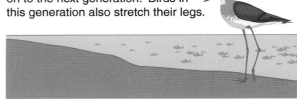

Over many generations, the wading birds' legs become much longer.

▲ Lamarck's theory of evolution.

Questions

a What are the advantages of wading birds having long legs?

b Use your knowledge of how characteristics are inherited to suggest a major weakness of Lamarck's theory.

Organisms compete for food

Individuals of the same species may have different characteristics, such as slightly longer legs.

Individuals struggle to survive. Some die because of lack of food or may be eaten by predators.

Individuals with useful characteristics are more likely to survive, and pass on their characteristics to the next generation.

Darwin and natural selection

Scientists' present ideas about the way species evolve are based on the theory of natural selection, which was first put forward by Charles Darwin. Natural selection brings about changes in species because:

- changes in genes (**mutations**) produce new forms of genes
- differences in the genes of individual organisms produce different characteristics
- individuals with characteristics most suited to the environment are more likely to survive and breed
- the genes which have enabled individuals to survive are then passed on to the next generation.

Natural selection can only occur when individuals of the same species show different characteristics. These differences occur because mutation produces new forms of genes. This is why the change in a species may become more rapid as new forms of genes are produced.

◀ Darwin's theory of natural selection.

Question

c Darwin's theory of how species change is very different from Lamarck's theory. Explain how wading birds would have developed long legs by the process of natural selection.

Different theories

Evolution has taken place over billions of years. There is not enough evidence from fossils and from the comparison of species to prove what caused species to change over this very long time period. This is why scientists cannot be certain about how life began on Earth and why there are conflicting theories to explain evolution.

Question

d What are the differences between Darwin's and Lamarck's theories?

Surviving and breeding

The effects of natural selection can be seen in a species called the peppered moth. There are two varieties of this species – a light variety and a dark variety. Both varieties feed at night and rest on trees during the day. The photograph shows the two varieties on a tree in a city.

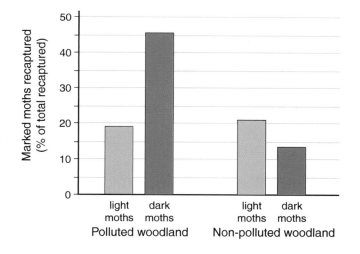

Question

e Which variety of moth is more likely to be eaten by insect-eating birds in a city? Explain your answer.

In an investigation:

- Large numbers of light and dark varieties of moth were caught in a trap.
- The moths were marked with a spot of paint on the underside of their bodies and then released.
- Equal numbers of moths were released into a polluted woodland and into a unpolluted woodland.
- After a few days the moths were trapped again and the number of marked moths was counted.

The results are shown in the bar graph.

Questions

f Suggest why the moths were marked with paint on the underside of their bodies.

g What percentage of light moths was recaptured in: (i) the unpolluted woodland; (ii) the polluted woodland?

h Explain why more dark moths than light moths were recaptured in the polluted woodland.

i Suggest why only a small percentage of both varieties of moth were recaptured.

Key points

- Some theories of evolution conflict with Darwin's theory.
- You should be able to interpret evidence relating to the theories of evolution.
- Darwin's theory is based on the natural selection of individuals most suited to their environment.
- There may be a more rapid change in a species when genes mutate.
- An investigation determines if a relationship exists between two variables.
- Scientists identify patterns and relationships to make suitable predictions.

The theory of evolution

When Charles Darwin presented his theory of evolution over 100 years ago people were astonished and even hostile. Darwin's ideas were only gradually accepted because:

- the theory of evolution undermined the idea that God made all the animals and plants that live on the Earth
- people believed that organisms had always been as they appeared.

People found it hard to believe that humans could have evolved. They laughed at the idea that humans as a species are closely related to apes such as chimpanzees. Although most people now accept that humans have evolved, scientists do not agree about how humans evolved, and how closely related we are to other species.

CHIMPS BELONG TO HUMAN BRANCH OF FAMILY TREE

A recent report says that chimps are so closely related to humans that they should be placed in the same branch of the evolutionary tree as us.

Evolutionary relationships

Studying the similarities and differences between species provides evidence of their evolutionary relationships. The diagrams show the skeletons of a human, an ape and a monkey. The features of these skeletons provide evidence to show how closely related these species are.

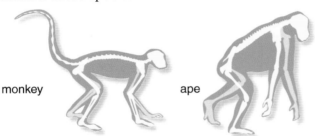

monkey   ape   human

Questions

a Describe two features of the ape and monkey skeletons that are not found in the human skeleton.

b Describe two features of the monkey skeleton that are not found in the human and ape skeletons.

c Which species, apes or monkeys, is more closely related to humans? Give reasons to support your answer.

Tracing human evolution

The diagram shows the evolutionary relationship between humans and other animals. Your family tree shows that you are more closely related to your parents than to your aunts and uncles. Similarly, species that have evolved from the same ancestors are related. The theory of evolution does not suggest that chimpanzees 'turned into' humans. Chimpanzees are themselves the result of evolution. Evidence suggests that an ancestral ape species gave rise to both chimpanzees and humans.

Question

d (i) Which species are most closely related to humans? (ii) Use the information in the diagram to explain your answer.

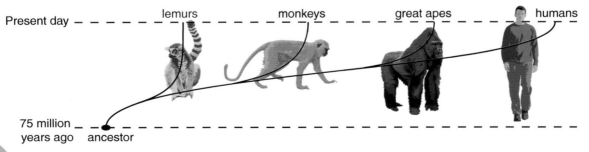

Present day — lemurs   monkeys   great apes   humans

75 million years ago   ancestor

Fossils of extinct species

One very important fossil discovery was the bones of a human-like creature that lived 3.2 million years ago. The scientists who found the fossil skeleton called it 'Lucy'. The skeleton has many features similar to chimpanzees, but the structure of the leg and hip bones show that Lucy walked on two legs, like us. Walking on two legs is a very important difference between humans and apes. This is why Lucy's species, called 'Southern Ape', is thought to be an extinct human ancestor.

Working out relationships

Scientists believe that humans share a common ancestor with extinct species such as Southern Ape and with chimpanzees. However, scientists are not sure how this common ancestor evolved into these three species. The diagram on the right shows how these three species could be related.

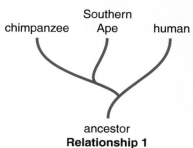

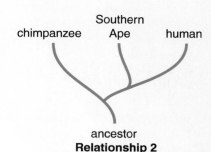

The table below shows some of the features of the skeletons of these three species.

Characteristic	Human	Southern Ape	Chimpanzee
thumb length	short	short	long
legs and arms	arms shorter than legs	arms shorter than legs	legs shorter than arms
brain size	large (1500 cm³)	small (620 cm³)	small (440 cm³)

Questions

e Which of the relationships is shown by (i) brain size, and (ii) the length of legs and arms?

f What evidence in the table suggests that the Southern Ape walked upright on two legs?

Charting human evolution

Scientists have pieced together the evidence from different fossils of extinct species to chart how human evolution may have occurred. The bars on the chart show when a species appeared and when it became extinct.

Questions

g How many years ago did 'Southern Ape' first appear?

h For how long did the species 'Handy Man' survive?

i Which species in the chart was the most intelligent? What evidence supports your answer?

Key points

- Darwin's theory of evolution was only gradually accepted.
- Scientists cannot be certain about how life began on Earth.
- The similarities and differences between species may provide evidence of their evolutionary and ecological relationships.

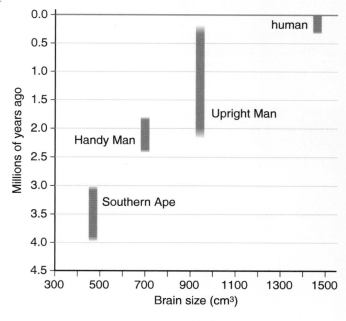

In 2003 Europe had the hottest summer ever recorded. The newspaper cuttings describe some of the effects of the heatwave. Was the summer of 2003 a sign that the Earth's climate is changing?

Parisians thronged the bank of the River Seine which has been turned into an urban beach with sand, cafes, deckchairs and palm trees as the temperature in the capital neared 40 °C (104 °F) again yesterday.

Amsterdam zoo fed its chimpanzees iced fruit and sprayed ostriches with cold water to keep them cool as temperatures in the Dutch capital edged towards 30 °C (86 °F), the Dutch news agency ANP reported.

Polish fire crews battled 35 forest fires on Monday and about a quarter of the country's woodlands were at serious risk of fire after temperatures topped 30 °C (86 °F) for much of July, authorities said.

13 Spaniards have died in the heatwave, and 30 taken to hospital because of the heat in Cordoba, Seville and Huelva in Andalusia.

The death toll from Portugal's biggest wildfires in decades rose to 11 after two bodies were found in charred woodland, but cooler overnight temperatures enabled firefighters to contain all but three major blazes.

Climate change

The impact that humans are having on our planet is always in the news. We are already beginning to see climate changes that may bring disasters to many parts of the world. For example, severe flooding in Bangladesh gets more frequent with each decade. The Earth is not ours to use as we wish; we hold it in trust for future generations, so we must look after the Earth and its resources.

The photographs show some of the concerns that people have about the environment.

▼ Forests in many parts of the world are being cleared to provide grazing land for cattle. In India the tiger has become an endangered species as its native forests are relentlessly cut back. Deforestation affects the Earth's climate.

▼ This satellite photo shows air pollution over China covering an area larger than the UK. Many developing nations are increasing the size of their industries. This can bring about air pollution on a massive scale.

▲ Climate change is bringing about more flooding. In recent years scenes like this have become much more common in many parts of the world.

▲ A huge area of land was flooded when this hydroelectric dam was built, destroying more animal and plant habitats.

For many years, scientists have made careful measurements of changes to the environment. From these measurements they have made predictions about the world in the 2050s. The map shows what many scientists think will happen if there is 'business as usual', that is if we do not change the way we treat our planet.

The map shows that several parts of the world, such as SE Asia, will have more frequent and more severe storms. Deforestation will continue in South America and crop yields in many parts of the world will fall, including India and southern Africa.

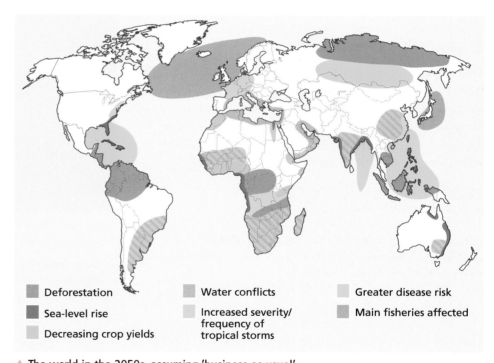

- Deforestation
- Sea-level rise
- Decreasing crop yields
- Water conflicts
- Increased severity/ frequency of tropical storms
- Greater disease risk
- Main fisheries affected

▲ The world in the 2050s, assuming 'business as usual'.

Think about what you will find out in this section

How is the increase in human population affecting the surface of our planet?	How do scientists investigate the effect of human activities on the environment?
How are human activities affecting the Earth's atmosphere and climate?	How can science help us to plan sustainable development?
How are humans making it difficult for some species to survive?	

The world's population

In 2005 the world's population was estimated to be 6.5 billion.

> **Question**
>
> **a** Look at the graph.
> (i) Describe how the world's population changed between 1750 and 2000.
> (ii) What proportion of the estimated world population in 2050 will live in less developed countries?
> (iii) Suggest reasons why the populations of less developed countries are rising faster than those of more developed countries.

Six thousand years ago, the population of the world was about 0.2 billion. People lived in small groups, and most of the world was unaffected by human activities.

Running out of raw materials

As world population increases, raw materials are rapidly being used up. Some of these resources, such as fossil fuels, are **non-renewable**. This means that once we have used them, no more can be made, so eventually supplies will run out. As we use these raw materials, a great deal of waste is produced. Much of this waste causes pollution.

Less space for wildlife

Every year, we have to build more homes to house the increasing numbers of people in the world. Before building began, this land provided habitats for animals and plants.

The new houses have to be supplied with electricity – so the demand for electricity is rising. Many parts of the world cannot afford to import fossil fuels to produce electricity, so they build dams for hydroelectric schemes. More habitats for animals and plants are lost.

Most houses are built using brick and cement. Bricks are made from clay which is obtained from quarries. Cement is made from limestone. Quarrying can threaten the habitats of rare species. The inhabitants of each new house will produce rubbish. This is dumped, tipped at landfill sites or even burned. Still more habitats are lost to animals and plants.

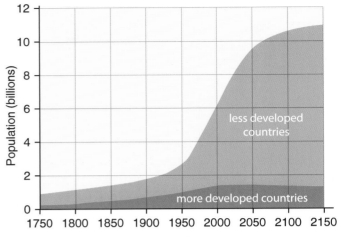

▲ World population estimates from 1750 to 2150.

▲ Satellite pictures at night show how much electricity is being used in Europe.

> **Question**
>
> **b** Give one disadvantage of each of the three methods of getting rid of rubbish.

▼ The more people there are, the more rubbish we make.

Each household also produces sewage. In this country most sewage is treated before being passed into rivers. But a lot of raw sewage is still dumped out at sea. This can be washed ashore by the tide to pollute beaches.

The increase in population means that more land is used for agriculture. Using land for agriculture reduces the number of habitats for wild animals and plants. The **pesticides**, **herbicides** and fertilisers used by farmers can cause further damage to local animals and plants.

▶ When treated sewage is dumped into rivers, microbes feed on it and multiply. Their respiration uses up the oxygen in the water, causing fish to suffocate.

Question

c Give three ways in which human activities reduce the amount of land available for other animals and plants.

DDT – the wonder pesticide?

In 1939, a pesticide called DDT was used for the first time to kill mosquitoes that carry malaria. DDT was seen as an ideal pesticide because it was toxic to a wide range of insects but it seemed to be harmless to mammals, fish and plants. DDT was widely used during World War II and was credited with saving the lives of millions of people who would have died of malaria.

But as DDT became more widely used, some insects became resistant. Even worse, in areas where DDT had been sprayed widely, scientists observed that bird populations had declined as well as mosquito populations. The scientists found that DDT interfered with the birds' ability to produce eggshells. The eggshells were thinner so most of them cracked before the young birds were hatched.

▲ A mosquito taking a meal.

DDT is now banned in developed countries, but the World Health Organization estimates that 22 of the world's poorest countries rely on DDT to fight malaria because of its effectiveness and affordability. Malaria affects more than 300 million people and causes at least one million deaths annually. More than 3000 people, mostly children, die from malaria each day in Africa alone.

Question

d Scientists have given politicians lots of data about DDT. Should DDT be banned in every country in the world? Explain your reasons.

Key points

- Human population growth means that raw materials are being used up quickly and more waste is being produced, causing more pollution.
- Humans are destroying animal and plant habitats by building, quarrying, farming and dumping waste.
- Some species are finding it difficult to survive.

Asian brown cloud

We need energy to power factories, homes and motor vehicles. But producing this energy can have serious effects on both humans and the environment.

The 'Asian Brown Cloud', a 3 km-thick blanket of pollution over South Asia, may be causing the premature deaths of half a million people in India each year, deadly flooding in some areas and drought in others, according to one of the biggest scientific studies of the phenomenon.

The grimy cocktail of ash, soot, acids and other damaging airborne particles is as much the result of low-tech polluters such as wood- and dung-burning stoves, cooking fires and forest clearing as it is of industry, the UN-sponsored study found.

More than 200 scientists contributed to the study. They used data collected by ships, planes and satellites to study Asia's haze.

The scientists say more research is needed but some trends are clear. Respiratory illness appears to be increasing along with the pollution in densely populated South Asia, researchers said, suggesting that the pollution plays a role in the 500 000 premature deaths that occur annually in India.

Scientists say it's too early to draw definite conclusions about the impact of the cloud and of similar hazes over East Asia, South America and Africa.

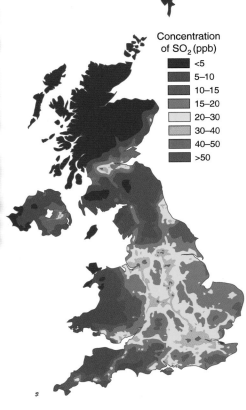

Concentration of SO_2 (ppb)

| <5 |
| 5–10 |
| 10–15 |
| 15–20 |
| 20–30 |
| 30–40 |
| 40–50 |
| >50 |

▲ Sulfur dioxide concentrations over the UK.

> **Question**
>
> **a** (i) Suggest what kinds of data the scientists collected in this study.
> (ii) Suggest why it is 'too early to draw conclusions' from this study.
> (iii) What could scientists do to help 'low-tech' polluters reduce pollution?

One effect of air pollution is the production of acid rain. Acid rain is formed mainly from gases released from car exhausts.

Petrol contains fuel molecules called hydrocarbons. These are oxidised when the fuel burns to release energy. The main gas released is carbon dioxide. Because petrol also contains nitrogen compounds and sulfur compounds, nitrogen oxides and sulfur dioxide are also formed. These gases pass into the atmosphere.

> **Question**
>
> **b** What evidence is there from the map that most sulfur dioxide in the atmosphere comes from motor vehicles?

How can scientists help?

You can now buy low-sulfur petrol and diesel from petrol stations. This reduces the amount of sulfur dioxide emitted by cars.

Nitrogen oxide gases are thought to contribute to asthma. Scientists have developed catalytic converters to convert the nitrogen oxides into nitrogen and carbon dioxide. The catalyst in the converter is the precious metal platinum. The diagram shows where the catalytic converter is fitted into the car.

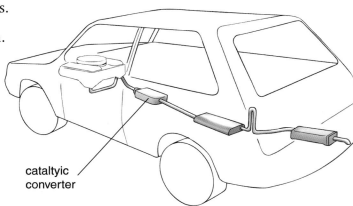

cataltyic converter

> **Question**
>
> **c** Not all cars in the UK are fitted with catalytic converters. Suggest a reason for this.

Acid rain

Carbon dioxide and sulfur dioxide in exhaust fumes from cars and lorries dissolve in rainwater and make it slightly acid. Acid rain has a pH of 4 or less. It has very damaging effects on the environment.

▶ Coal-burning power stations release sulphur dioxide into the atmosphere.

How does air pollution affect the environment?

Living organisms can be used to monitor the effects of air pollution and acid rain.

Lichens are organisms that live on the bark of trees and on stones. The table shows the number of species of lichen on the bark of trees at different sulfur dioxide concentrations.

	Concentration of sulfur dioxide in air (micrograms per m³ of air)					
	5	30	35	50	70	150
Number of species of lichen	14	10	8	7	5	2

Question

d *Could you use the number of lichen species to give an accurate prediction of the sulfur dioxide concentration in the air? Explain your answer.*

The larvae (young forms) of many types of insect live in fresh water. They are sensitive to the pH of the water. The table shows how the pH of the water affected the number of species of insect larvae and plants in five different ponds.

Pond	pH of water	Number of species of insect larvae	Number of species of plants
1	4.4	4	8
2	4.8	5	11
3	5.7	9	16
4	6.6	19	23
5	8.1	14	21

Question

e *Give two alternative explanations for the effect of pH on the number of species of animals found.*

Trees are also damaged by acid rain. One of the first signs of acid rain damage is that the young leaves near the top of the tree die. This is called 'crown-loss'.

Crown-loss is not the only damage caused by acid rain. The acid affects the covering of the older leaves. This makes it easier for disease organisms to attack the tree.

Question

f *How will the loss of its young leaves affect the tree?*

Key points

- Air is polluted by exhaust fumes from motor vehicles.
- Sulfur dioxide from exhaust fumes dissolves in rain to produce acid rain.
- Acid rain damages living tissues and some types of stones.
- Lichens can be used as indicators of the concentration of sulfur dioxide.
- Aquatic animals can be used as indicators of the acidity of fresh water.

The Brazil issue

Most forest clearance across the world is the result of slash and burn farming. In Brazil the government grants people land to farm for a short period of time. Once the land has become infertile, the farmers then move a little deeper into the forest and clear the next section of land.

Cattle ranchers also clear forests to provide grazing land. Over 74% of the beef consumed in Europe comes from Brazil. This is 80% of the beef Brazil produces, and most of it is produced on land that was once forest.

Greenhouse gases

Forest clearance, or deforestation, affects the atmosphere. Global warming is now regarded as a major problem facing the world. Some studies suggest that there has been an overall rise in temperatures by 0.3°C every decade across the planet. This rise is from an increase in the levels of greenhouse gases being released into the atmosphere. One of the most abundant of these gases is carbon dioxide. Levels of this gas in the atmosphere have risen 25% in the last 50 years. This is mostly due to industry in both developed and developing countries and the increased levels of car ownership and air travel in the developed world.

However, burning of vegetation in the areas where deforestation is taking place accounts for around 25% of the carbon dioxide released into the atmosphere. This equates to 2000 million tonnes of carbon dioxide every year.

CO_2 in balance

Plants remove carbon dioxide from the atmosphere during photosynthesis, and most living organisms pass carbon dioxide back to the atmosphere when they respire. These two processes balanced each other for thousands of years. But in the last few centuries humans have interfered with this balance in two major ways: combustion of fossil fuels and deforestation.

When trees are cut down, the branches are burned. This releases carbon dioxide into the atmosphere. The roots of the trees die and are decomposed by microorganisms. When microorganisms respire they release yet more carbon dioxide into the atmosphere.

Cutting down trees also means that the amount of photosynthesis going on in the world is reduced. Trees take in millions of tonnes of carbon dioxide every year.

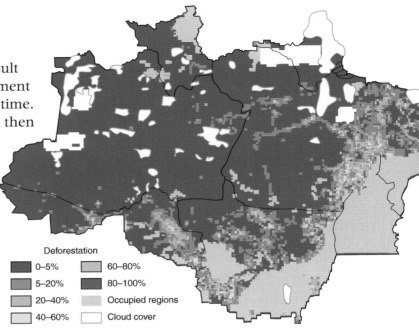

Deforestation
- 0–5%
- 5–20%
- 20–40%
- 40–60%
- 60–80%
- 80–100%
- Occupied regions
- Cloud cover

▲ Forests are disappearing at an alarming rate in Brazil.

Question

a Brazil is a developing country. Suggest why its government seems to be encouraging deforestation.

Questions

b Give two reasons why cutting down forests increases the amount of carbon dioxide in the atmosphere.

c In the USA large areas of forest are mature – the trees have stopped growing. How will these forests affect the composition of the atmosphere?

Biodiversity

Nobody knows how many species there are in the world. Scientists' estimations vary between 5 million and 80 million. Most scientists agree, though, that about half these species live in tropical rainforests. Another estimate is that deforestation is losing the world 150 species every day. Scientists call this a 'loss of biodiversity'.

Why does this matter? Approximately 40% of all prescription medicines are based on natural compounds found in microorganisms, plants and animals. Nature provides us with penicillin, aspirin, morphine and steroids. New medicines to fight breast cancer come from the bark of the pacific yew tree. The rosy periwinkle plant is used to fight Hodgkin's disease and childhood leukaemia.

Question

d Explain the possible consequences of loss of biodiversity.

Methane

The number of cattle in the world is rising rapidly, particularly in places like Brazil. Cows have a four-chambered stomach. Microbes live in these chambers and digest parts of the cow's food, producing methane. Methane is another greenhouse gas. Cattle produce about 100 000 000 tonnes of methane per year – 20% of the total methane in the atmosphere.

Most of the remaining atmospheric methane comes from rice fields. Rice fields are under water for long periods, so there is very little oxygen in the soil. Bacteria in these soils produce a lot of methane. As the world's population has increased, so has the total area of rice fields to provide food for all the people.

The increased concentrations of greenhouse gases are causing the temperature of the atmosphere to rise, slowly but surely. The diagram shows why this is happening.

▲ Methane is produced by bacteria living in flooded rice fields.

This rise will cause changes to climates around the world – some places will become wetter, others drier. The warming of the atmosphere is causing melting of the polar icecaps. This will cause sea levels to rise. Some low-lying pieces of arid land will become flooded.

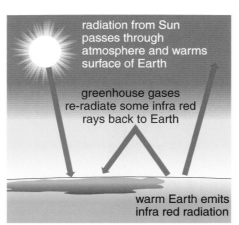

radiation from Sun passes through atmosphere and warms surface of Earth

greenhouse gases re-radiate some infra red rays back to Earth

warm Earth emits infra red radiation

Key points

- Carbon dioxide in the atmosphere is rising because of increased use of fossil fuels and increased deforestation.
- Loss of biodiversity is also caused by deforestation.
- Methane in the atmosphere is rising because of increased numbers of cattle and rice fields.

India moves forward

India is changing rapidly. It has a population of more than one billion. Its population grows by about 17 million each year (the population of the UK is about 60 million). Two-thirds of India's population lives in the countryside, but over the past 20 years cities have grown rapidly as industry has expanded and people have moved to find employment.

The increase in industrialisation and population has created problems:

- forests have been cut down for fuel and for farmland
- **water tables** have fallen and soils have become poorer
- use of pesticides and fertilisers has increased
- urbanisation has increased pollution of water, land and air
- rapid growth of the economy has led to increased numbers of motor vehicles and plastics, putting a strain on energy supplies.

There is no quick fix to India's problems. Different people have different views about the best way to tackle it.

▲ Millions of people in the world live in poor conditions.

Developing countries should protect their forests.

We only use a fraction of the energy you use per head of population.

Your pollution is ruining the planet.

Why shouldn't we try to improve our standard of living?

Your increasing population is taking too much of the world's resources.

America and Europe are using about 80% of the world's resources.

Conserving natural resources

Most energy used in industrialised countries comes from non-renewable energy resources. Industrial countries are using up non-renewable energy resources far more quickly than developing countries. The ways in which we can conserve non-renewable energy resources include:

- making our homes more energy efficient
- making less use of private motor vehicles by walking or by using public transport.

The Ecohouse has been designed to use energy in a sustainable way.

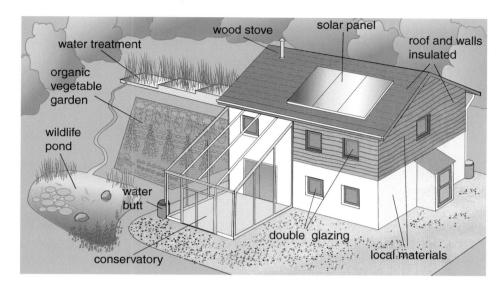

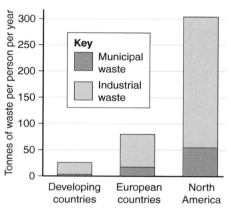

◀ Ecohouse – the sustainable house.

Question

a Explain how each of the labelled features helps the house to be sustainable.

Waste and recycling

The chart shows the amount of waste produced per head of population in different countries.

Municipal waste is the waste that is collected by refuse lorries from homes and shops.

▲ Getting rid of waste is a real problem – the more waste, the bigger the problem.

Question

b (i) Estimate the ratios of municipal waste to industrial waste for developing countries and for North America.
(ii) Suggest an explanation for the difference in the ratios.

One way of conserving precious natural resources is to recycle them. We can all contribute to this by using recycling bins. Many local councils now provide households with two bins – one for rubbish that can be recycled and one for waste that cannot be recycled. Many products are now designed so that the materials in them can be recycled.

The Government has given local councils recycling targets to meet. This means that a much higher proportion of waste is now being recycled rather than dumped. Recycling paper means that fewer forests are cut down. Recycling glass and metals means that fewer quarries are dug.

▼ Recycling materials helps to conserve natural resources.

Question

c How does recycling each of the following save natural resources? (i) newspaper; (ii) bottles; (iii) aluminium cans.

Key points

● Sustainable development means improving the quality of life without compromising the lives of future generations.
● This means using natural resources and energy carefully and in planned ways.
● Natural resources can be conserved by recycling paper, glass and metals.

Investigating climate change

People have differing views of climate change and whether global warming is really happening. Read the report below from a 'Greenforce' conference.

Climate change is with us. A decade ago, it was conjecture. Now the future is unfolding before our eyes. Canada's Inuit see it in disappearing Arctic ice and permafrost. The shantytown dwellers of Latin America and Southern Asia see it in lethal storms and floods. Europeans see it in disappearing glaciers, forest fires and fatal heat waves.

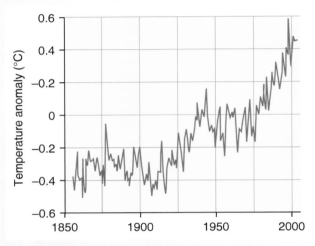

▲ How global temperatures have varied since 1860.

Question

a Are the above statements supporting the idea of global warming based on valid and reliable evidence, or on non-scientific observations?

The graph shows the how the global temperature each year differed from the mean temperature for the period. This difference is called the temperature anomaly.

Question

b (i) Describe the trend in global temperatures between 1860 and 2000. (ii) What is the advantage in recording 5-year averages rather than annual averages? (iii) Reliable measurements of the global temperature only go back to the 1860s. Suggest a reason for this.

▼ Every chunk of ice core tells the story of the atmosphere it was formed in.

To find out about the climate before 1860, scientists have to rely on 'proxy' records rather than direct measurements with instruments. For example, the width of tree rings is related to temperature. Other techniques that have been used include examining the time of crop harvests and other historical records.

Scientists needed much more reliable data if they were to prove that global temperature was rising, and to establish a link between global warming and carbon dioxide. To do this they obtained evidence from ice cores.

The photograph shows a scientist examining part of a 3 km-long ice core drilled from the Antarctic. As the ice was formed, air bubbles were trapped in it. Scientists can analyse these bubbles to find the composition of air trapped hundreds of thousands of years ago. They can also estimate the temperature of the atmosphere when the bubbles were trapped. The graph on the next page shows some of their results.

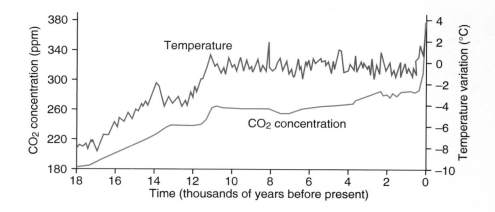

c (i) *What was the mean air temperature in Antarctica 14000 years ago?*
(ii) *Describe how the carbon dioxide concentration in the atmosphere changed from 18000 years ago to the present.*
(iii) *Explain how the data from the graph gives evidence that carbon dioxide is a greenhouse gas.*
(iv) *Explain why the graph does not prove that carbon dioxide is responsible for global warming.*

Different views

Read the newspaper cuttings about the heat wave of 2003 again (p 66). Some scientists are not convinced that the **greenhouse effect** was to blame. Below are some statements by these scientists:

'We must be wary of trying to link naturally varying weather events like fires and floods to simplistic events like 'global warming'. The highest recorded temperature for Australia was in 1889, for North America in 1922 and for Asia in 1974. If we junked every car, closed every factory, and shut down every power station, climate would still change, and we would still suffer heat waves and ice ages.'

The views of such scientists influence politicians. In 2004, Russia finally agreed to sign the **Kyoto treaty** that calls for industrialised nations to reduce their greenhouse gas emissions by 5% by 2012. This meant that nations responsible for 55% of greenhouse emissions had agreed to take action. But the USA, which is responsible for 25% of greenhouse gas emissions, still refuses to sign.

At the G8 summit in 2005, the US President George Bush said 'To a certain extent, [climate change] is [man-made], obviously.' But he defended US rejection of the Kyoto treaty, saying 'the Kyoto treaty would have wrecked our economy … my hope is to move beyond the Kyoto debate and to collaborate on new technologies that will enable the United States and other countries to diversify away from fossil fuels.'

d *Summarise evidence from this chapter that: (i) supports the views of the scientists above; (ii) supports the global warming theory for climate change.*

Key points

- Scientists collect data to provide evidence for environmental change.
- A correlation between two variables does not always mean that one is causing the other.
- We need to plan future development carefully to make sure it is sustainable.
- Different people have different ideas about how this should be done.

e *50% of electricity in the USA is generated by coal-fired power stations and this is expected to rise to 80% over the next 5 years.*
(i) Does President Bush now accept the scientific evidence that links global warming to carbon dioxide emission?
(ii) Why do you think that the USA will not sign the Kyoto treaty?

1 A class investigated how temperature affected the number of earthworms in soil.

Each soil sample was taken from the same field and was 1 m square and 15 cm deep. The air temperature was taken and earthworms were counted on the same day each month.

The results are shown in the table below.

	Jan	Feb	Mar	Apr	May	Jun	Jul	Aug	Sep	Oct	Nov	Dec
Air temp. (°C)	3	1	1	5	8	15	20	16	12	9	8	6
No. of worms	20	5	8	33	75	12	9	15	35	43	75	53

a **i** What were the control variables in the investigation? *(2 marks)*
    ii Give **two** ways in which the investigation could have been improved to give more reliable results. *(2 marks)*
b **i** Plot the data on one graph. *(2 marks)*
    ii In which month was the least number of earthworms found? Suggest an explanation for this. *(2 marks)*
c The class decided that another factor might also be affecting the number of earthworms. They decided to find out the rainfall for the area. Suggest where they might find this information. *(1 mark)*

The table below shows the monthly rainfall for the area.

	Jan	Feb	Mar	Apr	May	Jun	Jul	Aug	Sep	Oct	Nov	Dec
Total rainfall (mm)	45	33	28	55	75	25	8	12	35	45	60	55

    i Add this data to the graph. *(1 mark)*
    ii In which two months were most earthworms found? *(2 marks)*
    iii Which conditions do earthworms prefer? *(1 mark)*
    iv Outline an investigation you could do in a laboratory to find if earthworms prefer these conditions. *(2 marks)*

2 The table is about methods of producing offspring.

Match words from the list with each of the numbers **1–4** in the table.
    A asexual reproduction
    B genetic engineering
    C sexual reproduction
    D tissue culture

	Function
1	transferring genes from one species to another
2	produces offspring with no fusion of gametes
3	producing offspring from a small group of cells
4	produces offspring with a mixture of characteristics from two parents

3 The diagram shows the technique involved in adult cell cloning.

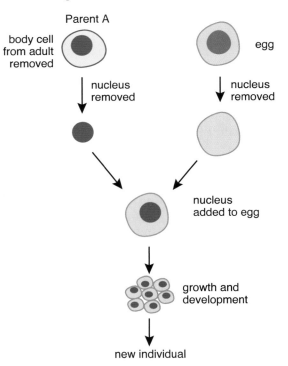

a This technique involves
    A asexual reproduction
    B fertilisation
    C mutation
    D sexual reproduction.
b The new individual is identical to Parent A because they
    A have the same genes
    B are formed by the fusion of gametes
    C have developed in the same conditions
    D have the same enzymes.

c Some people object to producing animals in this way. This is most likely to be because cloning raises issues which are

    A economic   **B** ethical

    C scientific   **D** social.

d Which one of the following is **not** contained in a nucleus?

    A cells   **B** chromosomes

    C DNA   **D** genes

4 Plant tissue culture is a method used to produce new plants. The flow diagram shows one method of plant tissue culture.

Small piece of tissue is removed from a plant, e.g. a piece of root or stem tissue
↓
The tissue is transferred to a culture medium
↓
New tissue develops containing unspecialised cells
↓
New tissue is transferred to a new culture medium
↓
New specialised shoots and root cells develop
↓
Developing plants are separated and grown under optimum conditions

a Name the type of reproduction involved in plant tissue culture. *(1 mark)*

b Describe **two** advantages of producing plants using this method rather than from seed. *(2 marks)*

c Explain why a disease is more likely to destroy a whole batch of plants grown by plant tissue culture than a batch of plants grown from seeds. *(1 mark)*

d Suggest **two** factors which need to be controlled to create the optimum growing conditions for the developing plants. *(2 marks)*

5 Fossils have been used to provide evidence of human evolution.

a **i** Explain why bones and teeth are normally the only fossils found. *(2 marks)*

    ii Usually, only a few bones from a single skeleton are found scattered around a wide area. Suggest reasons for this. *(2 marks)*

b Scientists use fossil evidence to work out how humans evolved. The diagram shows the skulls of a gorilla and a human and Neanderthal Man – an extinct species.

 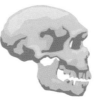 

gorilla   Neanderthal Man   human

Describe **two** features of the skull which suggest that Neanderthal Man is more closely related to humans than gorillas. *(2 marks)*

6 The land snail is found in grasslands and in woodlands. The shells of snails differ in colour and in the number of dark bands. The colour of the shells may be yellow or brown. Some shells have no bands and some have lots of bands.

Birds such as thrushes feed on snails.

The scattergraph shows the percentage of yellow unbanded snails in two different habitats.

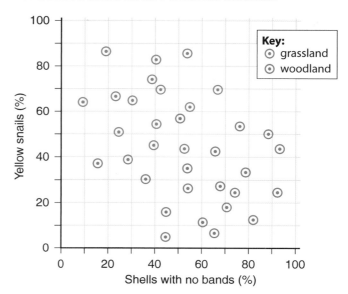

a Which of the following statements best describes the relationship between habitat and the colour and banding of the land snail?

   A There is no relationship.

   B The percentage of yellow snails with bands is higher in woodlands.

   C The percentage of yellow snails with no bands is higher in woodlands.

   D The percentage of yellow snails with no bands is higher in grasslands.

b Which of the following statements provides the best explanation of this relationship?

   A Snails which are more easily seen are more likely to be eaten by thrushes.

   B There are more thrushes in woodlands.

   C Thrushes only eat snails with banded shells.

   D Snails with yellow shells are better camouflaged.

c The differences in the appearance of the shells of the land snail is an example of

   A competition

   B cloning

   C natural selection

   D variation.

d Snails which are better suited to their habitat are more likely to survive and pass their genes on to their offspring. This is an example of

   A competition

   B mutation

   C natural selection

   D predation.

7 Human activities affect the environment.

Match words **A**, **B**, **C** and **D** with the spaces **1–4** in the paragraph.

   A carbon dioxide

   B fertiliser

   C methane

   D sulfur dioxide

Water may be polluted by ____1____. Burning wood produces ____2____. Acid rain is produced mainly by ____3____ dissolving in water. Rice fields add ____4____ to the atmosphere during the day.

8 Organisms affect or are affected by the composition of the atmosphere.

Match words **A**, **B**, **C** and **D** with the spaces **1–4** in the sentences.

   A cattle

   B lichens

   C microorganisms

   D trees

____1____ can be used as indicators of air pollution.

____2____ break down dead materials and return carbon dioxide to the atmosphere.

____3____ give off large amounts of methane into the atmosphere.

____4____ lock up large amounts of carbon dioxide for many years.

9 a Give **two** reasons why tropical rainforests are being cut down at a large rate. *(2 marks)*

   b Cutting down rainforests reduces biodiversity.

    i Explain what is meant by 'biodiversity'. *(1 mark)*

    ii Give **one** consequence for humans of a reduction in the biodiversity of tropical forests. *(1 mark)*

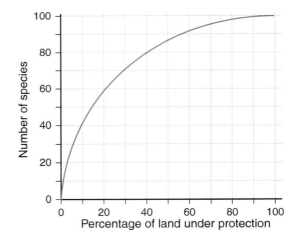

   c Biodiversity can be preserved by protecting parts of rainforests.

    i Describe, in as much detail as you can, the relationship between the percentage of land protected and number of species preserved. *(3 marks)*

    ii Explain why small-scale protection projects can be very effective. *(1 mark)*

10 In 1952 in London there was a thick fog for several days in December. This fog trapped air pollutants. The graph shows the concentration of sulfur dioxide and smoke particles in the atmosphere. It also shows the number of deaths per day.

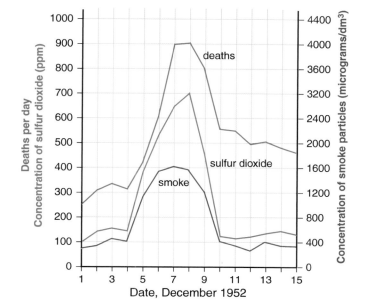

Date, December 1952

a What was the maximum number of deaths per day?

    A 400   **B** 700   **C** 900   **D** 3600

b What was the concentration of smoke particles on 7 December?

    A 400 micrograms per cubic decimetre
    B 650 micrograms per cubic decimetre
    C 900 micrograms per cubic decimetre
    D 1600 micrograms per cubic decimetre

c The data

    A proves that sulfur dioxide caused the large number of deaths
    B shows an exact correlation between sulfur dioxide concentration and the number of deaths
    C shows partial correlation between sulfur dioxide concentration and the number of deaths
    D shows that that the number of deaths depends on smoke particle concentration.

d Sulfur dioxide dissolves in water to produce
    A an acid solution
    B an alkaline solution
    C a neutral solution
    D sewage.

11 a Explain what is meant by 'sustainable development'. *(1 mark)*

b China has the largest population in the world. Demand for electricity there is increasing rapidly. Suggest **two** reasons for this increase in demand. *(2 marks)*

c The table shows how China plans to change its methods of generating electricity by 2020.

Year	Percentage of electricity obtained from energy source					
	Hydroelectricity	Coal	Oil	Gas	Nuclear	Other
2000	24.8	69.3	4.8	0.3	0.7	0.1
2002	27.1	58.6	1.6	7.5	4.2	1.0

Will the changes to China's electricity production help the environment? Use data from the table to explain your answer. *(3 marks)*

12 An 'ecological footprint' is the measure of how much land and water a human population needs to produce the resources required to sustain itself and to absorb its wastes.

The average American uses 25 hectares to support his or her current lifestyle.
The average Canadian uses 18 hectares.
The average Italian uses 10 hectares.

a Explain why Americans have larger ecological footprints than Italians. *(2 marks)*

b Suggest **three** ways in which ecological footprints can be reduced. *(3 marks)*

Everything we use comes from the Earth in one way or another. Rock is a material that we can often use straight from the ground. Blocks of stone are cut out of quarries. Limestone is a very common rock, and many old buildings were built using blocks of limestone. If you look closely you can sometimes see fossils in the limestone blocks.

▲ Many old buildings in Oxford are built from limestone.

Chemistry to the rescue

For modern buildings we don't use the natural, raw materials from the Earth directly. You can't build skyscrapers from blocks of limestone. Creative ideas in science and technology have helped us to develop new building materials. The raw materials have to be changed by chemical reactions before we use them.

New buildings such as the Lloyd's building in London are mostly made from concrete and glass. These materials have been used for a long time – the Romans used concrete for buildings nearly 2000 years ago. Over the last 100 years scientists have found out how to make stronger and more versatile concrete. It has become the most important building material of all.

The Romans also used glass – but only in small pieces. Some very old British houses still have tiny glass window panes, which were the best that could be made at the time. But glass technology has improved dramatically over the last 100 years. Now we can make huge sheets to cover our fantastic modern skyscrapers.

What are the raw materials?

Concrete is made from limestone and clay, mixed with sand and gravel.

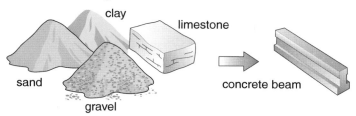

Glass is made from sand and limestone.

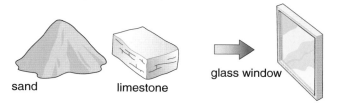

The effects of extraction

Digging out rocks leaves big holes – quarries. Unfortunately, the best limestone is often found in scenic areas, such as the Peak District. Quarries can be ugly places that spoil the natural beauty of the landscape. Of course, once the rock has been removed, the soil can be replaced and trees planted. Some old quarries have been successfully turned into nature reserves or country parks. Elsewhere, old quarries have been used to build shopping malls, such as Bluewater in Kent. More imaginatively, an old clay pit in Cornwall has been turned into the amazing Eden Project.

Quarries are noisy and dirty. Rock is blasted from the quarry face by explosives, spreading dust far and wide. Rock-crushing and sorting machinery rattles away all day and huge lorries rumble down local roads. Most people wouldn't like a quarry next to their home. But we need the limestone for making concrete and other important materials. Quarries also provide employment for local people, which helps the local economy.

▲ The Eden Project near St Austell in Cornwall.

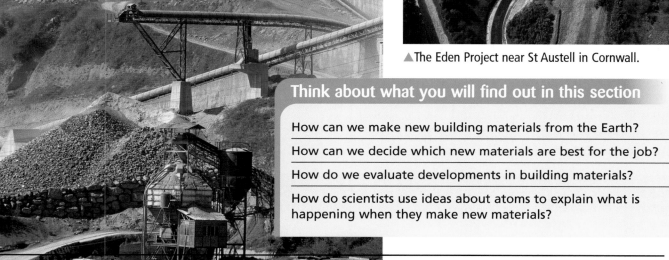

Think about what you will find out in this section

How can we make new building materials from the Earth?

How can we decide which new materials are best for the job?

How do we evaluate developments in building materials?

How do scientists use ideas about atoms to explain what is happening when they make new materials?

Tiny particles

If you crushed limestone to a powder, you would have a lot of tiny fragments of limestone. But limestone is made of really tiny atoms. There are about 3 million million million million (3×10^{24}) atoms in 100 g of limestone.

Naming the atoms

Most materials are made from atoms joined by chemical reactions. Limestone is made of three different types of atoms: calcium, carbon and oxygen. They make a chemical compound called calcium carbonate. Glass is made from calcium, silicon and oxygen atoms. These atoms make a chemical compound called calcium silicate.

There are about 100 different kinds of atoms – or elements. Each element has a symbol. Calcium is Ca, carbon is C, oxygen is O and silicon is Si. Calcium carbonate is $CaCO_3$ and calcium silicate is $CaSiO_3$.

Question

a How many atoms would there be in 1 kg of limestone?

Question

b Sulfuric acid has the formula H_2SO_4. What atoms does it contain? And how many of each?

Inside the atom

In their earliest ideas about atoms, people thought of atoms as simple balls. We often draw them like this when we are making simple models of chemical reactions. But 100 years ago, scientists discovered that the atoms themselves were made of even smaller particles.

Atoms have a small central **nucleus**. Whizzing in orbit around the nucleus are the tiny **electrons**. It is the moving electrons that give the atoms their shape. They also control chemical reactions between elements and compounds.

▲ This simple model of an atom shows electrons orbiting the nucleus in a similar way to planets orbiting the Sun in the solar system.

Electrons rule chemistry

When a chemical reaction takes place between atoms, electrons may move from one atom to another or be shared between atoms.

When metals and non-metals combine, the metals give up some electrons and the non-metals take them. Sodium and chlorine form a compound like this called sodium chloride. This is common salt. The sodium and chlorine atoms are stacked up in a **lattice**.

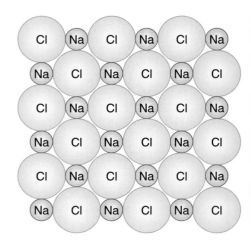

Question

c Describe what happens to some of the electrons when iron atoms react with oxygen atoms to form iron oxide.

When non-metals combine, the atoms share electrons and form molecules. Carbon and oxygen combine like this to form carbon dioxide (CO_2). Hydrogen and oxygen form water (H_2O).

Atoms of elements such as oxygen can also share electrons and make molecules all on their own. The oxygen in the air forms O_2 molecules.

This sharing or moving of electrons from one atom to another makes the **chemical bonds** that hold atoms together in chemical compounds.

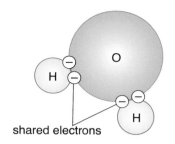
shared electrons

Conserving atoms

When chemicals react, the atoms just rearrange themselves. You always end up with the same number of each type of atom as you started with. You can show this as a balanced equation. For example, calcium oxide reacts with carbon dioxide to form calcium carbonate:

$$CaO + CO_2 \rightarrow CaCO_3$$

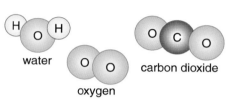
water   oxygen   carbon dioxide

Different properties

Different elements have different properties, but there is a pattern to this variation. You can see this in the periodic table. Each vertical column, or group, shows elements with similar properties.

When elements react to form compounds, the compounds have completely different properties from the elements that make them. For example, calcium is a metal, carbon a black solid non-metal and oxygen is a gas. Yet calcium carbonate, made from all three, is limestone.

Questions

d Which of these elements are metals and which are non-metals?
  barium (Ba)   selenium (Se)
  molybdenum (Mo)   radon (Rn)
  lithium (Li)
e Which group contains the most reactive metals?
f Which group contains totally unreactive non-metals?

Group number

1	2											3	4	5	6	7	0
																	He
Li	Be											B	C	N	O	F	Ne
Na	Mg											Al	Si	P	S	Cl	Ar
K	Ca	Sc	Ti	V	Cr	Mn	Fe	Co	Ni	Cu	Zn	Ga	Ge	As	Se	Br	Kr
Rb	Sr	Y	Zr	Nb	Mo	Tc	Ru	Rh	Pd	Ag	Cd	In	Sn	Sb	Te	I	Xe
Cs	Ba	La	Hf	Ta	W	Re	Os	Ir	Pt	Au	Hg	Tl	Pb	Bi	Po	At	Rn
Fr	Ra	Ac															

H

non-metals   metals

Key points

- Atoms have a small nucleus, around which are electrons.
- Atoms and symbols are used to represent and explain what is happening in chemical reactions.
- Elements form compounds by giving and taking electrons or by sharing electrons to form chemical bonds.

Using limestone

Limestone is a common rock with many uses. It is found in many of the most beautiful parts of the country. It is blasted out from the cliffs in large quarries. Some people say that these quarries spoil the natural beauty of the countryside.

Limestone has been used as a building stone for thousands of years. The castle in the photograph was made from blocks taken straight from a quarry. Today, most limestone is used to make something new. It is changed by chemical processes into other useful products such as cement, or is broken up for roads or concrete.

Limestone is a very important raw material. About 90 million tonnes of limestone are quarried every year in Britain alone. We use the limestone:

- for buildings or road 'chippings' (66 million tonnes)
- to neutralise excess acid in lakes or soils (1 million tonnes)
- to make cement (15 million tonnes)
- in other industrial processes (8 million tonnes).

Question

a Use the data to draw a pie chart showing the uses of quarried limestone.

Making new materials from limestone

Limestone is the compound calcium carbonate. Its chemical formula is $CaCO_3$. This means that for every calcium atom there is one carbon atom and three oxygen atoms. All carbonates have one carbon atom and three oxygen atoms arranged like this in a lattice.

▲ Calcite – the natural crystal form of calcium carbonate.

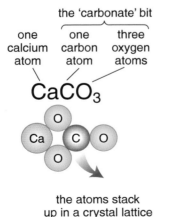

one calcium atom	one carbon atom	three oxygen atoms

the 'carbonate' bit

$$CaCO_3$$

the atoms stack up in a crystal lattice

If limestone is heated strongly, the compound breaks up and the atoms are rearranged.

- The carbon atom takes two oxygen atoms to form carbon dioxide.
- The calcium atom is left with just one oxygen atom. This is calcium oxide, which is also called **quicklime**.

calcium carbonate $\xrightarrow{\text{heat}}$ calcium oxide + carbon dioxide

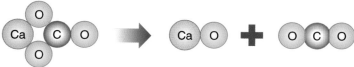

Question

b Copy and complete this equation. Make sure it is balanced.
$CaCO_3 \rightarrow CaO +$ _____

Breaking down a compound by heating it like this is called **thermal decomposition**. As in all chemical reactions you end up with the same atoms – they have just been rearranged. So the products have the same mass as the reactants. You can see the conservation of mass in these examples:

100 g of calcium carbonate gives 56 g of calcium oxide and 44 g of carbon dioxide

or

20 g of calcium carbonate gives 11.2 g of calcium oxide and 8.8 g of carbon dioxide

Reacting quicklime

Quicklime is a very strong alkali. It reacts with water to form calcium hydroxide, also known as **slaked lime**. A lot of heat energy is given out in this reaction.

calcium oxide + water $\rightarrow$ calcium hydroxide + heat energy
CaO + H_2O $\rightarrow$ $Ca(OH)_2$

Farmers have used slaked lime for centuries as a simple fertiliser to make their soil less acid. It also helps to break up the soil so that plants can grow well. Sometimes lakes are polluted by acid rain. Slaked lime can be used to get rid of the acid there as well.

Questions

c If 28 g of calcium oxide reacts completely with 22 g of carbon dioxide, what mass of calcium carbonate would you get?

d In the thermal decomposition of calcium carbonate, the solid calcium oxide left behind weighs less than the calcium carbonate. Why?

e Iron carbonate ($FeCO_3$) breaks down just like calcium carbonate. What new chemicals would you get if you heated this?

f Copper carbonate ($CuCO_3$) breaks down in the same way to give copper oxide (CuO). Write a balanced equation for this reaction.

g Quicklime has to be handled very carefully. Explain why.

h Mixing 56 g of quicklime with water makes 74 g of dry slaked like. What mass of water has reacted with the quicklime to make this?

Key points

- The formula of a compound shows the number and type of atoms in it.
- In chemical reactions, atoms are rearranged. No atoms are lost or made, so we can represent reactions using balanced equations.
- Limestone can be used as a building material or as a raw material for new products.
- Limestone ($CaCO_3$) and other carbonates can be broken down by thermal decomposition.

New rocks from old

Rock or 'artificial rock'?

These statues look very similar. One took a sculptor many weeks to make by shaping the limestone. The other was made by simply pouring concrete into a mould. Concrete is like an 'artificial rock'.

Making mortar, cement and concrete

Houses in many parts of Britain were traditionally built from bricks stuck together with **mortar**. The mortar is made by mixing slaked lime (made from quicklime) with water to make a thick paste. This dries and sets hard between the bricks, holding them together. Over time it reacts with carbon dioxide from the air and turns back to limestone. In many old houses this mortar has turned soft and crumbly. The bricks have to be 're-pointed' with fresh cement to stop the old mortar washing away in the rain.

Today, most quarried limestone is used to make **cement**. The limestone is heated with clay in a big oven and thermal decomposition occurs. The oven is called a rotary kiln because it keeps turning to mix everything up. The roasted product is then ground to form a light grey powder. This is cement. It forms a paste with water which soon hardens back to rock, like mortar, but the chemical reaction is more complicated. A series of chemical reactions take place involving calcium, silicon, oxygen, iron and aluminium. The new compounds form tiny crystals which interlock tightly to make a hard, rock-like material.

Cement is used to stick bricks together today instead of simple mortar. But most cement is mixed with sand, gravel and water to make **concrete**. This is cheaper and stronger than pure cement.

> **Question**
>
> **a** Heating limestone to make quicklime releases lots of the greenhouse gas carbon dioxide into the air. Why is this not a problem if the quicklime is turned into slaked lime and used to make mortar?

> **Question**
>
> **b** Every tonne of limestone that is turned into cement releases 440 kg of carbon dioxide into the atmosphere. Suggest one disadvantage of modern cement over old-fashioned mortar.

Concrete forms a thick liquid when first mixed, and can be poured into any shape. Slow chemical reactions make it set after a few hours and eventually it becomes rock hard. It is used to make roads, bridges and the frameworks and foundations of buildings.

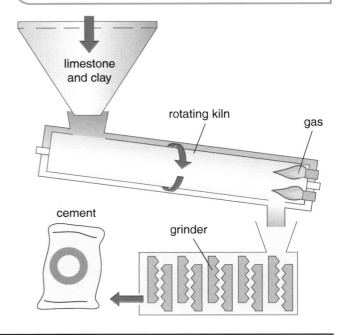

limestone and clay

rotating kiln

gas

cement

grinder

Making glass

Small pieces of glass have been used for thousands of years. But these days glass is a very important building material. Many modern buildings are completely covered in glass. Glass is also made from limestone. This time the limestone reacts with another common raw material – sand.

Pure sand is usually grains of silicon dioxide. Glass is made by heating very pure sand with limestone and a little soda (sodium carbonate). The chemicals react, melt, and carbon dioxide is released. When this liquid cools, it forms a hard, but brittle, transparent material – glass.

$$\text{calcium carbonate} + \text{silicon dioxide} \rightarrow \text{calcium silicate} + \text{carbon dioxide}$$

▲ The Swiss Tower, London (better known as the London Gherkin).

> **Question**
>
> **c** Copy and complete this to make a balanced equation.
> $CaCO_3 + SiO_2 \rightarrow$ _____ + _____

Smart glass

Sunlight can damage your eyes, so it is a good idea to wear sunglasses on a very sunny day. But what can you do if you already wear glasses? Smart glass to the rescue! Photochromic glasses contain special dyes in the glass of the lenses which darken in sunlight – but go clear again when the sun goes in.

> **Question**
>
> **d** The first photochromic glasses took a few minutes to clear when the light levels dropped. Why was this a problem for motorists driving into tunnels?

As this glass gets cheaper, it could be used for windows in sunny offices or classrooms instead of blinds.

One new form of glass even has a special coating that automatically cleans itself. This uses the energy from the ultra violet rays in sunlight to break down the dirt. Rain then simply washes it away!

> **Question**
>
> **e** Suggest some of the problems of working in a glass office building and of maintaining such a building.

> **Key points**
>
> ● Limestone can be used as the raw material for quicklime, slaked lime, cement and concrete.
> ● Limestone is also the raw material for glass, along with sand.

Concrete: beauty or the beast?

When architects designed the Royal Festival Hall in London over 50 years ago, they wanted to show off their new building material. They left the concrete exposed for all to see. Some people like it, but many find the buildings ugly. It doesn't help that the gleaming white concrete soon gets streaked and dirty in polluted London.

The Bahai Lotus temple in Delhi is also made of concrete. Concrete is so versatile you can build whatever you like from it. The only limit is your imagination. The world is dotted with brilliantly imaginative buildings that rely totally on concrete.

▲ The Royal Festival Hall was built in 1951 as part of the Festival of Britain.

Getting the best out of concrete

Building with quarried stone was a slow and labour-intensive process. Each block had to be carefully cut to shape and fitted into place by an expert craftsman. This made it slow and very expensive.

▲ The Bahai Lotus temple in Delhi, India, which was built in 1980.

In comparison, building with concrete is quick, cheap and easy.

- Cement is relatively cheap to produce on an industrial scale.
- Powdered cement is easy to store and transport.
- Sand and gravel can be found almost anywhere and are cheap materials. You can even recycle building rubble or ash from power stations to use as gravel.
- Liquid concrete can be easily mixed on site.
- Liquid concrete can be moulded into any shape you want: floor, girders, domes, ornaments.
- Once it sets it really is rock hard.

Concrete has one problem that it shares with quarried limestone. It is very strong if you squash it, so it can support very large buildings such as skyscrapers. But it is brittle, so if you stretch or bend it, it can crack easily. To overcome this problem, concrete beams or girders are reinforced with steel rods. These stop the concrete from stretching and cracking.

Questions

a Explain why it would be hard to build a limestone block skyscraper.
b Old buildings often had wooden beams over doors and windows to support the weight of stone or brick above. The wood was strong enough and could bend slightly without cracking. Today these beams are more likely to be made of concrete.
  (i) What advantage does wood have over simple concrete for this use?
  (ii) How could the concrete be made stronger, to overcome this problem?
  (iii) What's the disadvantage of using wood if you want your building to last a very long time? (Hint: What happens to wood eventually?)

Getting the best out of glass

Glass is a wonderful material. Glass-fronted offices give a feeling of space because you can see outside. Many people like to feel the warmth of the sun through the glass, and this can help to cut down heating costs as well. But this can be a problem in the summer, when the building could trap heat like a greenhouse and become too hot to work in.

Ordinary glass has one disadvantage. It is brittle and breaks into razor-sharp pieces. Fortunately, advances in technology mean glass can be made much tougher. One way is to heat it and then cool it quickly. This makes the glass five times as strong. Toughened glass is used in places where ordinary glass would shatter, such as car windscreens.

Car windscreen glass still shatters in a crash, but it breaks into small but chunky pieces that are not so sharp as ordinary glass slivers. More modern versions have an internal plastic layer that holds all the pieces together. As technology improves, glass keeps getting better and better. But even the best glass will shatter if there is an explosion or a building is shaken by a powerful earthquake.

Questions

c Suggest two ways to stop glass buildings overheating in summer.
d Suggest what problems there might be in winter.
e Suggest some places other than car windscreens where toughened glass ought to be used.
f Suggest a reason why we don't use toughened glass all the time.
g Describe how modern car windscreens have made it easier to replace a windscreen and clean up after a crash.

Key points

- Concrete is a strong, inexpensive and easy to use material for building. It is very versatile but needs to be reinforced with steel to stop it cracking if used for beams or girders. Some people think concrete buildings are ugly.
- Glass-fronted buildings can be good to work in as they are light and airy, but they can overheat in summer if not designed well. Broken glass is also very sharp and dangerous.

Useful metals

Technology relies on the strength of metals for constructing everything from aeroplanes to tin cans. Thousands of kilometres of electric cables snake across the country to bring us the power we need for our electrical equipment. We are very dependent on metals.

The useful properties of metals

It is the useful properties of metals that make them important.

- Metals are strong and hard, which makes them good structural materials. We use them to build machines, bridges and the frameworks for large buildings.
- Metals are easy to shape. Car body panels are pressed out of sheet steel.
- Metals have high melting points. This means that you can build engines that won't melt when you use them.
- Metals also conduct heat and electricity. They are used in electrical wiring and as 'heat sinks', to conduct heat energy away from microprocessors, to stop them overheating.

Are there problems with metals?

Some properties of metals are less useful.

- Some metals such as gold are very rare and so very expensive.
- Some metals are expensive because they are difficult to extract.
- Pure metals are too soft to be of much use, so scientists have worked out how to make **alloys** with improved properties.
- Metals corrode. We spend money and effort getting iron from the rocks – but leave any iron object lying about in the rain and you end up with a pile of rust.
- Metals pollute. Waste metal can corrode and get into the soil and groundwater. This can kill plants and animals. If it gets into the food chain it can harm us too.

▲ The *Pacific Princess* is a typical metal-hulled ship.

And what if we run out?

Modern technology relies on metals. But at present rates, using today's mining techniques, we may run out of many important metals over the next 100 years. What can we do to stop this happening? Some scientists are trying to find new sources of metals and new ways of extracting them. Others are looking for better ways to recycle the metals we have.

Steel or wood?

When builders and architects are looking at what materials to use, they have to evaluate the materials by looking at their properties, advantages, disadvantages, availability and costs.

In the USA, many houses are built using wooden beams, which cost 10% less than the steel equivalent. Overall, similar houses cost 10% more if built using steel. Wood is cheaper because it is a natural, renewable raw material. Steel has to be manufactured from finite iron ore sources. Wood can be cut and shaped on site, but steel beams arrive ready made in fixed sizes.

One of the disadvantages of wood is that it may rot in time. Steel is longer lasting, though it can rust if it is not protected. Although wood is strong enough for buildings of small to moderate size, it is not strong enough for large buildings. Steel beams are strong enough for even the tallest skyscraper.

▲ The Tamar road bridge.

▲ Japanese bullet train.

Think about what you will find out in this section

How do we get metals from their ores?

How are the most commonly used metals iron and steel made?

How can science help to make recycling easier?

How do we improve metals to make them better suited to their uses?

How can we evaluate our use of metals as structural and smart materials?

Getting at the metal

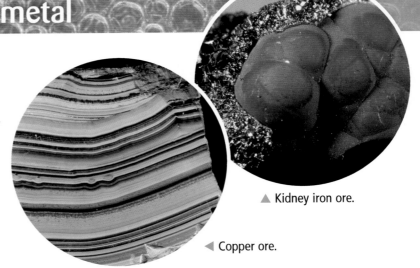

▲ Kidney iron ore.

Where do metals come from?

Metals are found in chemical compounds in the rocks of the Earth. Some metals are quite common. A field of mud contains tonnes of aluminium, and a lot of iron too. The trouble is the metals are far too difficult to extract. Fortunately, natural processes sometimes concentrate metals in certain rocks, which makes it easier and cheaper to extract them. Rocks like this are called **ores**.

◄ Copper ore.

Which metals are common?

Aluminium and iron are two metals we use a lot. As you can see from the table, they are also very common in rocks. But some other important metals, such as copper and gold, are really very rare.

Metal	Percentage of the rocks of the Earth's crust
aluminium	7
iron	4
magnesium	2
copper	0.004 5
tin	0.000 2
gold	0.000 000 5

> **Question**
>
> **a** How much more common is iron than gold? Choose from 8 thousand times, 80 thousand times, 8 million times or 80 million times.

Iron is king

Iron is the metal we use most. In 2004, the global production of iron topped 1 billion tonnes for the first time. That is 20 times as much iron as all the other metals put together. Production on this scale helps to make iron cheap compared to aluminium, even though aluminium is more common. But iron is also cheaper because of the way it is extracted from its ore.

Metal	Price per tonne (spring 2005)
aluminium	£1800
copper	£3300
iron	£300
tin	£8000

Reactivity and metals

Gold is a very unreactive metal. It does not react with other elements. It may be rare but, if you are very lucky, you could find a nugget of pure gold!

> **Question**
>
> **b** Explain why rare gold was discovered before common aluminium.

► Gold was well known to the Ancient Egyptians.

Aluminium is a very reactive metal. Because of this, the aluminium atoms are tightly combined in compounds with other atoms such as oxygen. Mud contains plenty of aluminium, but you cannot easily extract it. You never find aluminium as a pure element in the Earth's crust.

Carbon reduction and oxidation

Carbon is more reactive than metals such as iron and copper, so it can displace these metals from their compounds. We can use carbon like this to get less reactive metals from their ores.

▲ There is plenty of aluminium in this mud! But how could you tell?

Question

c Explain why you can't get aluminium from its ore by this method.

Metal ores are usually oxides. When we react the ore with carbon, the carbon combines with oxygen from the ore to form carbon dioxide. The carbon is oxidised. This is an **oxidation** reaction.

The metal oxide ore has its oxygen taken away. The oxide is reduced to the metal. This process is called **reduction**. Reduction is the chemical opposite of oxidation, and the two reactions always go together. For example, with copper oxide:

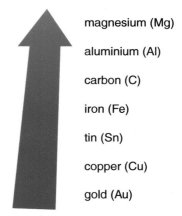

most reactive

magnesium (Mg)

aluminium (Al)

carbon (C)

iron (Fe)

tin (Sn)

copper (Cu)

gold (Au)

least reactive

$$\text{copper oxide} + \text{carbon} \rightarrow \text{copper} + \text{carbon dioxide}$$

reduction

oxidation

$$2CuO + C \rightarrow 2Cu + CO_2$$

Metals have been made using this method for thousands of years. Originally the carbon was in the form of charcoal. Today coke (made from coal) is used instead.

The Wealden Forest in Kent doesn't have any trees now. They were all chopped down to make charcoal for iron production at the start of the Industrial Revolution.

Questions

d Tin oxide (SnO_2) reacts with carbon to give tin and carbon dioxide. Write this as a word equation, showing the oxidation and reduction arrows.

e Copy and complete the equation. $SnO_2 + C \rightarrow$ _____ + _____

f Write a simple word equation for the reduction of iron oxide by carbon.

Key points

● Ores are found in the Earth and contain metal compounds from which the metal can be extracted. Some metals are more economic to extract than others.

● Metals such as copper can be extracted by carbon reduction.

Wanted by all

Iron is the most widely used metal, so we need to produce plenty of it to supply the world. Over the last 300 years scientists have refined the carbon reduction method to make it very efficient. But iron is not as easy to extract as copper, tin or other less reactive metals.

Iron plays hard to get

Carbon reduction reactions need a kick-start of energy to get them going. For copper and tin, the heat from a simple fire will do it. But for iron, much more energy is needed to get the reaction started. You can make charcoal burn at a very high temperature by providing more oxygen. Fanning a barbecue provides more oxygen and makes it hotter. This idea is used in a blast furnace to reach the very high temperatures needed to reduce the iron ore.

▲ Molten iron pours from a blast furnace.

Question

a Blacksmiths used bellows for pumping air. Why was this better than fanning the charcoal?

Inside the blast furnace

Iron ore (haematite, a type of iron oxide), coke (carbon) and limestone are tipped in at the top of the blast furnace. The main reaction is the reduction of iron oxide and the oxidation of carbon.

iron oxide + carbon → iron + carbon dioxide

Question

b Complete the balanced equation for this reaction:
$2Fe_2O_3 + 3C \rightarrow$ ___$Fe +$ ___CO_2

Most iron ore used today is only about 50% iron oxide. This will produce about 350 kg of iron per tonne (1000 kg) of ore. But the impurities from 1 tonne of ore will react with the limestone to make just under 1 tonne of waste material called slag.

Question

c *Here is a working 'recipe' for a blast furnace using the 50% ore. How much 'missing mass' is there? How can you account for it?*

Cast iron – carbon makes the difference

The iron that comes from the blast furnace is called cast iron. It's 96% iron with about 4% carbon (and some other impurities). The impurities make it very hard but quite brittle. If you hit it with a heavy hammer it would shatter. In the past, cast iron was used to make everything from manhole covers to bathtubs. It was used to make girders for the bridge at Ironbridge in Shropshire. Nowadays it is thought to be too brittle for most uses.

Question

d *Ironbridge in Shropshire was fine for horses and carts. Why couldn't this cast iron bridge be used for modern heavy lorries?*

Pure iron can be made by bubbling oxygen through the molten iron to burn out the carbon. But pure iron is very soft – too soft to use for construction. Fortunately it can be made much harder by leaving just a little carbon – just 1% or so. This new material is hard and tough! This alloy of iron is called steel. All the iron we use today is in this form.

The price of steel

The world price of metal changes over time, depending on what it costs to extract metal from its ore, the percentage of metal in its ore and its availability, as well as the supply and the demand for it in the world market.

Questions

e *Over the last few years, China and India have started to industrialise very rapidly. What effect do you think this has had on the demand for steel?*

f *What effect do you think that had on the price of steel on the world market?*

For every tonne of ore add:
850 kg limestone
and
50 kg coal

You should get:
350 kg iron
and
910 kg slag

Key points

- Iron is extracted from its ore in a blast furnace.
- Impurities make cast iron very brittle but pure iron is very soft.
- Iron is most useful when converted into steel with the addition of 1% carbon, making an alloy.

Why are alloys harder than pure metal?

In a pure metal all the atoms are the same, stacked up in a regular way. They are strongly held together, but the layers of atoms can slide over one another if a force is applied. In an alloy, a few different atoms have been added. These are not the same size as the rest.

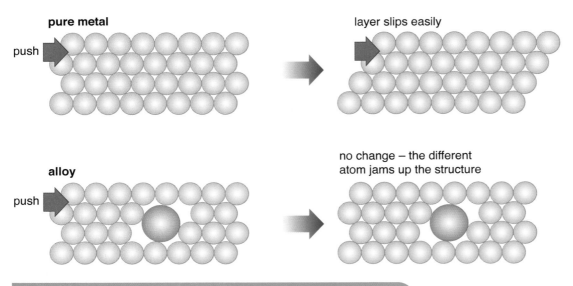

Question

a Use the diagram to explain how the different atoms stop the layers from sliding easily and make the alloy harder.

The best steel for the job

Adding carbon to iron makes it harder because the layers of atoms can't slide so easily. But adding too much carbon makes the lattice weaker. It becomes brittle. The graph shows how steel hardness and strength change with just a small change in the amount of carbon.

- Mild steel (<0.5% carbon) is quite soft. In thin sheets it can be pressed and moulded.
- Medium steel (0.5–1.0% carbon) is harder. It is strong enough to use for hammers.
- High-carbon steel (1–1.5% carbon) is hard enough to give a good cutting edge. It is not as strong as medium steel and can be brittle.

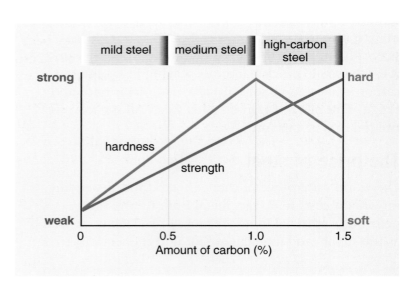

Question

b Which type of steel would be best for: (i) scissors and chisels, (ii) making car body panels and (iii) making hammers or spanners? Explain your answers, using the graph to help.

Special steels that don't corrode

Sometimes other metals are added to steel to give new alloys with special properties. Nickel is added to make a very tough steel. Tungsten is added to make a very hard steel. Adding 15% or so of chromium has a different effect. This stainless steel does not rust.

Question

c Stainless steel is perfect for cutlery, razor blades and the steam pipes of power stations. Explain the problems that corrosion would cause in each of these cases if stainless steel wasn't used.

Smart alloys

Pure copper, aluminium and even gold would be too soft to use on their own, so they are also mixed with other metals to make useful alloys which are harder.

- Gold is mixed with a little copper for jewellery.
- Aluminium is mixed with magnesium and a little copper for building aeroplanes.

Question

d Brass is made from copper and zinc. Why are bolts and hinges made from brass and not copper? Explain the difference in properties.

Metal scientists can now make fantastic new alloys with improved properties. At their simplest, some are *superelastic*. They can be bent and twisted without damage – great for making glasses that don't break if you sit on them! But some alloys have even smarter properties. They can be bent at low temperatures but they snap back to shape if they warm up. These shape memory alloys are made from metal combinations such as nickel/titanium or copper/nickel/aluminium.

Many people who suffer from heart disease have blocked or collapsed arteries. A wire grid can open the arteries up, but how can it be put in place? A grid made from a shape memory alloy can be cooled and squashed to fit in easily. As it warms up in the body, it snaps back to size and opens the artery.

collapsed artery   squashed grid in place   warms and expands

Key points

- There are many different types of steel, with different properties depending on the carbon content.
- There are many other alloys made with other metals to give useful properties.
- Smart alloys can return to their original shape after being deformed.

Question

e Orthodontists have to screw brace wires tight every few weeks to pull teeth into line. This is difficult and wires can sometimes be made painfully tight. Stretched cold 'smart wires' could be used which would contract in a much more controlled way when they warmed. How would this be better?

A hole in the ground

Copper is a very important metal, but there is only a thousandth as much of it in the Earth as there is iron. So when we find a big body of concentrated copper ore we just keep on digging till we've got it all out. The Bingham Canyon mine in Utah, USA, is now nearly 1 km deep!

What's so good about copper?

Copper is one of the **transition metals** from the central block of the periodic table. The transition block contains the 'everyday' metals. They are useful materials to make things from as they are hard and strong – unlike the metals in Groups 1 and 2. They can be bent or hammered into shape and will keep their new shape. Like all metals, they also conduct heat and electricity.

Copper is particularly useful as it is such a good electrical conductor. It is also soft and bendy, so it's great for electrical wires. Copper is not very reactive and so does not corrode like steel. This makes it useful for copper pipes for plumbing.

						B	
						Al	
Fe	Co	Ni	Cu	Zn	Ga	Ge
Ru	Rh	Pd	Ag	Cd	In	Sn
Os	Ir	Pt	Au	Hg	Tl	Pb

Getting out the metal

Digging copper ore out of the ground is just the start of the extraction process. The copper is usually in the form of copper sulfide crystals scattered through the rock. In the past, this was converted to copper oxide and then the copper was extracted from the ore by reduction.

Question

a In ski resorts, copper sheeting is sometimes used for roofs. Suggest two reasons why copper might be used here instead of cheaper steel.

▶ The Bingham Canyon copper mine, Utah, USA.

There are just a few major copper mines dotted around the world – in the USA, South America, Africa and some islands around the Pacific. The ore only contains about 1% of copper. Separating out the copper by reduction is too expensive, so nowadays other methods are used. One method is called leaching. Acid is sprayed onto the rock. Soluble copper compounds dissolve out of the rock and the solution is collected. The copper is then removed by **electrolysis** – breaking the compound apart using electricity.

We use large amounts of copper and the copper mines will soon be exhausted. Many old mines are now reworking their old waste tips to get out more of the copper by leaching.

So what's the future?

Leaching can get just a fraction of 1% of copper from the rocks, but scientists are working hard to find ways of extracting smaller and smaller fractions. One new method involves using special bacteria that 'eat' the copper from the rock.

Another problem is that even if we find a new source of copper, environmentalists have started to object to mining companies ripping great holes in the Earth! Open-cast copper mines are very large and very ugly.

A new leaching method that does not affect the environment so much involves drilling down to the ore. Acid is then pumped down to the ore and comes back up to the surface rich in copper for processing. You don't need to dig big, ugly holes in the ground and as long as you can collect all of the solution that comes back up, the environment is not polluted.

But will we still need copper?

Copper is mainly used for wiring. But new communications systems use laser light, shone along glass fibres, instead of sending information along electrical wires. The most modern systems are now completely 'wireless'. So perhaps we won't need so much copper in the future after all!

◀ 'Peacock' copper ore.

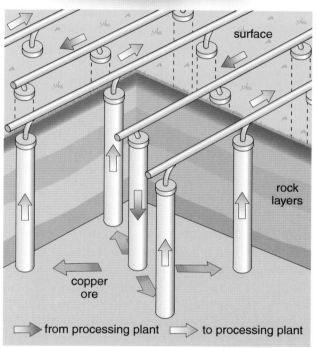
surface

rock layers

copper ore

⬜➡ from processing plant   ⬜➡ to processing plant

Question

b A mining company wants to develop a new open-cast copper mine near you. What objections would you have to the plan and what alternatives could you suggest?

Key points

- Transition metals are good conductors of electricity and heat and can be bent into shape – properties which make them very useful.
- Copper is extracted by electrolysis but other ways are being developed to use ores with low copper content and limit environmental impact.

Questions

c What will happen to the price of copper if demand falls?
d What will happen to the mines?
e What would be the wider effects on the society, the economy and the environment of mining areas if copper was no longer needed?

Useful metals with low densities

Steel may be fantastic for cars, trains and ships but its high density makes it useless for aircraft. An aircraft made from steel would weigh twice as much as a modern plane. It would never get off the ground!

Aluminium is not as strong as steel but its density is very much lower. This combination is just right to make a plane that is both strong enough *and* light enough to fly. Without aluminium there could be no commercial airlines.

▶ Commercial aircraft rely on lightweight yet strong aluminium.

▼ High-performance fighters need even stronger (but more expensive) titanium.

Metal	Density (g/cm³)	Strength	Melting point (°C)
pure aluminium	2.7	low	660
steel	7.7	high	1540
titanium	4.5	high	1670
Duralumin alloy	2.8	medium	600

Supersonic fighter jets need to fly so fast that the wings would get hot enough to melt aluminium. A new 'supermetal' was needed that was strong and had a low density but a high melting point. Titanium fitted the bill perfectly. Titanium is as strong as steel but its density is low enough to keep the weight down. An added bonus is that its melting point is higher than that of steel – high enough to withstand the frictional heating caused by supersonic flight.

Question

a *Pure aluminium is not used for aircraft. It is combined with magnesium and a little copper to make Duralumin alloy. Why do you think that is?*

The cost of extraction

Aluminium is more reactive than carbon. You can't use the carbon reduction method to get aluminium from its ores. Aluminium ore has to be melted and then split apart using large amounts of energy in the form of electricity. Aluminium plants have to have their own power station to provide this. This is a very costly process which makes common aluminium much more expensive than iron.

Question

b *Some of the first aluminium plants were built in the mountains of Scotland. What relatively cheap method of making electricity do you think they used? (Hint: Look at the photo.)*

Titanium is also more reactive than carbon and so can't be made by carbon reduction. But titanium is less common than aluminium and its concentrated ores are harder to find. It is also much harder to extract from its ore. This means that titanium is much more expensive even than aluminium. It is only used where high performance is more important than cost.

Question

c Some lower performance supersonic planes just use titanium for the nose-cone and leading wing edges. Suggest two reasons for this.

Resisting corrosion

Aluminium and titanium share another useful property. They both resist corrosion well. That is why aluminium foil stays shiny. Titanium resists corrosion much better than aluminium and stainless steel. It can be used safely where even stainless steel would corrode away, for example in nuclear power stations – or inside the human body!

Question

d What would happen in time if the hip replacement shown on this X-ray photograph was made from steel?

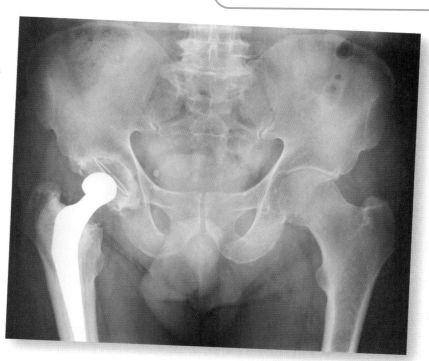

Recycling metals

The table shows which metals we **recycle** in Britain.

Metal	% recycled in Britain
aluminium	43
copper	45
iron	46
lead	61
tin	30
zinc	14

Questions

e Which metal is recycled the most?
f Aluminium is the commonest metal in the Earth's crust. Explain why it is particularly important to recycle aluminium despite this.

Key points

- Aluminium and titanium have two very useful properties: low density and resistance to corrosion. However, their extraction is expensive as it requires a lot of energy.
- We need to recycle metals as much as possible because the amount of ore is limited and extraction is costly in terms of energy and its impact on the environment.

Scarce resources

Earth is like a spaceship. We all live and get everything we need from it. There are nearly 6 billion people on the planet and we are consuming Earth's resources at an alarming rate. Fossil fuels like oil and gas will soon run out. Some metal ores will become scarce within the next 100 years or so.

Metal	Proven reserves will last until ...
tin	2030
copper	2030
tungsten	2050
aluminium	2050
nickel	2100

Questions

a Which metals might run out in your lifetime using today's mining techniques?

b Iron is unlikely to run out in the near future. But steels used for machinery or other high-performance uses are alloyed with metals such as vanadium and manganese that will run out. What problems would society face if we ran out of metals for these important alloys?

All mined out

Some optimists think that using up metal ore resources is not really a problem. As our technology improves it becomes possible to extract metals from poorer quality ores. The waste tips from early mines have often been successfully reworked. Also, if a metal starts to run out, the price goes up, so old mines that had to close when prices were low might reopen when prices rise.

Are we exploiting poorer countries?

Some countries are rich in mineral resources, while others have few. Industrial societies are buying up more than their fair share of the global resources. Sometimes it is because the countries of the developed world have used up their own resources. But even if the ore is still available in developed countries, it is often cheaper to mine in developing countries because the wages of the miners and other costs are so low. This does have some benefits as it provides jobs for people in the developing countries. But sometimes the working conditions are not very good and health and safety rules are not applied as strictly as they would be in the West.

Zambia is a poor country. Its economy relies on exports of copper from its huge copper mines. Forty years ago Zambia was encouraged to take out huge loans from the World Bank to develop these mines. They said it would raise the standard of living for all Zambians.

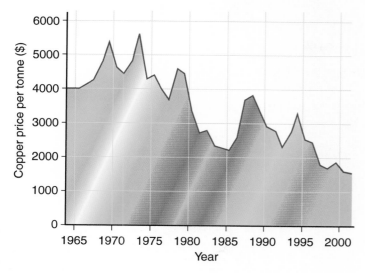

Questions

c What happened to the price paid for copper in the late 1970s?

d What effect do you think this had on the people and economy of Zambia?

e Do you think the advice from the World Bank was good or not? Explain your answer.

The economics of recycling

Recycling costs money. One of the problems is that waste material may well have lots of different metals mixed up. It is only economically viable at the moment for metals that are easy to separate such as iron and steel, or expensive metals such as gold. As technology improves, perhaps we will be able to do this for all metals.

Alucycle is a large company that produces 1 million tonnes of aluminium goods every year. It has its own plant for making aluminium from aluminium ore, but also uses recycled aluminium. The energy used for making the metal from its ore costs £100 per tonne. The energy used recycling aluminium costs just £5 per tonne. The company currently uses 40% recycled aluminium in its products.

Questions

f Calculate Alucycle's energy costs for its annual production of aluminium goods.

g The company hopes to increase the amount of recycled aluminium it uses to 50%. How much money a year would it save on energy costs?

The future is out there …

If we eventually colonise Mars, it will be too expensive to ship out our raw materials from Earth. Mars may have its own metal ores, but just outside the orbit of Mars lies the asteroid belt. This is made up of millions of orbiting chunks of rock. Many are several kilometres across – and about half of them are made entirely from iron and nickel, just like the core of the Earth. It is a space technologist's dream that one day we will be able to mine these 'flying mountains' of metal.

Question

h List a few of the problems you would have to overcome before you could set up a mining operation on an asteroid.

Key points

● Mining, extracting and recycling metals have economic, social and environmental impacts.

● The supply of metals on the Earth is finite so we need to develop ways of using and recycling them effectively.

Oil: black gold

Our shiny new technological world relies on oil. We need oil to fuel our cars, machines and power stations. Oil helps the economy grow so we can afford new buildings and transport systems.

▲ Oil money pays for developments like this in Bahrain.

▲▼ But oil can do great damage if handled badly…

Environmental impact

But there is a price to pay for economic success. The catastrophic pollution caused by burning oil wells after the first Gulf War is just an extreme example of the environmental hazards posed by oil.

Coastal areas from Alaska to Cornwall have been devastated by oil spills from wrecked tankers over the years. Sea birds are the most obvious casualties, but the whole ecosystem suffers. Oil usually contains a little sulfur. If this is not removed before burning, sulfur dioxide gets into the air and causes acid rain. The carbon dioxide from burning could be causing global warming.

Human impact

Around 50 years ago only a minority of families owned cars. Today, almost everybody expects to own a car – often two or three per family. Exhaust gas pollution causes the brown haze that hangs over many cities on hot summer days.

About 50 years ago asthma was uncommon. Today 15% or so of children suffer from asthma, and need to use chemical inhalers to help them breathe when they have an attack. Attacks happen more often on high pollution days.

The rise in asthma seems to match the rise in air pollution. Does that mean air pollution causes asthma? The graph alone does not prove anything – it could just be chance or some other factors that have changed with the change in lifestyle over the last 50 years. Research suggests that pollen and even thunderstorms can also trigger asthma attacks, but air pollution *may* trigger the problem in the first place. Science has not yet proved conclusively that this pollution causes asthma. Even so, the pollution levels are monitored carefully and 'high pollution' alerts go out with the weather forecasts to help warn asthma sufferers.

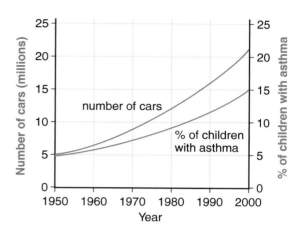

Economic impact

North Sea oil has been great for Britain. The production of over 2 million barrels of oil per day for the last 30 years has helped to keep our economy healthy and created many new jobs. But not all countries have been so lucky. Nigeria is the biggest oil-producing country in Africa. Despite producing roughly the same amount of oil as Britain since the 1970s, the standard of living for ordinary Nigerians has been declining steadily. Most of the oil money has gone to a few rich people while other industries have been neglected.

Political impact

At the rate we are using oil, it will all run out within your lifetime. The economy of the USA powers the global economy. It was built on vast supplies of cheap oil, but it has almost exhausted its own oil and now needs to buy in oil from the rest of the world. Information about oil reserves shows why the USA takes such a political interest in the Middle East. Many people suggest that the recent Gulf Wars in Kuwait and Iraq had more to do with oil than democracy. Further wars could break out in the future in other parts of the world over the last, dwindling oil supplies.

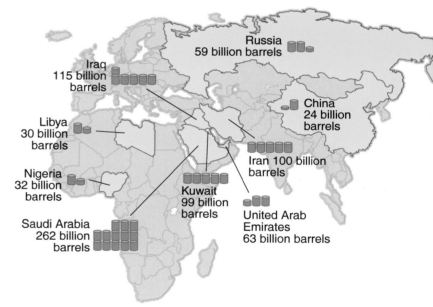

▲ Oil reserves of the major oil-producing countries in and around the Middle East in billions of barrels of oil.

Think about what you will find out in this section

What is crude oil made of?

How can science help to overcome any pollution problems caused by oil?

How can we make useful products from crude oil?

How can science help to develop new energy sources for the future, when oil runs out?

What environmental problems are linked to the use of crude oil?

How did crude oil form?

Crude oil is an ancient biomass. If dead plants or animals get buried quickly, they are broken down by microbes that do not need oxygen. Oil and natural gas are formed by this process. The oil and gas trapped in rocks has formed in this way over millions of years.

What is crude oil made of?

Crude oil is a mixture of many different compounds. Mixtures are not chemically combined, so each compound has its own properties. On their own, they may be runny liquids, thick liquids, solids or gases. Mixed up together they are a thick, gooey black liquid. As a mixture, crude oil is useless. The different compounds must be separated out before they can be used.

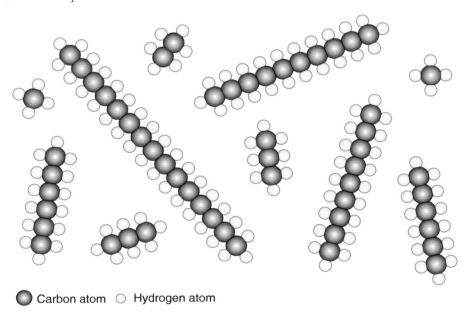

● Carbon atom   ○ Hydrogen atom

What kind of compounds?

Most of the compounds in oil are made from two types of atom only: hydrogen and carbon. Compounds like this are called **hydrocarbons**. The hydrocarbons shown here have molecules of different sizes.

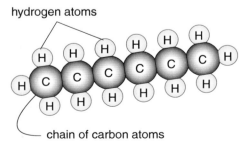

hydrogen atoms

chain of carbon atoms

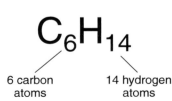

This has 6 carbon atoms. It can be written as:

$$C_6H_{14}$$

6 carbon atoms   14 hydrogen atoms

Carbon atoms can form chains. Big molecules have long chains and small molecules have short chains. The molecules are often drawn like this, showing how the atoms are joined by single chemical bonds. If you look closely, you will see that every carbon atom has four bonds. Two bonds link the carbon atom into the chain and two are linked to hydrogen atoms. At each end, there is an extra hydrogen atom.

$$H-\underset{\underset{H}{|}}{\overset{\overset{H}{|}}{C}}-\underset{\underset{H}{|}}{\overset{\overset{H}{|}}{C}}-\underset{\underset{H}{|}}{\overset{\overset{H}{|}}{C}}-\underset{\underset{H}{|}}{\overset{\overset{H}{|}}{C}}-\underset{\underset{H}{|}}{\overset{\overset{H}{|}}{C}}-\underset{\underset{H}{|}}{\overset{\overset{H}{|}}{C}}-H$$

The alkane family

This family of hydrocarbons is called the **alkanes**. Every chemical bond is a single bond, either between two carbon atoms along the chain (C–C) or between a carbon and a hydrogen atom (C–H). Each alkane has as many hydrogen atoms as it is possible to take – the molecules are 'full' of hydrogen. The word chemists use for 'full' here is *saturated*. Alkanes are known as **saturated** hydrocarbons.

Question

e *What are the physical properties of carbon and hydrogen? Compare them with the physical properties of oil.*

Properties of alkanes

For a liquid to boil, the molecules have to move fast enough to break free from one another. The molecules move faster when the liquid is heated. When they have enough energy to escape, the liquid boils.

Formula	Boiling point (°C)
C_5H_{12}	36
C_6H_{14}	69
C_7H_{16}	99
C_8H_{18}	
C_9H_{20}	151
$C_{10}H_{22}$	174

Questions

f *From the data, which are easier to make move faster, short-chain or long-chain molecules?*
g *Plot a scatter graph of number of carbon atoms against boiling point and draw a line of best fit. Use this to predict the boiling point of C_8H_{18}.*

Questions

c *(i) Look at the molecular models for these hydrocarbons. If n is the number of atoms of carbon in these molecules, how many hydrogen atoms will there be? (Hint: Don't forget the ends!)
(ii) Complete the general formula for this type of hydrocarbon: $C_nH_{\underline{}}$.*
d *Give the formula for hydrocarbons like this with chains of:
(i) 7 carbon atoms
(ii) 22 carbon atoms
(iii) 125 carbon atoms.*

Key points

- Crude oil is a mixture of different compounds. Most of these compounds are saturated hydrocarbons called alkanes.
- C_2H_6 is an example of an alkane. The general formula is C_nH_{2n+2}.
- Different sized hydrocarbon molecules have different numbers of carbon atoms joined in a chain. Short chains have low boiling points and long chains have high boiling points.

A mixture of hydrocarbons

Crude oil is a mixture of many useful hydrocarbons that need to be separated out before they can be used. This is done by a form of distillation using the physical property of boiling points.

Fractional distillation

If you heat crude oil enough it will boil. In an oil refinery, crude oil is heated strongly in a furnace so that it all boils. The gas then passes up through a tower, which is hot at the bottom but cold at the top.

Question

a Steam condenses back to water at 100°C. Paraffin boils at 200°C. At what temperature will paraffin gas condense back to liquid?

Long-chain alkanes with high boiling points will condense out quickly. Short-chain alkanes with low boiling points will have to be cooled down much more before they condense. So the different alkanes condense out at different levels of the tower. They are collected in trays and can be piped off.

This method gives a good separation, but it is not perfect. The liquid that collects at each level is still a mixture, but has a much narrower range of carbon-chain lengths, all with very similar properties. Petrol, for example, contains a range of molecules that have between 6 and 10 carbon atoms. Each liquid that is collected is called a **fraction**, so the process is called **fractional distillation**. This process can run continuously, which helps to keep the costs down.

Question

b Where will short-chain alkanes condense out, at the top or bottom of the tower?

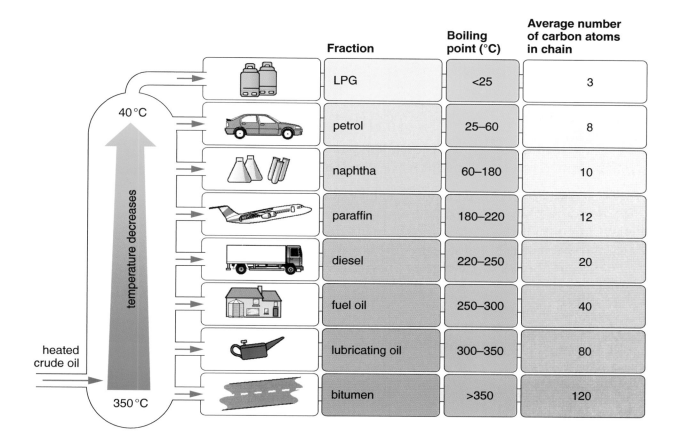

Fraction	Boiling point (°C)	Average number of carbon atoms in chain
LPG	<25	3
petrol	25–60	8
naphtha	60–180	10
paraffin	180–220	12
diesel	220–250	20
fuel oil	250–300	40
lubricating oil	300–350	80
bitumen	>350	120

Supply and demand

Petrol makes up about 40% of all the crude oil products sold. Oil from different regions gives different amounts of each fraction when distilled.

Source	Petrol (%)	Paraffin (%)	Diesel (%)	'Heavy oils' (%)
Arabian	18	12	18	52
Iranian	21	13	20	46
North Sea	23	15	24	34
Demand	39	11	30	20

Questions

c Refineries have to make enough petrol and diesel to meet the demand. To make 39 barrels of petrol they will need to distill nearly 200 barrels of crude oil. Which fractions will be left over 'unsold' if they do this?

d From the figures and your answer to c, why do you think North Sea oil is sold at a higher price than Arabian oil?

You will find out what they do with all the leftover fractions in Section 4 of this unit.

Key points

- The physical property of boiling point can be used to separate the mixtures in crude oil by fractional distillation.
- Long-chain hydrocarbons have high boiling points and condense at the bottom of the tower. Short-chain ones condense at the top of the tower.

Carbon dioxide and global warming

Oil is mostly made from hydrocarbons. We burn oil to get energy from the reaction:

hydrocarbon + oxygen → carbon dioxide + water + **energy**

For example, for methane:

$$CH_4 + 2O_2 → CO_2 + 2H_2O$$

These waste products of burning are not 'dangerous' compounds. You make them in your body and breathe them out when you respire!

Burning fossil fuels has increased the amount of carbon dioxide in the atmosphere by over a third over the last 200 years. This may have caused **global warming**, raising the temperature of the Earth by a few degrees. This might not sound much, but it makes the weather more extreme, melts polar ice and causes the sea level to rise.

Sulfur and acid rain

Oil contains traces of sulfur. When sulfur reacts with oxygen and then water it makes sulfuric acid which causes **acid rain**.

$$S + O_2 → SO_2$$
$$2SO_2 + 2H_2O + O_2 → 2H_2SO_4$$

Forty years ago, sulfur dioxide from power stations and factories in Britain formed clouds of acid rain that caused great environmental damage both here and abroad. Acid rain from northern Britain blew all the way to Norway and killed trees and poisoned lakes there.

Today sulfur is removed from petrol and diesel before it gets to the pumps. Power stations remove sulfur dioxide from their waste gases by spraying slaked lime to neutralise the acid.

Question

a What are the waste products of burning hydrocarbons?

Question

b Explain how we think carbon dioxide causes global warming.

Questions

c What compound will you get if you use slaked lime (calcium hydroxide, $Ca(OH)_2$) to neutralise sulfuric acid?

d Complete the balanced equation for this reaction:
$Ca(OH)_2 + H_2SO_4 →$ ____ $+ 2H_2O$

Soot and global dimming

Diesel cars and lorries release billions of tiny carbon particles into the air. They are much smaller than soot from coal. You can sometimes see clouds of black smoke coming from the exhaust of a badly running lorry or bus engine.

Over the last 20 years, the sunlight falling on the Earth has been getting weaker and weaker. Scientists have taken measurements that show that energy levels reaching the Earth have dropped by 20%. They call this **global dimming**. Measurements from space show no change from the Sun itself, so scientists looked for the cause of this mysterious effect.

The tiny particles of carbon formed when oil burns get up into the atmosphere and water droplets form around them, making clouds. These clouds act like a mirror, reflecting some of the Sun's energy back out into space.

Global warming versus global dimming

So burning oil seems to be warming the Earth up with its carbon dioxide, but cooling it down with its carbon particles. The effect of global warming is kept in check by the global dimming.

Question

e *Jet engines leave 'vapour trails' of tiny ice crystals that form from their waste gases. Normally the congested skies over the USA are full of these vapour trails. After the attacks on the Twin Towers on 11 September 2001, all flights over US airspace were grounded for three days. The difference between the day and night temperatures over the USA rose markedly as the area warmed up more by day. The pattern returned to normal when air travel resumed. Suggest a reason for this.*

Questions

f *What will happen as we try to clean up the pollution caused by the carbon particles? Scientists (and politicians) will need to think very hard about this issue and be very careful about the action they take if we are to overcome this global problem.*

g *Your friend suggests we could stop global warming by making more diesel smoke pollution. Is she right? Explain why this might not be such a good idea.*

Key points

- Most fossil fuels contain a little sulfur. This combines with oxygen to produce sulfur dioxide, which causes acid rain.
- The carbon in fuels produces carbon dioxide, which causes global warming. Some carbon particles are also released from burning fuels, which cause global dimming.
- Sulfur can be removed from petrol and the sulfur dioxide removed from waste gases to reduce pollution.

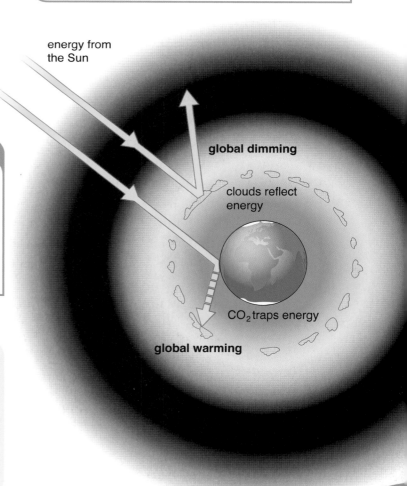

energy from the Sun

global dimming

clouds reflect energy

CO_2 traps energy

global warming

Burning fuels and global warming

Scientists agree that carbon dioxide is a **greenhouse gas** and that the level of carbon dioxide in the atmosphere is rising, at least in part due to our burning oil and other fossil fuels. There is evidence that the Earth's climate is changing as global temperatures rise. The finger of blame for global warming points to us and our use of fossil fuels. But is it really that clear-cut?

Question

a Compare the trends shown by the two lines. Does this graph prove that carbon dioxide causes global warming?

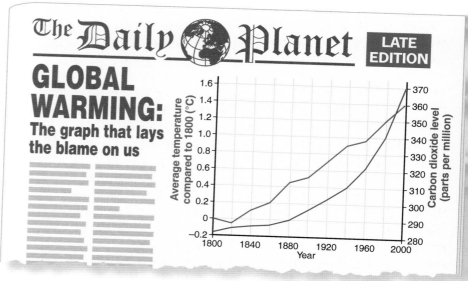

The Daily Planet — LATE EDITION

GLOBAL WARMING: The graph that lays the blame on us

▲ How carbon dioxide levels and global temperature have changed over the last 200 years.

Is it just us?

We put another 8 billion tonnes of carbon dioxide into the air every year just by burning oil. But the picture is complicated by the fact that there are other major natural sources of atmospheric carbon dioxide.

- Wildfires in Indonesia in 1997 burnt for many weeks. Over that short period it is estimated that as much as 2 billion tonnes of carbon dioxide were released into the air.
- Volcanoes release billions of tonnes of carbon dioxide into the air when they erupt.

Both of these natural sources are sporadic but at times spectacularly large. They make simple **correlation** of human action to global warming very difficult.

Questions

b Natural forests re-grow after fires. How will that affect the carbon dioxide levels in the atmosphere?

c The amount of carbon dioxide we add by burning fossil fuels is probably matched by natural sources. But every 1000 years or so you might get 100 times as much from a single 'super' volcano eruption. What would you expect this to cause?

▲ Erupting Guagua Pichincha volcano looms over Quito, Ecuador.

Global warming could be worse

Computer models of our climate predict that if all the carbon dioxide we produce stayed in the atmosphere, global warming would be much worse. But 'only' 3 billion tonnes of the gas seems to stay in the air. Let's look at where the rest goes.

Plants absorb carbon dioxide during photosynthesis and use some of it for plant growth. In old forests new growth using carbon dioxide is balanced out by dead wood that rots and produces carbon dioxide. But new forests can take up to 2.5 tonnes of carbon dioxide from the air per hectare every year!

Carbon dioxide dissolves in the oceans. Some is then taken out permanently by shellfish in their shells and ends up as limestone. Floating seaweed takes up carbon dioxide as it grows. When it dies, it sinks to the bottom and is buried in the rocks, forming the fossil fuels of the distant future.

How can we help?

The link between burning oil and global warming is not completely proven. However, we should try to limit the amount of energy we use and so reduce the amount of fossil fuels we burn.

Science to the rescue?

One possible answer to global warming is to find ways to trap the carbon dioxide before it gets into the atmosphere. We currently get our natural gas from the North Sea oilfields. The gas is trapped beneath domes of clay, deep below the seabed, but this gas will soon run out. Scientist are now trying experiments to see if carbon dioxide from power stations can be pumped back down these old wells and stored safely underground.

Key points

- Burning fossil fuels has contributed to an increase in carbon dioxide levels.
- There are natural sources of carbon dioxide, such as wildfires and volcanoes.
- Some carbon dioxide is absorbed by plants and oceans.
- We still need to try to reduce our fossil fuel use to reduce the impact on the environment.

Question

d Look at the table below. From these figures, which country looks better placed to significantly reduce its net carbon dioxide emissions by planting new forests? Explain your answer.

Source	UK	Canada
area (million hectares)	24	850
annual net carbon dioxide production (million tonnes)	550	740

Question

e The Sargasso Sea is a great mass of floating seaweed in the middle of the Atlantic Ocean. The Amazon jungle is an ancient forest. Which is better at removing carbon dioxide from the atmosphere? Explain your answer.

Question

f We have raised our own standards of living by burning oil. Are we morally justified in trying to stop developing countries from following our example?

▼ Could old oil or gas wells save us from global warming?

What's left?

Many people think we're approaching the halfway mark on our oil reserves. When will the oil run out, and what can we do about it?

Type of oil reserve	Billions of barrels of oil
oil used in the last 100 years	620
known oil reserves	1050
estimated reserves as yet undiscovered	450

Question

a From these figures you might think we have enough oil left for another 200 years. Why won't the remaining oil last anything like that long?

Hydrogen as a future fuel?

Whatever happens, oil will run out eventually, so scientists are looking for new sources of energy. Hydrogen has been used to fuel the Space Shuttle for decades, but now scientists are developing hydrogen as a fuel for buses. When this burns it just makes water, so it is completely pollution-free.

hydrogen + oxygen → water + **energy**

Some school bus fleets in California have already converted their buses to run on hydrogen.

But there are problems with hydrogen. It has to be compressed and can be quite dangerous to store if not handled properly. Also, at the moment it can only be made in large amounts by electrolysis of water using electricity.

Questions

b Hydrogen only becomes a 'renewable' fuel if the electricity used to produce it is generated by a renewable source. List three possible generating methods using renewable resources.

c At night, power stations make more electricity than they need, which is simply wasted. How could hydrogen-generating plants be used to 'store' this waste energy?

Countries with no oil

Many scientists are looking for renewable fuel resources to replace the oil as soon as possible. A vast amount of energy pours onto the Earth from the Sun every day. We can harness this for the natural process that gave us our oil reserves in the first place – photosynthesis.

Brazil has no oil of its own so took a novel approach to fuelling its cars. Instead of petrol, Brazilian motorists use alcohol. Sugar cane grows well in the hot sunshine of tropical Brazil. This sugar is fermented with yeast to produce a solution of alcohol in water. The alcohol is called **ethanol**. This is then distilled to give pure alcohol, which works well in petrol engines. Ethanol is a clean, renewable fuel. It has helped Brazil to halve its oil imports. The downside has been that large areas of rainforest have been cleared to grow the sugar cane.

▲ Sugar cane grows well in hot climates.

Questions

d Complete this equation for burning ethanol:
$2C_2H_5OH + 6O_2 \rightarrow$ _____ $+ 6H_2O$

e List the environmental advantages and disadvantages of using ethanol for cars instead of petrol. Look at the complete 'life-cycle' of the fuel, from production through to combustion.

f (i) Suggest a reason why we can't grow sugar cane in Britain.
(ii) We can grow sugar beet. What would be the advantages of making alcohol from this to run our cars?
(iii) Britain is a small country with a very large number of cars. Suggest a problem we might face if we tried to go over to alcohol instead of petrol.

Many other plants store energy in their seeds as oil – olives, sunflowers, soya beans and so on. These oils can be made to burn well in engines. This new fuel is called **biodiesel**. You will find out more about it in Section 5 of this unit.

Key points

● Oil will run out one day but scientists have already developed new fuels, such as ethanol and biodiesel.
● The use of hydrogen as a fuel is still being developed.
● Some countries are already making good use of renewable fuels.

1 **a** Match words **A, B, C** and **D** to the formulae in the table.

    A calcium hydroxide
    B carbon dioxide
    C calcium oxide
    D calcium carbonate

1	$CaCO_3$
2	$Ca(OH)_2$
3	CaO
4	CO_2

b Complete and balance these chemical equations.

    i $CaCO_3 \rightarrow$ _____ + _____
    ii $CaO +$ _____ $\rightarrow Ca(OH)_2$ *(2 marks)*

2

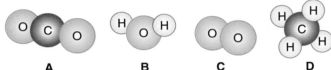

    A   **B**   **C**   **D**

a Which of these diagrams shows a molecule of an element?   *(1 mark)*

b Which of these diagrams show a molecule of a compound?   *(1 mark)*

c **i** Give the chemical formulae for molecules **A–D**.   *(2 marks)*
    ii Give the chemical names for molecules **A–D**.   *(2 marks)*

d Which subatomic particle is shared between atoms in molecules like this, to make the chemical bonds?   *(1 mark)*

3

This building is made from concrete and glass.

a What are the raw materials used to make **i** cement and **ii** glass?   *(2 marks)*

b What problem might you face working in a glass-fronted building like this on a sunny day?   *(1 mark)*

c Suggest **one** advantage of building with concrete rather than blocks of limestone.   *(1 mark)*

d List **three** environmental problems that are associated with quarrying limestone.   *(3 marks)*

4 Limestone ($CaCO_3$) breaks down to quicklime (CaO) when heated. Zoe, Mumtaz and Tomi performed an experiment to see how much quicklime they could get by heating 10 g of limestone. They set their balance to zero with a crucible in place and measured out exactly 10 g of limestone. They then heated the crucible strongly, reweighing it regularly. They kept heating until the mass stopped going down. They each repeated their experiment three times. Here are their results.

	Quicklime produced from 10 g of limestone (g)			
	Expt 1	**Expt 2**	**Expt 3**	**Mean**
Zoe	5.6	5.7	5.5	
Mumtaz	5.65	5.66	5.64	
Tomi	5.62	5.68	6.92	

a Why does the mass as measured on the balance go down during this reaction?   *(1 mark)*

b Why did they have to keep heating 'until the mass stopped going down'?   *(1 mark)*

c Calculate the mean result for each of the three students.   *(3 marks)*

d **i** Which student had been given an older, less precise balance to work with?   *(1 mark)*

    ii How will this have affected her results?   *(1 mark)*

e Which student appears to have obtained the most reliable results? Explain your answer.   *(2 marks)*

f Which student ran out of time and didn't heat her final piece of limestone long enough? Explain your answer.   *(2 marks)*

g i The theoretical amount of quicklime produced from 10 g of calcium carbonate is 5.6 g. Whose final answer appears to be the most accurate? *(1 mark)*

ii A detailed analysis of the limestone used shows that the residue after heating is indeed slightly greater than 5.6 g. Suggest a possible reason for this. *(1 mark)*

5 Iron is made by heating iron oxide with coal in a blast furnace.

a Which element is coal mostly made of? *(1 mark)*

b Complete this word equation.

iron oxide + carbon → iron + _____ _____ *(1 mark)*

c Which reactant is oxidised in this reaction? *(1 mark)*

d Which reactant is reduced in this reaction? *(1 mark)*

e Why can't aluminium be produced from aluminium oxide by this reaction? *(1 mark)*

6 Myanmar is a poor country with underdeveloped heavy industry. Bamboo grows well in its hot climate.

In London, scaffolding is built from steel tubes that are screw-clamped together. In Myanmar, scaffolding is built from bamboo poles lashed together with natural string.

a Which do you think would be stronger, the steel or bamboo? *(1 mark)*

b What would you notice if you picked up a steel pole and a bamboo pole? *(1 mark)*

c Suggest **two** reasons why bamboo is used in Myanmar rather than steel. *(1 mark)*

d Steel scaffolding poles last longer than bamboo poles. Why is that not a problem in Myanmar? *(1 mark)*

e Broken bamboo poles are simply thrown away. Why is that not a problem? *(1 mark)*

f Large bamboo poles cost more in the UK than their steel equivalents. Suggest **two** reasons for this. *(2 marks)*

7 Look at the table:

Metal	Melting point (°C)	Strength (1 = low, 50 = very high)	Cost (£/tonne)	Density (g/cm³)
aluminium	660	1 (pure) 5 (alloyed)	18000	2.7
steel	1540	20	300	7.7
titanium	1670	10	12000	4.5
tungsten	3400	50	9000	15.3

a For each use below, suggest a suitable metal and give a reason (from the property table).
i the barrel of a Bunsen burner *(1 mark)*
ii the wing of a supersonic fighter *(1 mark)*
iii the filament in a light bulb *(1 mark)*
iv a commercial aeroplane *(1 mark)*

b Why is aluminium never used in its pure form? *(1 mark)*

c Explain in simple terms why alloys are harder and stronger than the pure metal. *(2 marks)*

8 The permitted levels of some metal ions in drinking water are:

copper	1 mg per litre
lead	0.05 mg per litre
zinc	5 mg per litre

a From these figures, which metal is most toxic, and which is least toxic? *(1 mark)*

Cattle in the fields around the river shown on the map became ill and metal poisoning was suspected. Water samples taken from the rivers at **A**, **B**, **C**, **D** and **E** were analysed and the results were:

	Concentration (mg per litre)		
	copper	lead	zinc
A	0.05	0.001	0.05
B	5.00	0.1	3.0
C	6.0	5.0	10.0
D	1.00	0.02	0.6
E	1.6	1.0	2.0

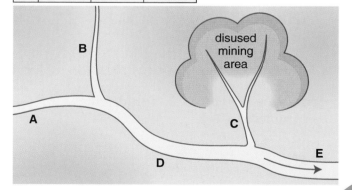

b **i** Which site would give safe drinking water (in terms of metal content)? *(1 mark)*

  ii Which site shows the most polluted water? *(1 mark)*

  iii Where do you think this pollution has come from? *(1 mark)*

c **i** The rivers flow from **A**, **B** and **C** to **E**. Why are the metal levels lower at **E** than at **C**? *(1 mark)*

  ii From the figures, which river carries more water, the main river at **D** or the side river from **C**? By how much (to the nearest whole number)? *(1 mark)*

d **i** Site **A** has a full range of wildlife. How would you expect site **E** to compare with this? *(1 mark)*

  ii You find water snails at site **A** but they have disappeared from the river at site **D**. Which metal do you think the snails might be sensitive to? *(1 mark)*

e The herd of cattle could only get to the river to drink at **E**. Which metal is most likely to be responsible for the poisoning? Explain your answer. *(2 marks)*

f **i** Scientists have suggested that the pollution problem could be tackled by throwing scrap iron into the rivers at **B** and **C**. How would this work? *(1 mark)*

  ii Which metal would not be affected? *(1 mark)*

  iii Which metal ion would increase in the water at **E**? Would this be a problem? *(2 marks)*

9 1

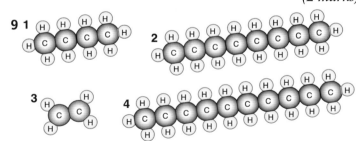

The picture shows some hydrocarbon molecules.

a Write the chemical formulae for molecules **1–4**. *(4 marks)*

b Which molecule is not an alkane? Explain your answer. *(2 marks)*

c Propane (C_3H_8) is another alkane. Complete and balance this equation for the combustion of propane. *(3 marks)*

$C_3H_8 +$ _____ $O_2 \rightarrow$ _____ $H_2O +$ _____

d **i** Oil often contains sulfur as an impurity. What compound forms when this burns? *(1 mark)*

  ii What problem could this cause if the sulfur was not removed from fuel oils? *(1 mark)*

10 When hydrocarbons burn they produce carbon dioxide and water. The number of molecules of each produced by burning one molecule of the hydrocarbon is shown below.

Hydrocarbon	Number of CO_2 molecules	Number of H_2O molecules	Ratio H_2O/CO_2
CH_4	1	2	
C_2H_6	2	3	
C_3H_8	3	4	
C_4H_{10}	4	5	
C_5H_{12}	5	6	
C_8H_{18}	8	9	
$C_{20}H_{42}$	20	21	

a Complete the column showing the ratio of the number of water molecules to the number of carbon dioxide molecules. *(1 mark)*

b Plot a scatter graph of the number of carbon atoms against the ratio you have just calculated. *(1 mark)*

c Draw a suitable curve and describe in words the pattern you reveal. *(2 marks)*

d What global problem is thought to be caused by carbon dioxide in the atmosphere? *(1 mark)*

e Natural gas is CH_4. Fuel oil has much longer carbon chains. From your graph, suggest a reason why oil-fired power stations are worse for the environment than natural gas-fired ones. *(1 mark)*

11 a Crude oil is split into fractions by distillation. Choose from the phrases below to label **1–4** on the diagram.

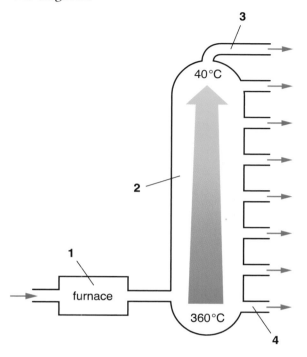

A short-chain hydrocarbons out
B crude oil vaporised
C long-chain oil out
D the vapour rises and cools   *(4 marks)*

b Petrol and lubricating oil contain hydrocarbons. Petrol catches fire (ignites) easily.

Lubricating oil does not ignite easily.

Choose from the list the **two** statements that are true.
A Petrol is less volatile than lubricating oil.
B Petrol has shorter-chained hydrocarbons than lubricating oil.
C Petrol has smaller molecules than lubricating oil.
D Lubricating oil is a better fuel than petrol.
E Lubricating oil has a lower boiling point than petrol.   *(2 marks)*

12 Most forms of transport work by burning fossil fuels. The table shows approximately how much carbon dioxide is produced for a 1 km journey.

bus	1 000 g
large car	300 g
small car	150 g
walking	15 g

a Why is it better for the environment to drive a small car than a large one?   *(1 mark)*

b Some firms run 'car pools' where people take it in turns to give each other lifts. How does this help?   *(1 mark)*

c A bus can take 50 people. How much carbon dioxide is produced per person per kilometre?   *(1 mark)*

d Why isn't it zero for walking?   *(1 mark)*

13 Methane (natural gas) is 30 times worse than carbon dioxide as a greenhouse gas.

a Some oilfields burn off unwanted methane from the oil wells, forming carbon dioxide. Others just release the methane into the air. Which of these two options is worse for the Earth? Explain your answer.   *(2 marks)*

b Trees take in carbon dioxide from the air. Cows each produce about 24 litres of methane a day from their digestive systems. In many parts of South America, the forests have been cut down to graze cattle to produce beef for hamburgers. Give **two** reasons why this is harmful to the Earth.   *(2 marks)*

Oil is not just for energy!

Crude oil is more than just a rich source of energy. In fact it has so many other uses that many people think it's a waste to just burn it. The lubricating oil and bitumen for the roads that come straight from the fractionating tower are just some of the useful products from crude oil. With a little bit of chemical know-how, many other materials can be made from oil fractions.

▼ All our plastics come from oil.

Plastic fantastic

Where would we be without plastics? From polythene shopping bags to vinyl car upholstery; from polypropene carpets to polystyrene computer housings; from a baby's bottle to false teeth and gumshields; from a Teflon non-stick coat on a frying pan to PET 'pop' bottles … Countless products are made from crude oil. Oil is a truly versatile raw material.

Smart plastics

Chemists are developing new plastics with new 'smart' properties. Some polymer gels can be made to grow or shrink. Perhaps they could be used as the muscles of future robots. New polymer transistors will make electronic devices flexible. Soon you may have a TV screen as big as your wall which rolls up neatly like a blind when you don't need it. There seems to be no limit to the possibilities of smart polymers.

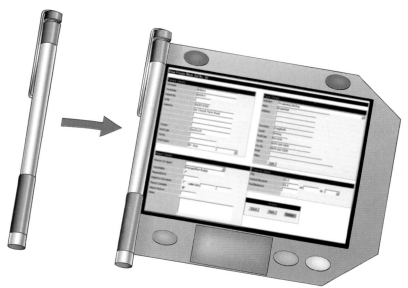

▲ How about an electronic notebook that unrolls out of a pen?

Alcohol from oil

Ethanol is the alcohol in alcoholic drinks. It is made by fermenting sugary liquids like grape juice or malt mash. But vast amounts of ethanol are used in industry as an industrial solvent for varnishes, inks, paints and glues. It is also used in perfumes and aftershave. All of this industrial ethanol is made from oil.

But there are disadvantages

Plastics are easy to use in large-scale, automated industrial processes. As customers we get cheap goods, but many skilled craftsmen from carpenters to leatherworkers have been put out of work. These people need to be retrained so they can find new jobs.

Because plastics are cheap to produce, many disposable plastic products have been created, from carrier bags to cutlery, crockery and cameras. We have become a 'throw away' society. Now environmentalists are trying to encourage us to reduce, reuse or recycle what we use. Or better still, use products that aren't intended to be disposable.

Using plastics has also meant that we no longer use local, natural renewable materials such as wood and leather. Instead we rely on oil, which we will have to import when our North Sea oil runs out. Oil prices change rapidly on international markets and this can lead to economic instability. And what will we do when *all* of the oil finally runs out?

Plastics can also cause environmental problems. They are difficult and expensive to dispose of. You will consider this issue further in Spread 4.5.

Think about what you will find out in this section

What are plastics and why do they have such useful properties?

How can science help to develop fantastic new smart materials?

How are plastics made from crude oil?

How do plastics affect the environment?

How is alcohol made from oil?

Oil fractions and demand

The fractional distillation of crude oil makes many useful products. Unfortunately the demand for these does not match the supply from the refinery.

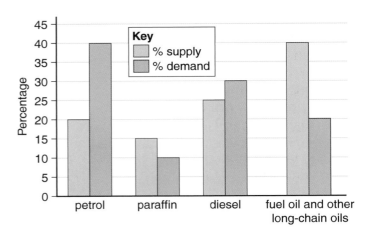

Question

a How does the supply of the different fractions compare with the demand?

To keep up with the demand for petrol by distillation alone, a refinery would end up with vast amounts of 'unwanted' long-chain oils. For every barrel of petrol it sold, there would be another three barrels of long-chain oil it couldn't sell.

Industrial cracking

Fortunately it is fairly easy to 'chop up' long-chain hydrocarbons. If they are heated, they can be broken up by a thermal decomposition reaction. This is called **cracking**.

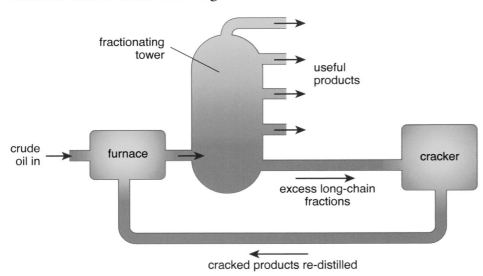

The cracking process takes place in the oil refinery.

- First the unwanted long-chain fractions are boiled.
- The vapour is then passed over a hot catalyst (this makes the reaction work faster).
- The long-chain molecules break up into smaller pieces.
- The shorter-chain products are then passed back through the fractionating tower to separate them.

The extra petrol needed is produced in this way, as well as other important chemicals used to make ethanol and plastics.

Question

b Suggest why this cracking takes place at the oil refinery, rather than in a separate plant elsewhere.

More about cracking and its products

Alkanes make their chemical bonds by sharing electrons. When an alkane is cracked, a carbon–carbon bond (C–C) is broken and the electrons are no longer shared. Broken bonds like this are very unstable, so the atoms rearrange themselves. One hydrogen atom from the smaller piece joins the larger piece to make another alkane.

This leaves the smaller piece short of two hydrogen atoms – and with two broken bonds. These bonds snap together, forming a carbon–carbon double bond (C=C). Hydrocarbons with double bonds like this are called **alkenes**. The simplest alkene, with just two carbon atoms, is called ethene.

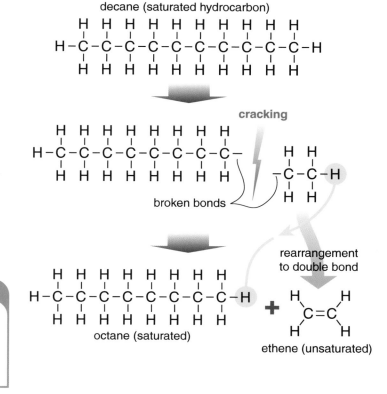

Question

c The diagrams show an alkane called decane being cracked to give an alkane called octane and an alkene called ethene. Write out the reaction as both a word equation and a balanced chemical equation. (Hint: You will need to count the atoms.)

◀ Some other members of the alkene family.

Question

d What are the formulae of the alkenes shown here? What is the general rule for the formula of an alkene?

Alkenes have two hydrogen atoms less than alkane with the same chain length. So alkenes do not have the full number of hydrogen atoms. Alkenes are called **unsaturated** hydrocarbons.

Ethene is a hydrocarbon and can be burnt. In the past, because petrol was the product needed from the process, ethene was seen as a waste product and simply burnt off. Now we have lots of uses for ethene. It is used as a raw material to make a range of things from ethanol to plastic.

Question

e For every 170 kg of decane cracked in this way you could in theory get 142 kg of petrol (octane) and 28 kg of ethene. Suggest a reason why you might not actually get that much of either. What might you get instead?

Key points

- Hydrocarbons can be cracked by thermal decomposition using a catalyst to produce smaller, useful molecules.
- The products of cracking are unsaturated alkenes with the general formula C_nH_{2n}. An example is ethene, which has the formula C_2H_4.
- Some of the fractions from cracking give petrol, which is much in demand.

Traditional ethanol

Ethanol is the alcohol in wines, beers and spirits. People have been making these drinks for thousands of years. Fermenting grape juice or malt mash makes a weak solution of ethanol in water. Distilling it gives a stronger alcoholic drink with more alcohol such as whisky or brandy.

▶ Wine and beer have been around for thousands of years.

Product	Source	How it's made	Proportion of ethanol
beer	barley mash	fermentation	5%
wine	grape juice	fermentation	11%
whisky	barley mash	fermentation and distillation	40%

Question

a Explain why there is more alcohol in whisky than in beer or wine.

Ethanol in industry

Pure (100%) ethanol is also a very important industrial chemical. It is used as a solvent in glues, varnishes, inks and paints. It evaporates quickly so it is also used as a 'carrier' for perfumes and aftershave.

For large-scale industrial use, pure ethanol has to be made as cheaply as possible. Alcoholic drinks are relatively expensive – partly due to the high tax paid on them. Almost pure ethanol can be made in the same way as whisky or brandy, but the fermentation and distillation process is slow and relatively costly, even without the tax the government adds. A new source was needed and oil provided the answer.

Question

b Suggest two reasons why vodka costs so much more than methylated spirits.

85% ethanol   40% ethanol

▲ Methylated spirits is mixed with poisonous methanol, a dye and a bitter chemical to stop people drinking it.

Ethanol from waste

The cracking process that produces more petrol from oil also makes ethene as a waste product. Chemists discovered that they could react ethene with steam to give ethanol. The carbon=carbon double bond in ethene is relatively weak. With a little heat energy and a suitable catalyst the double bond breaks. The loose 'bond arms' then grab hold of passing water molecules from the steam to make ethanol.

This process is called **hydrolysis**, which just means 'adding water'. This is an addition reaction, because new atoms are added to the compound.

ethene + water → ethanol

$$C_2H_4 + H_2O \rightarrow C_2H_5OH$$

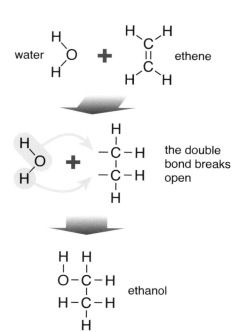

Question

c What compound would you get if you made ethene react with hydrogen (H_2)?

So which method is best?

It depends what you want the ethanol for – and whether you are thinking about now or the future.

	Fermentation	From ethene
type of process	This is a batch process. Fixed amounts of sugary solution are fermented at a time. The weak solution of alcohol is then distilled.	This is a continuous, automated process. Ethene and steam are constantly fed over the heated catalyst.
speed of production	Fermentation is a slow process that takes days or weeks.	The reaction takes place as fast as the reactants can be pumped in.
quantity of product	Limited by the size and number of fermentation vats.	In a large refinery the amount of alcohol produced can be tailored to meet demand.
quality of product	The proportion of alcohol may be low, but the impurities give it the flavour.	Pure ethanol is produced with ease. Impurities may be added later to stop people drinking it.
the raw material	Sugar comes from photosynthesis. Plants are a renewable resource.	Ethene is produced from fossil fuels. These are non-renewable.
cost	The use of batch processing and the long timescale makes this relatively expensive.	The continuous processing makes this relatively cheap – but that could change if oil prices go up.

Questions

d Breweries need to employ more people than refineries. Why do you think that is?

e What are the advantages and disadvantages of these two methods of making ethanol? Draw up a table.

Key points

- Ethene can be reacted with steam using a catalyst to produce an industrial alcohol, ethanol.
- The industrial method of producing ethanol relies on ethene, which is a by-product of cracking long-chain hydrocarbons from non-renewable oil.
- The fermentation method of producing ethanol relies on renewable plant resources.

Polymerisation

The small alkene molecules made by cracking have a huge range of astounding uses as plastics. These small molecules, or **monomers**, can be made to 'pop' together like beads to make very long chains called **polymers**. There may be thousands of monomers popped together in a polymer chain. The process is called **polymerisation**. The long chains stick together like a tangled mass of spaghetti. It is this structure that gives polymers their useful properties.

Polymers are plastics. They are very easy to shape and are great for making objects from mobile phone cases to sink units. Plastics are very versatile and are used from the 'cheap and cheerful' end of the market to high-tech luxury.

> **Question**
>
> **a** List five objects made from plastic in the room around you. Suggest why plastic was used in each case.

It's that double bond again...

In this type of polymerisation, the double bonds in the monomers break open. The 'loose' bonds from neighbouring monomers then join up to form a long polymer chain. This is called **addition polymerisation** as the chains are simply added together.

Poly(ethene)

Polymers are named by putting 'poly' in front of the name of the small molecule. The simplest molecule is called ethene, so the polymer made from this is called poly(ethene). We often shorten this to polythene.

Poly(ethene) is a waxy solid that is very easy to shape. We can mould into bottles that can be used for drinks, or even for dangerous chemicals such as bleach or acid. It can also be rolled into thin but tough, flexible and waterproof sheets. These are ideal as a food wrap or for plastic bags.

> **Question**
>
> **b** Why are polythene bags preferred to paper ones by most people? Suggest one disadvantage of using polythene bags.

ethene monomers	double bonds open	and join with neighbours	to form a polymer

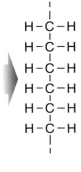
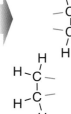

Cracking makes small ethene molecules.

These can be made to pop together to form poly(ethene).

The chains stack up like molecular spaghetti.

Poly(propene)

Poly(propene) is made from the alkene called propene (C_3H_6). It is a tougher plastic than poly(ethene) and it's not so flexible. It is used to make hard-wearing things such as bowls, crates or even school chairs. It is also made into fibres for carpets and ropes. Poly(propene) can be made brightly coloured so it is often used for children's toys.

Question

c Poly(ethene) chains are smooth and can slide over one another. Poly(propene) chains are 'knobbly' and can't slide easily. What property does this give poly(propene)?

The polymer for the job

Different polymers have different properties that make them suitable for different jobs.

Question

d Which polymer would you use for these products and why? (i) Insulation on an electrical cable; (ii) the case for a stereo system; (iii) the coating on a frying pan; (iv) a 'shatter-proof' window.

Polymer	Flexibility	Toughness	Relative cost	Other property
poly(ethene)	high	low	low	
poly(propene)	medium	high	medium	easy to colour
poly(styrene)	low (brittle)	brittle	medium	can be precisely moulded
poly(chloroethene) (PVC)	high	high	high	resistant to corrosion a very good electrical insulator
poly(ethane terephthalate) (PET)	high	medium	medium	transparent easy to 'blow mould'
poly(tetrafluoroethene) (PTFE)	high	medium	high	low friction – 'non-stick'
poly(methyl methacrylate) (acrylic)	low	medium	high	highly transparent

Smart polymers

Scientists are continually developing new polymers. Many of these new polymers seem to work well in the human body. New dental polymers are being made to replace old-fashioned metal fillings, for example. But some of these new polymers have unusual – 'smart' – properties.

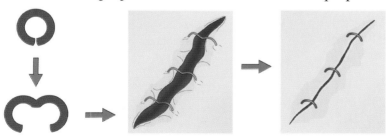

Question

e Shape memory polymers can be used to make moulds for casting plaster or concrete. You could make the mould by warming the polymer, stretching it into shape and then cooling it.
(i) Explain how this material could be used over and over again for different moulds.
(ii) Even if these special polymers cost three times as much as the traditionally used latex rubber, why might they still end up saving money?

Shape memory polymers can stretch like rubber when warmed but will 'stick' in their new shape if cooled. When they are warmed again they revert to their original shape. Large wounds can now be closed using special 'shape memory' polymer clips. These tight rings can be stretched out, cooled and fitted loosely into place. As they warm up, they pull back to their original shape, gently and securely closing the wound.

Key points

- Alkenes monomers such as ethene and propene can be used to make polymers such as polyethene and polypropene in a process called polymerisation.
- Polymers have many uses depending on their properties.
- Scientists are now developing 'smart polymers' with strange but useful properties.

From PVA to hydrogels

Slime is wonderful stuff, isn't it? You can mix your own in the kitchen sink. But what is it? And how can you change it from soft dripping slime to the bouncing variety?

Simple slime is made from PVA. PVA is short for poly(vinyl alcohol) – the old name for poly(ethanol). On its own it is not particularly strong, but it mixes well with water, making PVA glue. As the water dries out, the polymer chains stick to each other and whatever it is they are sticking together.

But PVA glue is not a simple mixture. The water molecules get between the polymer chains and are held weakly in place. If PVA reacts with a chemical such as borax, weak chemical bonds form 'cross-links' between the polymer chains, making a loose grid. Water molecules can get into this grid, but are held more tightly than in plain PVA. This gives slime its properties. Slime with few cross-link bonds is very runny. Slime with more cross-link bonds is much more viscous.

The open structure and trapped water makes slime soft and easy to pull apart, breaking the cross-link bonds between the chains. When two pieces of slime are pushed back together, the cross-link bonds re-form and the slime forms a single piece again.

Materials like this are called **gels**. You can make weak, low viscosity gels like slime by having lots of water and less cross-linked polymer. Or you can make strong, high viscosity, bouncy gels with more polymer and more cross-links.

Using different polymers, you can make gels with much stronger cross-links. These can hold their shape – but they can also trap lots of water. These **hydrogels** are used to make soft contact lenses.

Other hydrogels can be used in hospitals to cover wounds. They keep the wounds safe from infection, but allow small molecules like oxygen and water to move through, allowing the flesh beneath to 'breathe'.

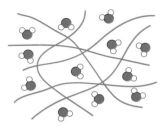

PVA: polymer chains – no cross-links

PVA glue: polymer chains – no cross-links, water molecules held loosely between chains

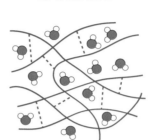
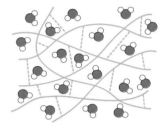

slime: polymer chains – weak cross-links, water molecules trapped loosely between chains

hydrogel: polymer chains – strong cross-links, water molecules trapped between chains

Question

a *Explain how the number of cross-link bonds affects the physical properties of slime.*

Question

b *Which would a hydrogel work best on – a graze or a large open wound?*

▼ Soft contact lenses are made from hydrogels.

Keeping the water out

Hydrogels keep water in – but other polymers are used to keep the water out. PTFE (polytetrafluoroethene) is the polymer used to make non-stick frying pans. A slightly different version of PTFE is used to make clothing waterproof. A thin layer of the tangled mass of polymer strands has millions of tiny pores to every square centimetre. When you sweat, the water molecules in the water vapour you give off can escape through these pores. The layer 'breathes' like cotton. But rainwater falls in droplets containing billions of tightly packed water molecules. These stick together and the whole droplet is much too big to get through the pores. So the layer is as waterproof as a polythene sheet!

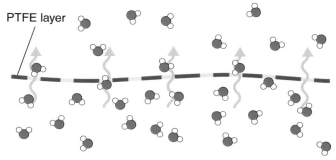

water vapour from sweat can escape

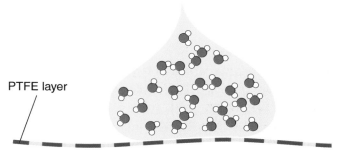

water in raindrops can't get in

Question

c What are the disadvantages of wearing polythene clothes?

Futuristic applications

Scientists have now made plastics that conduct electricity. Going further, they have developed plastics that can be used to make transistors and microchips. These plastics partially conduct electricity in a similar way to silicon. Normal microchips are very expensive to make. You have to grow silicon crystals in carefully controlled conditions. If any dust gets in, it's all ruined! Plastic microchips could be made by simply printing them using special inks on special plastic sheets. All you need is an industrial-sized version of the bubble jet printers we use at home.

Question

d What advantages will 'plastic' computer chips have over the silicon ones we use now?

In the future, plastics might dominate all aspects of our lives. Athletes will have computers built into their clothing to monitor their performance. You might have computers built into your clothing that monitor your health!

Question

e Silicon is made from sand, plastic is made from oil. What are some possible disadvantages of changing to plastics for our microchips and computers?

▲ Smart shirts could easily write backwards for mirror viewing!

Key points

- The properties of polymers depend on what they are made from and how they are produced.
- Polymers have many useful applications and new uses are being developed all the time.
- Hydrogels are useful new polymers.

Great plastics

Plastics are everywhere today. Much of our food now comes pre-packed in plastic. At home, our plastic-cased electronic equipment comes packed in plastic foam to keep it safe, and we put our rubbish into plastic bin bags before we throw it all out.

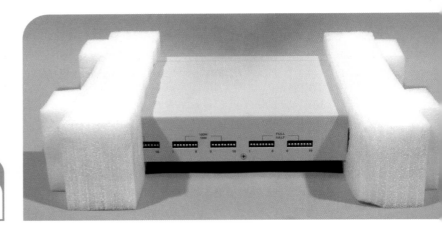

> **Question**
>
> **a** Suggest what materials were used for packaging before plastics. What were their disadvantages?

The down side

Disposing of plastics is a problem. The plastic age is also the over-packaged, throw away age. Over a million tonnes of plastic packaging are produced per year in the UK. In the worst case, this plastic ends up as litter – an ugly reminder of our waste on our streets, in the countryside and on the beach.

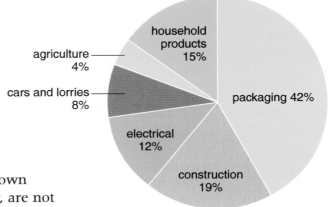

Biodegrade, tax or ban?

We throw paper away too, but this natural material rots down rapidly in the soil – it is **biodegradable**. Plastics, however, are not biodegradable, and may take tens or even hundreds of years to break down. Most plastic rubbish ends up in the dustbin and then on the local tip, which is usually a landfill site – perhaps an old quarry. The problem is that these are filling up fast.

Scientists are working on the development of smart plastics that are biodegradable. Some of these are based on natural polymers such as starch, which break down easily without leaving toxic waste. They would be more expensive than oil-based plastics, but it would be worth the extra cost to stop damage to the environment. And the price would soon come down if their use increased.

> **Question**
>
> **b** Using the pie chart, explain why a reduction in the amount of plastic packaging we use would make a significant contribution to the overall amount of plastic waste.

In Ireland they tax plastic bags. In New York State in the USA some counties have banned plastic bags completely. Food shops have to use paper bags instead.

Recycling and energy use?

Plastics are made from non-renewable oil. One way to use less oil is to recycle wherever possible. Most plastics have stamps that say what type they are. Many countries have set up separate recycling bins for different plastics, so that people can separate their waste at source. Maybe it should be compulsory.

Recycling uses a lot of energy, often more than it would take to make new plastic. Plastic waste contains as much stored energy as fossil fuels. Sweden already recovers 52% of the energy from plastics by burning plastic waste as fuel in power stations. Think how much oil you could save!

A detailed cost-benefit analysis shows that, overall, plastics use less energy and cause less environmental damage than traditional materials. For example, glass bottles are made from sand, but this has to be melted first. It takes 230 kg of oil to make 1000 glass bottles. You could make 1000 plastic bottles from just 100 kg of oil.

Different countries, different ways

The graph shows how different countries are dealing with plastic waste.

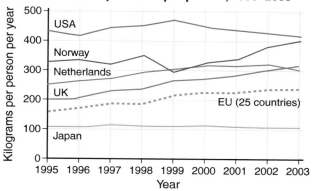

Amount of waste produced per person, 1995–2003

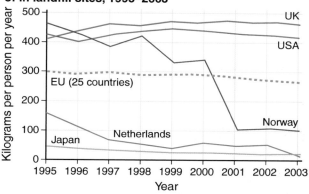

Amount of municipal waste per person disposed of in landfill sites, 1995–2003

Questions

c How does Norway compare with the UK in terms of:
  (i) the amount of waste produced?
  (ii) how they dispose of that waste?
d How has this pattern in Norway and the UK changed over time?
e Norway has banned the dumping of biodegradable materials in landfills. Do you think this accounts for all the change in their graph?
f Suggest other ways in which Norway might have reduced the scale of the problem.
g In the Netherlands, campaigns have encouraged people to reuse the plastic carrier bags they get from the supermarket instead of using new bags every time and then throwing them away. Does the waste graph suggest this has been effective?
h Japan and the USA both have advanced high-tech societies. What difference do their waste graphs suggest about these two cultures?
i Compare the proportion of waste (as an approximate fraction) that ends up in landfill for Japan and the USA. Suggest a reason for this difference.
j The EU has put a tax on landfill sites. How do you think this might affect the way local councils deal with their waste? Is it helpful?
k Copy the table below. From the information on this spread, list the social, economic and environmental impacts of each action.

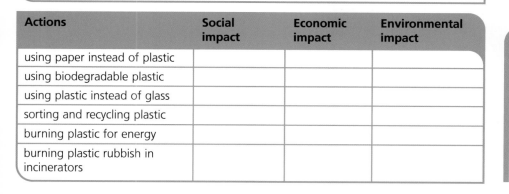

Actions	Social impact	Economic impact	Environmental impact
using paper instead of plastic			
using biodegradable plastic			
using plastic instead of glass			
sorting and recycling plastic			
burning plastic for energy			
burning plastic rubbish in incinerators			

Key points

● Many polymers are not biodegradable, which causes a problem with waste disposal.
● The disposal or recycling of polymers costs money and can have social environmental and economic impacts.

Plants and oil

All plants make glucose by photosynthesis, but some plants change this glucose to oil. Oil is a more concentrated store of chemical energy than glucose. Many plants make oil in their seeds, to provide energy for their growing seedlings. We can eat these seeds and use the energy directly. Or we can take the oil from them to use in other ways, for example as fuels.

Extracting the oil

Olives have been used to make oil for thousands of years all around the Mediterranean. Traditionally, the olives were crushed by giant stone wheels rolling over them, or squashed in large, hand-turned presses. Now these are replaced by industrial hydraulic presses.

The oil is squeezed out of the crushed pulp, runs out and is collected. The oil is then separated out from any water or other impurities. Even with modern methods olive oil is expensive, as olives are difficult to harvest and contain less than 20% oil.

Oil is sometimes removed from plants by distillation, but this can alter the flavour and smell of edible oils. Some plants like lavender produce small amounts of scented oils. These can be removed by distillation with water, which works at a lower temperature.

Oilseed crops

For cooking olives have been replaced by oilseed crops that can be harvested and processed cheaply and easily. In Southern Europe, sweetcorn and sunflowers grow well. In cooler Britain, the favourite oilseed crop is oilseed rape, as it grows well in our climate and the seeds contain up to 50% oil by mass.

This close relative of cabbage with its bright yellow flowers has changed the colour of the English countryside in summer over the last 20 years. Rapeseed oil is produced cheaply by industrial-scale processes. It is also a 'healthy' oil in your diet (see Spread 5.1). But the seeds are scattered easily and you can now see this plant growing along roadsides and invading fields. There is a danger that it will push out native wild flowers.

Vegetable transport fuel?

Oils are fuels for our bodies. Vegetable oils can also be made into biodiesel as a fuel for cars and lorries. Biodiesel itself is non-toxic to plants and animals and breaks down easily in the natural environment if it is spilt. Its exhaust contains fewer pollutants than ordinary diesel. It does give off carbon dioxide when it burns, but the plants that it is made from took in carbon dioxide when they grew. So it is a renewable fuel that does not cause global warming.

This could be the renewable fuel of the future, but you would need to grow a lot of oilseed. You can get about 1000 litres of oil from a $4000\,m^2$ field of oilseed rape. That's enough to run an average car for a year. But there are 24 million cars in Britain. You would need to turn $96\,000\,000\,000\ m^2$ of land over to oilseed farming if you wanted to replace all the petrol and diesel. That's almost half the total land area of Britain, so we could never become self-sufficient here. Biodiesel could still make a significant contribution to our energy needs in the future.

Think about what you will find out in this section

Which plants provide vegetable oil and how do their oils differ?	What additives are used in processed foods?
How can science help us to understand more about healthy eating?	How can we evaluate our increasing use of vegetable oils for fuels and food?
How are oils changed physically or chemically before use?	Could vegetable oils become the fuels of the future?

Healthy or not?

We seem to get conflicting messages about fats or oils in our food. But if you understand the science it helps.

▲ Oily food is bad for you!   ▲ Oily food is good for you!

Oils for energy

You must have some oil in your diet for your body to work properly. For example, you get vitamin A from oily foods. Oils and fats are primarily energy foods; fats are just solid oil. You need energy for life and the more active you are, the more energy you use. Oils are a more concentrated energy food than carbohydrates. Every gram of oil provides 39 kilojoules (kJ) of energy – double that from carbohydrates. An averagely active adult needs about 12 000 kJ of energy every day, which is the equivalent of 300 g of oil.

What sort of oil?

Vegetable oils have long carbon-chain molecules but they are not just simple hydrocarbons. At their simplest, all the C–C bonds are single bonds. These are called saturated oils. Animal fats are also 'saturated' like this. Scientists think than eating too many saturated oils or fats can lead to the build-up of a fatty chemical called cholesterol in the body. This can block arteries and cause heart disease.

But vegetable oils also contain some molecules with C=C double bonds – unsaturated oils. These seem to be much better for our health. Olive oil and sunflower oil contain a lot of unsaturated oils.

Questions

a The main oil available in Mediterranean countries is olive oil. In Britain, people traditionally cooked with butter or lard. Why would you expect Mediterranean people to have a healthier diet?

b Suggest how people have changed the way they use oil for cooking in the last 50 years.

Oils for health

The main health problem associated with eating large amounts saturated fat such as lots of fried food is the increased risk of heart attack or stroke. This appeared clear-cut at first, but scientists studying the diets of the Inuit of Canada found that their results did not fit the simple pattern.

Further study of the Inuit diet showed that their health depended on the fact the animal oil they ate was from fish, and fish has a particular type of oil in it.

People studied	Main oil source in diet	Risk from heart disease
Greeks	olive oil	low
Scots	lard, beef suet or butter	very high
Canadian Inuit	whale or seal blubber and fish oil	very low

Your body can make most of the oils it needs if necessary, but there are two types of unsaturated oil you must get from your diet because your body can't make them. They are called omega-3 and omega-6 oils. Oily fish and seafood are rich sources of these oils. The large amounts of these oils in the Inuit diet counteracts the saturated fats they get from whale and seal meat. It helps to 'thin' the blood and stop the build-up of cholesterol. Omega-3 oils are also good for your brain and help your memory work efficiently.

Vegetarians need omega oils too. Fortunately some seed oils contain these special oils. Flaxseed oil has just the right balance of omega-3 and omega-6 oils for the human body. Many people now buy flaxseed oil capsules from health food shops as a dietary supplement.

How can you tell which is which?

Bromine water is an orange–brown solution containing bromine (Br_2) molecules. It is not reactive enough to react with saturated oils. But the C=C double bonds in unsaturated oils make them more reactive than saturated oils. The double bonds break open and react with bromine and an addition reaction occurs. The new compounds that form are colourless, so the bromine water loses its colour. This reaction is used as a test for unsaturated oils. A weak, brown iodine solution can be used in a similar way.

Question

c The Greek and Scottish people studied followed the pattern seen elsewhere. In what way were the Inuit results anomalous?

Question

d Why might it be a good idea to eat mackerel or salmon when revising for an exam?

▲ A field of flax.

Question

e Which is more likely to decolorise iodine solution, olive oil or lard? What is happening to cause this colour change?

Key points

- Vegetable oils are important foods because they provide lots of energy and nutrients.
- Different types of oils have different effects on our health.
- Unsaturated vegetable oils with carbon=carbon double bonds can be detected using bromine or iodine.

Ready to eat

Fresh food may be best for our health, but in our busy modern world processed foods are certainly quicker. What happens to food when it is processed?

Changing vegetable fat

Fats are just oils that are solid at room temperature – they have higher melting points. Most natural fats come from animals, for example lard from pigs, suet from cows or butter from milk. Fats are better than oils for making cakes or pastry, but they are linked to heart disease. And they are also 'not suitable for vegetarians …'.

Saturated oils have higher melting points than unsaturated oils. Some vegetable products like coconut oil are high in saturated oils and do turn solid when cold. But these also have a strong flavour that isn't suitable for all food. Scientists have found a way to change cheap unsaturated oils into saturated fats for cooking.

The oil is warmed to 60 °C and hydrogen gas is bubbled through it. The double bond snaps open and 'grabs hold' of a passing hydrogen molecule to become saturated. Nickel is used as a catalyst to speed up the reaction. The process is called **hydrogenation**. Hydrogenated oils are used as fats for margarine, to replace butter. They are also used in cakes and pastries – and in chocolate!

▲ Fresh cooked spaghetti and calamari, or …
▼ a TV dinner … which is healthier?

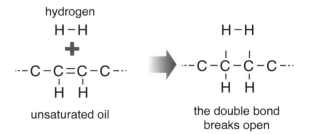

hydrogen
H–H
+
--C–C=C–C--
　　H　H
unsaturated oil

--C–C–C–C--
　H　H
the double bond
breaks open

H　H
　|　|
--C–C–C–C--
　|　|
H　H
saturated oil

Question

a Expensive chocolate is made with the unsaturated fats found naturally in cocoa butter. Why do you think this is often partly replaced by hydrogenated vegetable oil?

Additives in our food

Processed foods can lose some of their flavour and natural colour. They also need to last a long time on supermarket shelves. Processed foods have additives put in to overcome these problems. Some of these are 'natural' chemicals that have been used for thousands of years. Others have been created by scientists to do specific jobs.

- *Flavour enhancers* – We all like a little salt and maybe vinegar on our chips, or sugar in our baked beans. Monosodium glutamate is used in Chinese cooking, and we find it in lots of foods. It may sound as if it comes from a chemistry lab, but it is actually made from fermented soya beans!

- *Colour enhancers* – Processing dulls the colours of foods like peas and tomatoes. Some products use food colours to improve the appearance of the food. Some are natural, like the 'carotenes' extracted from tomatoes and carrots. Other are synthetic – made in the laboratory – such as yellow tartrazine and carmine red.

- *Preservatives* – Vinegar for pickles and sugar for jam have been around a long time; chemicals such as benzoic acid or sulfur dioxide are more recent additions. These preservatives all stop microbes growing in the food. Another group, called antioxidants, stop fats and oils going rancid and tasting bad.

- *Vitamins and minerals* – These are sometimes added to replace those lost during processing. Others are added to improve the product. Calcium is sometimes added to milk products, while ascorbic acid (vitamin C) is added to many fruit-flavoured drinks.

Are all these chemicals good for us?

Used wisely, some chemical additives help us make the most of our food. But there are some potential problems.
- Some people might be allergic to some additives.
- Additives might be used to disguise substandard ingredients.

Additives have all been tested, but there are concerns that long-term consumption of some additives could cause health risks. Many people believe that some of the bright colours used in sweets and drinks may cause children to lose concentration and become hyperactive.

Question

b Look back at the types of additives and give four reasons why they can be helpful.

How can we tell what's in our food?

By law all processed food products have to list their ingredients. As some of these have long 'chemical' names, the government has produced a list of permitted additives and given them 'E-numbers'. For example, E100–E199 are colours, E200–E299 are preservatives and E300–E321 are antioxidants. Some people reject any food with E-numbers in them as they think additives must all be nasty, harmful chemicals. But some of them are perfectly 'natural'. E300 is vitamin C while E260 is acetic acid, or vinegar.

Questions

c Explain to a friend who is against foods containing E-numbers why some additives can be beneficial.

d Suggest as many reasons as you can why people eat processed foods rather than fresh food.

Key points

- Vegetable oils can be hardened by hydrogenation so they can be used in spreads, cakes and pastries.
- Processed foods contain additives to improve taste and appearance, and to preserve them, but there are also disadvantages of using additives.
- Permitted additives are classified using the E-number system.

Just paint?

You may have used a can of white emulsion to paint your bedroom. But you use emulsions more often than you might think.

So what is an emulsion?

Oil and water do not mix. If you shake water with a small amount of oil, tiny droplets of oil will spread throughout the water. An **emulsion** is a mixture of tiny droplets of oil in water or water in oil. If you let the mixture stand, the oil and water will separate out. This happens quickly with an oil and vinegar salad dressing.

> **Question**
>
> **a** Why does the oil rise to the surface?

The trick with emulsions is to stop them from separating out. This happens naturally in emulsions such as milk, cream and butter. Milk is an emulsion of a few per cent of tiny droplets of butterfat in a watery liquid. Cream is similar but has more fat and less water. In butter, the emulsion is the other way around – with just a few per cent of milky water as droplets within the fat.

Even milk and cream separate eventually, however. The oil in milk slowly rises to the surface where it can be skimmed off – as cream. Butter is made by churning cream, which concentrates the fat even more. But some water is left. Once you melt butter, however, it separates completely and you can't get the butter texture back. The resulting butterfat is called ghee.

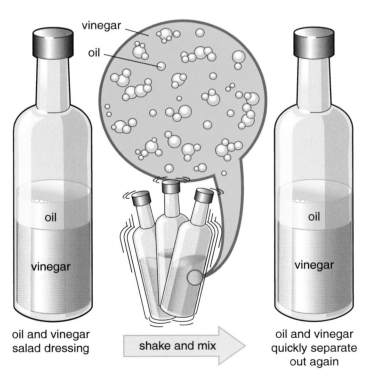

oil and vinegar salad dressing

shake and mix

oil and vinegar quickly separate out again

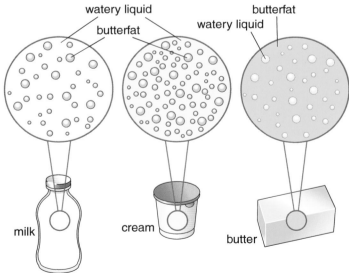

milk   cream   butter

> **Question**
>
> **b** Why do people on diets drink skimmed milk rather than ordinary milk?

Preventing separation

Mayonnaise is made from oil and vinegar but it doesn't separate out because it also contains a little egg yolk. Chemicals in the egg yolk stop the tiny droplets of oil from joining together when they collide, so the emulsion does not separate out. Chemicals that act like this are called **emulsifiers**. They are so important in the food industry that they have a whole section of E-numbers to themselves (E322–499).

Emulsions are very versatile, but even with the best emulsifiers they will separate out in time. This limits the shelf-life of products containing emulsions.

Why are emulsions so useful anyway?

Emulsions are thicker than oil or water. The thickness depends on the amount of oil and water, and how it is arranged. How we use them depends on their special properties.

Emulsion paints were first introduced to make paint more 'user-friendly' for the DIY market. They had less oil in them so they smelt less and dried quicker. You could even wash your brushes in soapy water instead of needing white spirit. But making an emulsion also changed the texture. Emulsions were less runny than oil-based paints and with a little tweaking could even be made 'non-drip'. They stay in place on the brush and do not run on walls.

This thicker texture is also important in food emulsions. Emulsions may be made to coat other foods, to keep particular shapes or simply to give a creamy, even texture. Mayonnaise is much thicker (more viscous) than salad dressing. It doesn't pour, it dollops – and sticks nicely to your chips.

Cream is less runny than milk; double cream is even 'thicker' as it has more fat. But whisk in some air bubbles and you get stiff whipped cream that sticks to your strawberries or can be piped into pretty shapes on your trifle. Ice cream is another water/fat emulsion that has the added complexity of tiny air bubbles – and ice crystals.

Question

e Presentation is very important when selling food. Give examples where the careful use of emulsions improves the presentation of processed food.

The way emulsions change the physical properties of the ingredients is vitally important to the food processing industry. Creamed cake mixture is an emulsion of water in fat. It is soft enough to be poured into a tin, but firm enough to keep the ingredients well mixed until it is cooked. Soft margarines are also water-in-oil emulsions. The water in the margarine makes it soft enough to be spread straight from the fridge.

Questions

c Some emulsifiers give the droplets a positive electrical charge. Like charges repel one another. How does this stop the droplets joining together and the emulsion from separating?

d Jars of very old and stale mayonnaise often have an oil layer in them. Explain what has happened.

Key points

- Emulsion are mixtures of oil and water, which can be made to stay together using emulsifiers.
- Emulsions have different uses depending on their properties. Examples are milk, butter, mayonnaise and paint.

Sudan 1

Fresh chillies can be bright red. When they are dried and processed to make chilli powder the colour usually darkens. Food colours may be added, to make them look fresher and more appealing.

Harmless colours are fine but sometimes dyes are used that should not be put in food. Some of these could cause long-term health problems such as cancer. Sudan 1 is one of the dyes that is not allowed in food. In 2005, Sudan 1 was found in processed food. Around 400 products had to be withdrawn from supermarket shelves.

> **Question**
>
> **a** List five types of food that might have contained chilli.

How can we tell what's in our food?

Foods are mixtures. We have to separate out the chemicals in the food before we can identify them. One of the simplest ways to separate out artificial food colours is to use **chromatography**. You put a spot of food colour onto a piece of filter paper and let water soak up through it. The different colours move up the paper with the water at different rates. You can then compare the dyes in the food with a pure sample of the dye you are investigating.

Chemical analysis

Simple chromatography might be fine if you just want to check what to avoid in your food. But before withdrawing millions of pounds worth of food from the supermarket shelves you need to be very sure of your facts. Supermarkets use analytical laboratories which can pinpoint chemicals accurately even at very low concentrations.

To test for Sudan 1, scientists used a special kind of chromatography to separate out the different chemicals in chilli powder. These were then fed into a machine called a mass spectrometer, which gives a printout that acts like a chemical fingerprint. The 'fingerprint' was then matched against a database of known dyes.

Of course, this system is only as good as its database. Just as a fingerprint found at the scene of a crime is of no use unless the police can match it to a known criminal, this system is only effective for 'known' chemicals. Laboratories in many universities across the world are constantly analysing new chemicals and adding their results to the global database. But some companies will only release their data if you pay for it.

From database for comparison

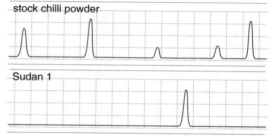

Chilli powders being tested

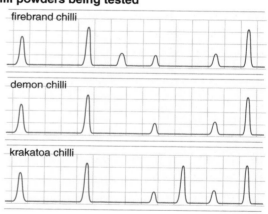

> **Question**
>
> **b** Which of these chilli powders contains Sudan 1?

> **Question**
>
> **c** Should all chemical data like this be freely available? Suggest reasons why companies might want to sell their data rather than give it away.

Reliability

Labs need to provide reliable results. Their machines need to be calibrated carefully – tested on known standard samples and adjusted so that they are accurate and give repeatable results with very little variation.

Modern laboratories are very 'high-tech' and rely on automated systems. These system are:

- *fast* – using automated systems samples can be tested continuously, one after the other, 24 hours a day!

- *accurate* – once calibrated the machines will give repeatable and reliable results. Even so, they will need to be recalibrated regularly, to make that the settings have not slipped during use.

- *sensitive* – these systems can deal with microscopic amounts, or detect chemicals that make just a tiny fraction of a complex mixture.

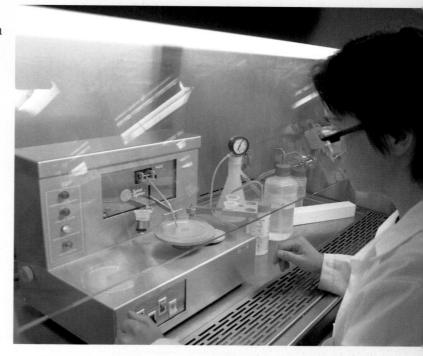

The machines are connected to computers which do the 'number crunching', produce the charts and help with the identification. This takes away much of the boring repetition that can lead to human error, which allows the human operators to concentrate on what we can learn from the data.

Question

d *Environmental scientists use similar machines. What chemicals might they be looking for?*

Even with sophisticated high-tech systems errors can still creep in:

- machinery can malfunction
- human error might lead to incorrect calibration
- mistakes might be made with samples mixed or muddled up before testing
- printouts might be read incorrectly or accidentally misinterpreted
- data might be maliciously falsified for political or commercial reasons.

Because of this, the chemical data is usually cross-checked at two or more independent laboratories before any important (or expensive) decisions are made.

Key points

- Chromatography and other chemical analysis can help us find out what additives are in our food.
- Measuring instruments need to be calibrated so that they give accurate readings.
- Repeated readings are needed to give reliable measurements when averaged out.

Ever since people have had accurate maps of the world they have wondered at how some of the continents seem to fit together like a jigsaw.

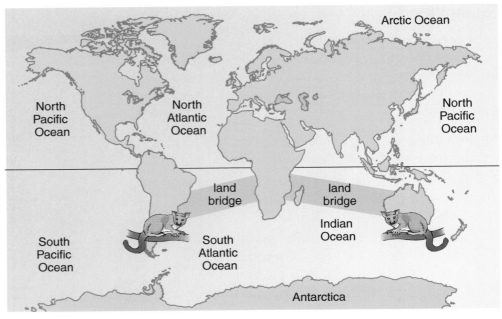

Moving continents

People have also wondered at why the same types of land animals are found on different continents. Why are marsupials such as possums found in South America and Australia yet nowhere else? How could they have crossed deep oceans to get from one continent to another? Some scientists thought there must once have been land bridges that linked the continents. They knew that mountains rose up and then were worn away over time. Perhaps this had happened in the oceans between the continents.

In 1912, a scientist called Alfred Wegener looked closely at South America and Africa. The shapes fitted together like the two halves of a torn picture.

- Ancient mountain ranges that stopped at the coast of South America continued across the Atlantic in Africa.
- The same rocks and fossils were found on both sides.
- There was evidence of an ancient shoreline that matched.

He thought they must been part of a bigger continent that had split and moved apart. He called this process **continental drift**, but he didn't know how it worked.

When his work was published in English translation in 1924 it immediately caused uproar. Most scientists thought the idea was nonsense.

- It went against the current ideas about land bridges.
- Wegener could not explain why the continents moved.
- Errors in his data made him suggest that the continents were moving apart at 250 cm every year – that's 100 times faster than they are actually moving.
- Physicists said (rightly) that it would be impossible for continents to 'plough through the crust' without breaking up.

Today

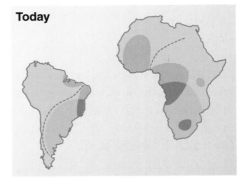

Millions of years ago

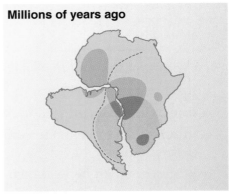

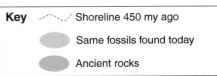

Key	
˜˜˜	Shoreline 450 my ago
	Same fossils found today
	Ancient rocks

▲ These maps show how the continents are today and how Wegener thought the land must have been millions of years ago.

The scientific community shut Wegener out. He couldn't even get a job as a professor in Germany. He had his 'great idea' too soon, without enough evidence to back it up. He died in 1930, frozen to death on an expedition over the Greenland ice cap. He left one or two supporters, but most scientists stuck with the 'old' idea of stable continents and land bridges.

Unexpected mountains under the sea

One of Wegener's problems in getting his ideas accepted 80 years ago was that nobody knew what was at the bottom of the oceans. When scientists began a survey of the floor of the Atlantic Ocean, which is up to 7 km deep, they were amazed to discover a chain of undersea volcanoes running down the middle of the ocean! No one expected there to be mountains under the sea. In the 1960s they realised that the line of volcanoes was along a crack in the crust. Magma from the mantle pushed into this crack, cooled and set to rock. The sea floor was spreading apart and the ocean was getting wider. This was how the continents moved apart.

The seal of approval

In 1964 the Royal Society in London announced that it had enough evidence to support Wegener's idea of continental drift. Wegener's explanations were not accurate, as the whole crust moved, not just the continents. The continents were on plates made of bits of crust. But his idea finally gave birth to the theory of **plate tectonics** which revolutionised the study of the Earth.

▼ Iceland sits astride the mid-Atlantic rift. The central valley gets wider every time its volcanoes erupt.

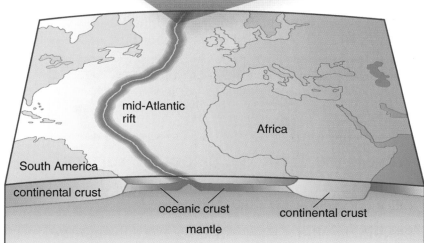

mid-Atlantic rift

Africa

South America

continental crust

oceanic crust

continental crust

mantle

Think about what you will find out in this section

Why can it take a long time for some scientists' ideas to become widely accepted?

Why is the Earth so 'restless'?

Can we use our understanding of Earth's structure and processes to help save lives?

How has the Earth and its atmosphere changed over time?

Can we use science to reduce harmful effects of human activity on the atmosphere?

Unchanging Earth?

Living in Britain it is easy to think that the Earth is a peaceful place geologically, but don't be fooled. Over millions of years continents move around and mountains rise and are worn away. Even on a human timescale, many parts of the world are shaken by terrible earthquakes or menaced by explosive volcanoes.

> **Question**
>
> **a** Where have you heard of earthquakes occurring or volcanoes erupting recently?

Mountain building

Mountain ranges such as the Himalayas are built from folded rocks. A hundred years ago, some scientists thought that the Earth must have shrunk as it cooled down. They thought that this caused the crust to get wrinkles, just like a plum turning into a prune. They thought mountains were just big wrinkles! To understand how mountains are really made, we need to know more about the inside of the Earth.

> **Question**
>
> **b** Some mountains are huge and still rising while others are just eroded stumps. Does this fit the 'wrinkle' theory? Explain your answer.

What is the Earth like below the surface?

We live on the surface of the Earth. This surface layer is called the **crust** – it is a thin hard layer.

Beneath the crust is a hot rock layer called the **mantle**. This can move slowly at a rate of just a few centimetres a year. The continental crust 'floats' on the denser rocks of the mantle. The continents on the crust and the top part of the mantle are divided into a number of large pieces called **tectonic plates**. These move, carrying the continents with them.

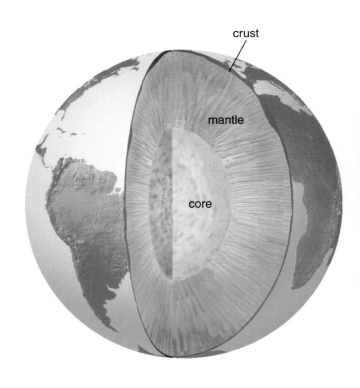

> **Question**
>
> **c** Which scientific objection to Wegener's idea of continental drift does the concept of the moving mantle overcome?

Why do they move?

If you heat a liquid from below, warm currents rise up and make the liquid swirl and mix. These are called **convection currents**. The rocks in the mantle and core are heated by natural radioactivity. This heating causes convection currents in the mantle, too. They are very slow currents but they make the tectonic plates move. The plates move very slowly, just a few centimetres a year, but they have been moving for hundreds of millions of years. Over such a long time, these tiny movements can make continents move around the Earth and force new mountains high into the air.

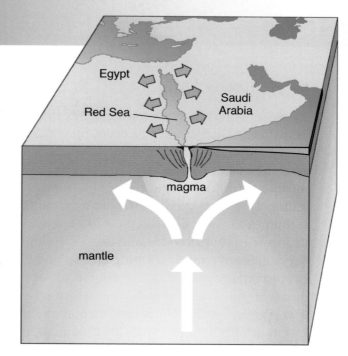

Questions

d Iceland is a volcanic island in the northern part of the Atlantic. The mid-Atlantic rift runs right through the middle. Iceland is now 2 m wider than it was 100 years ago. What is the spreading rate for the Atlantic?

e The Atlantic Ocean is approximately 5000 km wide. How old must it be if it is getting wider by 2 cm every year?

Most of the continents are now moving apart, carried along by their plates. That means that if you go back in time, they must have been closer together. Go back 250 million years and the world looked very different. All the continents were stuck together in a supercontinent called Pangaea.

Mountain building cycle

In the Atlantic the plates are moving apart. In the Pacific, on the opposite side of the Earth, they are moving together. This pushes the old ocean crust back down into the mantle, where it is slowly recycled. Rocks are folded up to form new mountains, volcanoes erupt and powerful earthquakes shake the ground. Eventually old oceans will disappear completely in this way. Great mountain chains like the Alps and the Himalayas formed when oceans disappeared and the continents on each side collided. The sediment caught between the continental blocks was squeezed and folded.

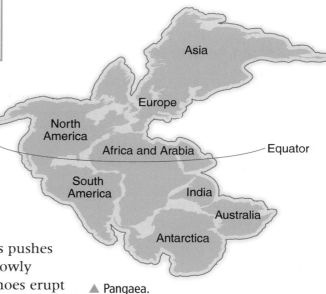

▲ Pangaea.

▼ Mountain building where plates collide.

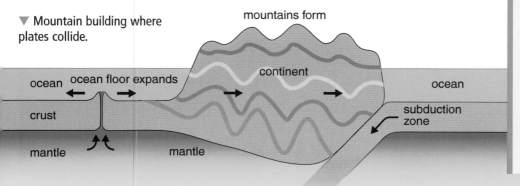

Key points

- Scientists used to think that the Earth's surface features were the result of the crust shrinking as the Earth cooled down.
- The Earth's surface consists of tectonic plates, carrying continents, which move by convection currents.
- When the plates crash into each other, they force up new mountains.

Boxing Day 2004

Every now and then the news brings stories of devastating earthquakes or erupting volcanoes. Most of these centre on uninhabited regions, and so cause few problems, but in 1999 a terrible earthquake struck Izmit in Turkey, killing 40 000 people. In 1976 an earthquake ten times as powerful killed 600 000 people in China. Volcanoes can also be deadly, though they often give more warning and so give people time to escape. The eruption of Mount Pinatubo in 1991 in the Philippines killed 350 people, but 25 000 people died after the eruption of Nevado del Ruiz in Colombia in 1985, which sent a giant mudslide down onto an unsuspecting town.

At 8 am local time on Boxing Day 2004, just off the northern tip of Sumatra in the Indian Ocean, the Earth moved. Pressure that had been building up for centuries finally caused rock to shatter and slip, triggering a massive earthquake. It was the most powerful quake for 40 years, giving out a shock wave as powerful as a thousand nuclear bombs.

The Earth's crust moved along the boundary between the Indian and Eurasian plates. One side was lifted by 10 metres – and so was the ocean above it. The water slumped back creating a huge surge wave, or **tsunami**, which spread across the ocean as fast as a jet plane.

In deep water the tsunami was not a problem. But as it approached the shore the moving water bunched up, raising the wave into a solid wall of water up to 10 metres high.

From the shore the first sign of this impending doom was a sudden drop in sea level, as if the plug had been pulled from the ocean. The unwary may have walked out to view the strange spectacle of fish stranded on the sand or suddenly exposed rock pools or reefs. And then the roar in the distance and the first sign of the tsunami wave approaching, moving faster than you could run … Within hours 250 000 people had been killed.

Question

a Earthquakes send shock wave vibrations out through the rocks. Soon after the Sumatran earthquake, elephants in Thailand trumpeted and rushed inland to safety. Suggest one way could they tell that something was wrong.

Where do quakes and eruptions occur?

Earth movements cause these sudden and disastrous earthquakes and volcanoes. Powerful earthquakes only occur along the plate boundaries. The destructive ones occur where the plates are crashing into each other like cars colliding head-on and crumpling or sliding sideways past each other.

Earthquakes and volcanoes are common. If you plot them on a map they occur in clear belts across the globe:

- along the 'ring of fire' around the Pacific Ocean
- along the Alps and Himalayas belt where new fold mountains are created
- in zones such as the San Andreas Fault zone in California
- in the middle of the Atlantic and Pacific Oceans where undersea volcanoes are forming
- where one plate is slipping down under another and disappearing.

Earthquake-proof buildings

Britain has no powerful earthquakes but we have the occasional weak ones. We are a long way from the edge of the Eurasian plate. Our traditional brick houses would simply shake apart in a powerful quake. Reinforced concrete should fare better, but many of the deaths in Turkey and China were caused by the collapse of poorly built buildings. San Francisco is a city of skyscrapers built over a major earthquake-prone plate boundary. Oddly enough, steel-girder framed skyscrapers survive earthquakes quite well, though they do sway alarmingly.

▼ These skyscrapers are built to withstand a good shake!

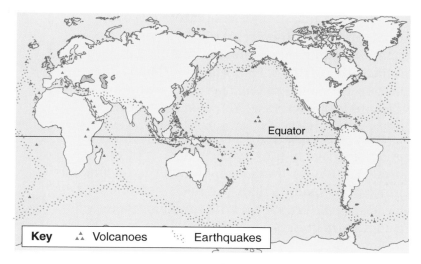

▲ Earthquakes and volcanoes occur where plates meet.

Questions

b Earthquake power is measured on the Richter scale. Each number is ten times as powerful as the number below. Izmit was magnitude 7 on this scale. What number would you give to the Chinese earthquake in 1976?

c The Sumatran earthquake was magnitude 9 on the Richter scale. Would the death toll from the Sumatran earthquake have been lower or higher if it had happened on land, under a big city?

Question

d Japan lies in the Pacific 'ring of fire'. Why do you think that Japanese houses were traditionally built with bamboo and paper walls?

Key point

- Tectonic plate movements can be sudden and disastrous, causing earthquakes and volcanoes at plate boundaries.

Vesuvius sleeps

The great volcanic cone of Vesuvius looms over the city of Naples in Italy. Nearly 2000 years ago, a gigantic eruption sent a cloud of red-hot gas down on the thriving city of Pompeii, killing all its 5000 inhabitants. Should the million people who live in Naples today be worried? You'd better believe it!

Vesuvius last erupted in 1944, when lava stopped just on the edge of the city. Since then it has been quiet – but it is far from dead. Vesuvius has a long history of dormant periods like this, often followed by catastrophic eruptions. Without doubt there will be another major eruption. The question is not 'if' but 'when'.

> **Question**
>
> **a** *What was different about the 1944 eruption, compared with the one that destroyed Pompeii?*

▲ A killer on the doorstep … if history is right.

When will it happen?

If the people of Naples are to have a chance of survival, they need to have advance warning so that they can evacuate the city. Scientists must try to predict when the volcano will blow, and that is far from easy. But there are some warning signs.

- *increased temperature* – There is a great chamber full of molten magma beneath a volcano, and hot gases from this escape into the crater. The temperature of this gas is about 90 °C – hot enough to cook eggs. If the temperature rises, it might mean an eruption is coming soon.

- *more earthquakes* – You get a lot of small earthquakes around a volcano. These earthquakes get stronger and more common before an eruption. Hundreds of small earthquakes have occurred recently, making it the most active period since the last eruption.

- *more gas* – The gas that comes out of a volcano is mostly carbon dioxide and toxic, foul-smelling hydrogen sulfide. You get more gas before an eruption.

- *rising land* – As magma pushes in below the volcano, the ground rises. A harbour near Vesuvius has risen nearly 4 metres out of the sea in the last 30 years.

For earthquakes, these warning signs are:

- *animal behaviour* – Local tales often talk of animals behaving strangely just before an earthquake: dogs start to bark or all the birds go silent. In the Sumatran earthquake, elephants stampeded inland to safety.

- *pre-shocks* – Minor shocks often occur before a big shock. Perhaps these are what make the animals behave strangely.

- *changes in the water levels in wells* – This often seems to drop in the period before an earthquake.

> **Questions**
>
> **b** *La Sulfatara is a small crater to the West of Naples. Sulfurous gas is escaping at 165 °C. The region has had lots of small earthquakes recently and the crater floor has risen by a few metres. There is a large housing estate built on the rim. Write a letter to the local residents' association, warning them of the dangers.*
>
> **c** *What are the 'natural' signs that an earthquake may be on its way?*

Time to evacuate?

All this activity shows an earthquake or eruption is about to occur. Will it happen tomorrow, in a few months or not for years? The best way to save lives is to evacuate the danger zone. But do this too soon, and people will get bored and drift back to their homes.

Scientists are working hard to find ways of making precise predictions about eruptions, but it is not easy. Some volcanic craters remain open, so it is relatively easy to monitor what is happening. You can see whether the lava level is rising or falling, whether it is getting hotter or cooling down, whether there is more or less gas. But with many of the more dangerous volcanoes lava sets solid in the vent, plugging it and stopping gas escaping. Building pressure eventually blows this out in a massive eruption, but it is hard to tell *how much* pressure is building up inside and *how strong* the lava 'plug' is. And there are many thousands of volcanoes in the world. Some are near large population centres in rich countries and so are monitored carefully. But poorer countries do not have the resources to do this.

For earthquakes, as you have seen there are a lot of plate edges and ocean ridges to monitor. Even if you know how they move they don't always move steadily and the stress points may be deep underground or at the surface. Since the Sumatra tsunami, scientists are considering installing an early warning system for tsunamis so people can at least be evacuated from the low-lying land.

There is a random unpredictability about many natural phenomena. Some people think it will never be possible to predict accurately the time of an eruption.

How big is the problem?

Some volcanoes have bubbling lava in their craters, which simply spills over the edge during eruptions. Vesuvius is far more dangerous as the lava has set to form a plug in the crater neck. The pressure builds up and up inside until the plug 'blows'. Look at the data table for Mount Vesuvius.

Year of eruption	Years since last eruption	Millions of cubic metres of lava erupted
1794	34	27
1858	64	120
1872	14	20
1906	34	80
1929	23	12
1944	15	25
20??		

Questions

d If you blow up a balloon and keep blowing it will eventually burst. You cannot predict the exact moment of bursting because the rubber is not perfectly uniform. If there is just a tiny flaw here, or a thinner patch there, that is where the break will begin. Use this or any other analogy to explain why it may never be possible to predict the eruption time of a volcano exactly.

e (i) Plot a graph of the amount of lava against the time between eruptions. Draw a line of best fit.
(ii) What pattern does this graph show?
(iii) Use this line to predict the volume of lava produced if Vesuvius erupted today.
(iv) Given where the 1944 lava stopped, should the people of Naples be worried? Explain your answer.

Key point

- Although scientists monitor for earthquake and volcano activity, they find it very hard to predict accurately when they will occur.

The air that we breathe

What's in the air?

The Earth's atmosphere has been more or less the same for 200 million years. Without it, we could not exist. Dry air is 21% oxygen, the gas you need to breathe; 78% is the unreactive gas nitrogen. There is just 1% of 'other gases'. Normal air also contains varying amounts of water vapour. The 21% of oxygen is very important to animals on the Earth. The carbon dioxide is very important to plants.

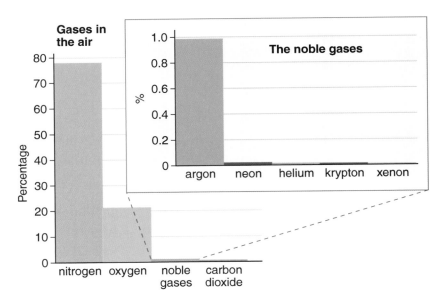

Gases in the air

The noble gases

What are the 'other gases'?

A hundred years ago, nobody knew that these 'other gases' existed. They were hidden in the fairly unreactive nitrogen.

But nitrogen reacts with burning magnesium. Careful experiments showed that there was 1% of air that refused to react even with magnesium. This was called **noble gas**, as it was so unreactive. (Unreactive gold is called a noble metal.) We now know that there is a whole family of noble gases. The most common is argon.

The noble gases form Group 0 of the periodic table. The noble gases are typical non-metals in many ways:

- they have very low melting/boiling points
- when solid they are soft and crumbly
- they do not conduct electricity.

They are, however, very unreactive. You may think that such unreactive gases will not be of much use, but sometimes their very inactivity is just what is required.

Group 0

| He |
| Ne |
| Ar |
| Kr |

Question

a Oxygen boils at −183 °C, argon at −186 °C and nitrogen at −196 °C. Suggest another way that argon could be separated from air.

Using the noble gases

Helium is not very soluble in water, even under pressure. This makes it an excellent substitute for nitrogen in the 'air' that deep-sea divers breathe. When a diver surfaces nitrogen bubbling out of the blood can cause the 'bends'. Helium doesn't do this but does have the side effect of making you sound like Donald Duck when you talk!

Question

b Methane (in natural gas) boils at −162 °C, while helium boils at −269 °C. Explain what would happen if you cooled natural gas to −180 °C. Why do you think it is easier to separate helium completely from natural gas than it is to separate argon from air?

Helium's low density means that it is very easily lost from the atmosphere, into space. Helium forms in the rocks of the Earth during radioactive decay. For the last 50 years or so, helium has been produced commercially from natural gas.

Helium's low density also makes it a safe alternative to hydrogen for modern airships – or party balloons.

Question

c (i) Why is helium a safer gas to use in airships than hydrogen?
(ii) Why wasn't it used for the early airships of the 1930s?

▶ The Hindeburg disaster in 1937 showed the danger of using hydrogen for airships.

Neon is most commonly used for another property. It glows if an electrical discharge is passed through it. These discharge tubes can be coloured, making them ideal for flashy neon signs.

Argon is the cheapest of the noble gases to produce as it makes up 1% of the air. Argon is used inside ordinary light bulbs, to stop the filament from burning. It is also used to give an unreactive atmosphere for welding which could be dangerous if done in air.

Question

d Why is argon used rather than helium or neon?

Krypton is used in some lasers. These are used for laser surgery and for removing birthmarks and tattoos, as well as for 'laser sights' on rifles. They can also be used to cure some eye defects.

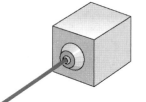

Key points

● For 200 million years the Earth's atmosphere has consisted of roughly 80% nitrogen and 20% oxygen. There is a small proportion of carbon dioxide and water vapour and noble gases.
● Noble gases are in Group 0 of the periodic table and are chemically unreactive, which can be a useful property.

The first atmosphere

The Earth formed 4½ billion years ago. In the beginning things were very different from our present atmosphere of oxygen and nitrogen. The Earth was very hot and was covered with volcanoes. Gas from these volcanoes formed the first atmosphere. This first atmosphere was thought to be made mostly of carbon dioxide and water vapour, with a little methane and ammonia. Scientists have come up with the theory of the origin of the atmosphere by studying the gases from modern volcanoes, as well as by looking at the atmospheres of Mars and Venus.

▲ The Earth 4.5 billion years ago may have looked like this.

Questions

a *Near Naples in Italy there is a cave known as 'the mouth of hell' that fills up with invisible, odourless volcanic gas. Any dogs that wander in die by suffocation. What gas causes this, do you think?*

b *Which type of organism wouldn't have been able to survive in a carbon dioxide atmosphere?*

As the Earth cooled the water vapour turned to water, forming the oceans. The atmosphere was almost 100% carbon dioxide, just like on Mars and Venus today. We know that there was no oxygen as iron found in the sediments is not oxidised.

Simple microbes lived in this oxygen-free environment. Then about 3 billion years ago simple plants evolved in the oceans. These plants changed the world. Fossils show that they became bigger and more sophisticated. Eventually they colonized the land as well.

▲ 3 billion years ago.

The first pollutant on Earth

Plants use photosynthesis to make the food they need from carbon dioxide and water. They do this by tapping into the vast amounts of energy that pour onto the Earth from the sun. This gave them a competitive edge over the pre-existing organisms, so plants grew, evolved and spread rapidly through the oceans. But plants make oxygen when they photosynthesise. To the simple microbes, oxygen was a poison! So the growth and spread of plants led to a pollution of the world's oceans with oxygen because oxygen dissolves in water. You can see evidence for this in the thick beds of oxidized iron that formed at this time.

Question

c *Imagine a new form of life evolved that produced chlorine gas. What effect would that have on the microbes, plants and animals that live on Earth today?*

▲ 2 billion years ago.

By 2 billion years ago, early life forms were nearly wiped out. Just a few survived in oxygen-free deep ocean mud or stagnant pools.

Locking up the carbon

As plants evolved and spread, carbon dioxide was removed from the atmosphere and locked up in the plant biomass. Some of this became trapped in the rocks, forming the fossil fuels of the future. By 300 million years ago great swamp forests covered much of what is now Britain. You can find the stumps of fossil trees in many parts of the country.

Meanwhile, oxygen started to build up, first in the oceans and then finally in the atmosphere. Just under 1 billion years ago the first animals appeared in the oceans, exploiting the 'new' oxygen to get the energy they need for life by respiration.

Some of these ocean organisms built shells from calcium carbonate. They took carbon dioxide from the oceans for this, so more dissolved out of the air to take its place. When they died their shells formed limestone which locked the carbon away in the rocks. So carbon dioxide levels in the atmosphere fell as oxygen levels rose. By about 200 million years ago, the oxygen and carbon dioxide levels reached their presents values and the atmosphere has remained fairly stable ever since.

The graph shows how the percentage of carbon dioxide and oxygen in the atmosphere has changed over time.

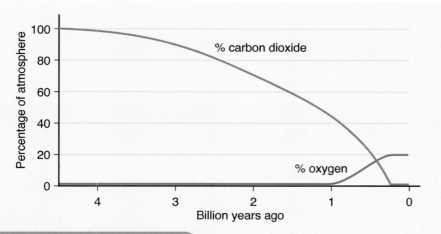

Question

d Why couldn't animals have evolved before plants?

Questions

e Every tonne of coal will have removed 3.7 tonnes of carbon dioxide from the atmosphere. What happens if that coal is burnt?

f Every tonne of limestone will have removed 0.44 tonnes of carbon dioxide from the atmosphere. Limestone is a very much more common rock than coal (coal beds are just a few metres thick, limestone beds may be hundreds or even thousands of metres thick). Which has removed more carbon dioxide from the atmosphere, coal or limestone? Explain your answer.

Question

g (i) For roughly what proportion of Earth's history has the oxygen level been as it is today?

(ii) Simple plants had been producing oxygen for 2 billion years before it started to build up in the atmosphere. Where did the oxygen go over that first period?

Key points

- In the first billion years of the Earth's existence the atmosphere was very different from today.
- Theories suggest that the early atmosphere was mainly carbon dioxide, until plants developed and produced oxygen.
- Most of the carbon dioxide from the early atmosphere is now locked up in fossil fuels and limestone rock.

Tipping the balance

For 200 million years our atmosphere has been in balance. Plants take in carbon dioxide and animals breathe it out. Recycling at its best! But over the last 200 years we have upset the balance. We've been burning up the fossil fuels a million times faster than they took to form. What effect will this have on the Earth?

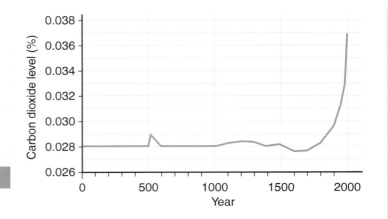

▲ Carbon dioxide level in the atmosphere over the last 2000 years.

Question

a Look at the graph.
  (i)   Describe in words what the graph tells you.
  (ii) There was a huge volcanic eruption in 500 AD. What effect did this have on the carbon dioxide level?
  (iii) How long did this effect last – 50, 200 or 500 years?
  (iv) How long has the recent rise in carbon dioxide level been going on for?
  (v)   Do you think this could have been caused by volcanic activity? Explain your answer.
  (vi) What human activity over the last 200 years might have caused this?

Theories and evidence

Environmentalists are certain that the Earth's climate is changing and point the finger of blame at fossil fuels. Most scientists agree that the climate is changing and that the billions of tonnes of carbon dioxide that we put into the air every year when we burn fossil fuels is contributing to this change, but this may not be the sole cause. There are several different theories about what effect human activity is having on the Earth's atmosphere now. Beyond that, there is little agreement.

Carbon dioxide to blame?

Environmentalists believe we need to reduce the amount of carbon dioxide produced to try to stop the climate from changing. In a meeting in Kyoto in 1997, leaders of the developed world, including Britain, agreed to set targets for reducing the amount of carbon dioxide they produce.

But the biggest polluter of all, the USA, has not agreed to this. They say using less oil could harm their economy and people would suffer. They also point out that India and China, both countries with huge populations, are industrialising fast and will soon produce more carbon dioxide than even the USA.

Question

b Look at the table below.
  (i)   From these figures, calculate the total mass of carbon dioxide produced every year by each country.
  (ii) Over the last 20 years, the figure for the USA has been constant, while the figures for India and China have doubled. Suggest a reason for this.
  (iii) What would be the overall effect on global carbon dioxide emissions if this trend continued for another 20 years?
  (iv) Would a 15% reduction by the USA over this period be significant for the environment?

Country	Population	Tonnes of carbon dioxide produced per person annually
USA	300 million	20
China	1300 million	3
India	1000 million	1

Natural climate change

Environmentalists often give the impression that the climate would stay the same if it were not for us. Four hundred years ago, Britain was so cold in winter that the River Thames froze over in London and fairs were held on it. Eight hundred years ago it was much warmer than today, and grapes were grown to make wine in northern Britain.

Going further back, 20 000 years ago the world was in the grip of the Ice Age. Britain was covered by great ice sheets and woolly mammoths roamed the country. So much water was locked up in the ice that the sea level fell so far that you could walk to what is now France. Then 10 000 years ago the ice started to melt and sea levels rose, flooding communities that lived in low-lying areas.

Research shows that the Earth's climate has been alternating between ice age and much warmer periods when all the ice melted every 100 000 years or so for millions of years. No-one is quite sure why, though cycles of solar activity or passing interstellar dust clouds have been blamed. Our climate is currently about halfway between the two extremes.

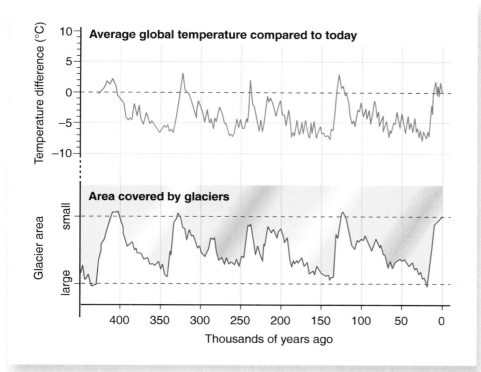

Key points

- We are releasing carbon dioxide locked up in fossil fuels from the Earth's early atmosphere and this is increasing the carbon dioxide level in today's atmosphere.
- We can evaluate theories about the changes occurring in today's atmosphere by looking at the evidence.
- We can evaluate the effects of human activity on today's climate by analysing data.

Questions

c Why is it extremely unlikely that the Earth's climate will stay constant?
d From the graph, which is usually more rapid, the onset of an ice age or its retreat?

1 **a** Which of the following shows a saturated hydrocarbon?

A
$$H-\overset{\overset{\displaystyle H}{|}}{C}-\overset{\overset{\displaystyle H}{|}}{C}-\overset{\overset{\displaystyle H}{|}}{C}-\overset{\overset{\displaystyle H}{|}}{C}-H$$
(with lower H's)

B
$$H-\overset{\overset{\displaystyle H}{|}}{C}-\overset{\overset{\displaystyle H}{|}}{C}=\overset{\displaystyle H}{C}-\overset{\overset{\displaystyle H}{|}}{C}-H$$

C
$$H-\overset{\overset{\displaystyle H}{|}}{C}-\overset{\overset{\displaystyle H}{|}}{C}=\overset{\displaystyle H}{C}-H$$

D
$$\overset{H}{\underset{H}{}}C=C\overset{H}{\underset{H}{}}$$

b Which of the following could represent an alkene?

A C_5H_{12} B $C_{16}H_{34}$

C $C_{18}H_{36}$ D $C_{42}H_{86}$

c Unwanted long-chain hydrocarbons are
   A cracked to make the monomers needed to make addition polymers
   B combined with bromine water to make polymers
   C are used as the monomers to make addition polymers
   D converted to alkanes to make addition polymers

d Small alkene molecules are
   A cracked to make the monomers needed to make addition polymers
   B combined with bromine water to make polymers
   C are used as the monomers to make addition polymers
   D converted to alkanes to make addition polymers

e Some people think plastic polymers are an environmental hazard because they
   A are biodegradeable
   B are not biodegradeable
   C are easily moulded into shape
   D are not easily moulded into shape.

2

Polymer	Properties
poly(propene)	semi-rigid, easily coloured
poly(ethene)	cheap, flexible
poly(styrene)	rigid, easily moulded
PVC	tough, resists damage, shiny, electrical insulator
PET	transparent or black, microwave-proof

For each use below, suggest a suitable plastic and give a reason why.

a a supermarket carrier bag   *(1 mark)*
b the packaging for a CD player   *(1 mark)*
c 'artificial leather' for a sofa   *(1 mark)*
d a washing-up bowl   *(1 mark)*
e a lemonade bottle   *(1 mark)*
f coating for an electric cable   *(1 mark)*
g the tray for a microwave dinner   *(1 mark)*

3 The graph shows how much energy you get by burning 1 kg of plastic waste compared to 1 kg of oil and coal.

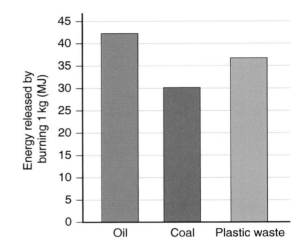

a Describe how the energy from plastics compares to the energy from fossil fuels.
(1 mark)

b **i** Most waste plastic in Britain ends up in landfill sites. Give **two** reasons why this is not a good way to deal with plastic waste. *(2 marks)*
   ii Suggest a reason why it might be difficult to recycle plastic waste. *(1 mark)*

c **i** We are responsible for up to 0.5 kg of waste plastic every day. Suggest **two** advantages of burning this material in power stations instead of coal or oil. *(2 marks)*
   ii What are the **two** main compounds that will be formed when plastic burns?
   (2 marks)

d Some plastics contain nitrogen or chlorine. Why might these cause a problem? *(1 mark)*

4 A third of all plastic used goes in packaging – which is then simply thrown away. Manufacturers now stamp many plastic containers with the plastic type to aid recycling.

PET   low-density polythene

high-density polythene   polypropene

PVC   polystyrene

a i How easily would it be to separate out mixed plastic waste using these codes (could it be automated)? *(1 mark)*

ii Some councils have recycling bins to allow people to sort their waste by hand into the different groups. Suggest a way to encourage people to do this. *(1 mark)*

Some supermarkets are experimenting with carrier bags made using polymers made from corn starch that are biodegradeable.

b i Suggest **two** ways in which these would be better than polythene. *(2 marks)*

ii Suggest **two** possible problems that might stop the general introduction of these bags. *(2 marks)*

Scientists are now looking at ways to break down waste plastics into smaller chemicals which could then be fractionated, cracked and used as 'feedstock' for new plastics. The problem is that expensive equipment is needed and large amounts of plastic waste would need to be available to make it economically viable (at least 50 000 tonnes a year).

c i Why is it easier to separate out oils and other chemicals formed by breaking down plastics than it is to separate the plastics themselves? *(1 mark)*

ii Suggest **two** factors that are slowing down the introduction of this technology. *(2 marks)*

5 Match words **A**, **B**, **C** and **D** to the sentences in the table.

    A whipped cream   **B** egg yolk
    C cream   **D** butter

1	This is a 'water' in oil emulsion made by churning milk.
2	This oil in water emulsion separates out from milk.
3	This oil in water emulsion has added air bubbles.
4	This is added to oil and vinegar in mayonnaise as an emulsifier.

6 Read this passage and answer the questions.

Oils are a much more concentrated energy store than carbohydrates. Many plants store oil in their seeds, to provide the energy for the growing seedling. When we eat vegetable oils, we can utilise this energy store to give us the energy we need for life. There is a concern that eating too much saturated oil could lead to the build up of cholesterol in the arteries, which can lead to heart disease. But many vegetable oils are unsaturated, and these seem to have the opposite effect, keeping us healthy.

We all need to have some oil in our diet, as it is needed for important reactions in our cells. Fortunately we can make most of the oil we need, but some oils – called omega-3 and omega-6 – have to come from our diet. Omega-3 oils are particularly good for our brains. They are found in fish oils, but also in some vegetable oils such as flaxseed oil.

a i Explain the terms saturated and unsaturated. *(2 marks)*

ii How could you use bromine water to tell these two types of oil apart? *(1 mark)*

b i Which chemical causes heart disease if it builds up in the arteries? *(1 mark)*

ii Which types of oil seems to prevent this effect? *(1 mark)*

iii One 'old wives' tale' was that 'fish is good for your brain'. Could there be any truth in this? *(1 mark)*

iv How can vegetarians keep their brain in good shape? *(1 mark)*

7 Vegetable oils are usually unsaturated, but animal fats are saturated.

    a What health problem is associated with eating too much animal fat? *(1 mark)*

    b Olive oil is a healthy oil for salads but not so good for frying as heating for a long time breaks down the C=C double bonds in unsaturated oils. In what way does this 'spoil' the oil as a food? *(1 mark)*

    c **i** Vegetable oils are turned into solid fats for margarine by bubbling hydrogen through the hot oil. What happens in this reaction? *(1 mark)*

        ii Nickel is added to this mixture. What effect does it have on the reaction? *(1 mark)*

8

Fuel	Energy content (MJ/litre)	Source	Main pollutants produced compared to petrol engine *		
			Particulates	Nitrogen oxide	Carbon monoxide
petrol	26	crude oil	*	*	*
diesel	29	crude oil	high	*	*
biodiesel	27	vegetable oil	low	high	*
ethanol	18	sweetcorn	*	low	low

    a **i** How does biodiesel compare to petrol and diesel in terms of energy content per litre. *(1 mark)*

        ii How does ethanol compare to petrol and diesel in terms of energy content per litre. *(1 mark)*

    b Cars can be converted to run on either petrol or ethanol. Which do you think would give more miles per litre? *(1 mark)*

    c **i** City smog is caused by a mixture of nitrogen oxides, carbon monoxide and particlulates. Is ethanol more or less likely to cause city smog. *(1 mark)*

        ii What pollution disadvantage does biodiesel have compared to ethanol. *(1 mark)*

        iii What big advantage do biodiesel and ethanol have over petrol and diesel in the long term? *(1 mark)*

    d You would need a 4000 m² field to produce enough biodiesel to run a car for a year. There are 24 million cars in Britain. What is the big limitation on using biodiesel to replace fossil fuels in Britain? *(1 mark)*

9 The ideas about how mountains form have changed dramatically over the last 100 years.

    a How did early scientists think that mountains were formed as the Earth cooled? *(1 mark)*

    b We now know that the crust is broken up into slabs called plates that move slowly. What makes these plates move? *(1 mark)*

    c Describe how moving plates can cause mountains to form. *(1 mark)*

    d The edges of plates often stick and jam, but eventually they will jerk apart and move. What does this cause? *(1 mark)*

10 Yellowstone Park is a vast area in the Rocky mountains of Wyoming, USA. It is famous for its geysers that squirt boiling water into the air in great fountains. It also has bubbling pools of mud and sulfurous fumaroles. Recently there have been many small earthquakes, and the ground has risen by a metre or so in some areas.

    a Give **two** features that suggest that Yellowstone is a volcanic region. *(2 marks)*

    b Give **two** features that suggest an eruption might be on the way. *(2 marks)*

Scientists think that Yellowstone Park contains a 'supervolcano' that, when it blows, would be a thousand times as large and powerful as any other eruption in recorded human history. It would produce 1000 times as much ash, carbon dioxide and sulfur dioxide.

    c Suggest some effects that this type or eruption might have on the Earth's climate. *(2 marks)*

11 This question is about the atmosphere and how it has changed over Earth's history.

    a The composition of the air today is approximately
        A 1/5 nitrogen and 4/5 oxygen
        B 1/5 carbon dioxide and 4/5 oxygen
        C 1/5 oxygen and 4/5 carbon dioxide
        D 1/5 oxygen and 4/5 nitrogen.

b Four billion years ago the Earth's atmosphere was mostly made from
  A nitrogen
  B oxygen
  C methane
  D carbon dioxide.

c There is oxygen in the atmosphere because
  A animals need oxygen to breathe
  B animals make oxygen when they respire
  C methane reacts with carbon dioxide
  D plants make oxygen during photosynthesis

d There is less carbon dioxide in the atmosphere on Earth than there once was because
  A we burn fossil fuels on Earth
  B lots of carbon is locked up in limestone and fossil fuels
  C animals breathe out carbon dioxide
  D it has turned into nitrogen

e Just under 1% of the air is a gas called argon. This gas was not discovered for a very long time because
  A it is invisible
  B it just has single atoms
  C it is an unreactive gas from Group 0 of the periodic table
  D it is very similar to oxygen so it was very hard to tell the two gases apart

12

Location	Type of building
England (traditional)	brick and mortar
Japan (traditional)	wood and paper
USA (California – modern)	concrete and steel

a **i** Which of the regions shown above suffer from powerful earthquakes? *(2 marks)*
  ii What is the reason for this? *(1 mark)*

b **i** During an earthquake the ground shakes violently. What would happen to a traditional English house in a powerful earthquake? *(1 mark)*
  ii Why would this be very dangerous to people in the house? *(1 mark)*

c **i** What would happen to a traditional Japanese house in a powerful earthquake? *(1 mark)*
  ii Why would this be less dangerous to people in the house compared to an English style house? *(1 mark)*

d **i** Concrete and steel-frames buildings are flexible and can sway without breaking. Are skyscrapers more or less vulnerable than 'bricks and mortar'? *(1 mark)*
  ii Which material used extensively in modern skyscrapers might be more vulnerable to earthquake damage? *(1 mark)*

13 Water levels in the rocks appear to change before an earthquake. Look at this table from a Chinese mine, from the three weeks before the 1976 earthquake. It shows how fast water had to be pumped out to stop the mine from flooding.

Time before the earthquake (days)	Pumping rate (m^3 per second)
21	70
14	65
10	55
7	45
5	35
4	30
3	25
2	25
1	50
0	75

a Draw a graph of these figures and describe the pattern. *(4 marks)*

b Describe what would have happened to the water level in local wells over the period. *(1 mark)*

c What happened just before the earthquake? *(1 mark)*

d Suggest why water levels should be studied carefully in earthquake zones. *(3 marks)*

Heat is one form of energy. To heat an object, for example a building, we need to supply it with energy. To keep it warm, we need to stop it losing energy. Understanding how heat is transferred from place to place helps us to use it efficiently and conserve it effectively.

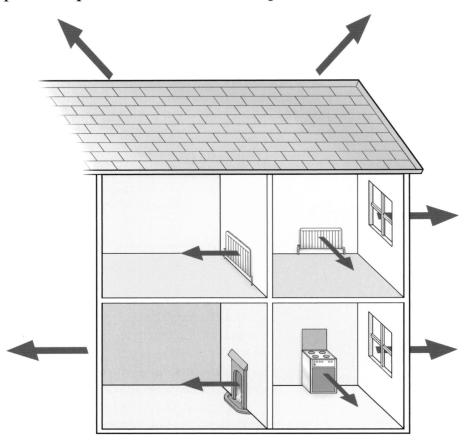

▲ Heat transfer in a house. Heat moves into the rooms from sources such as the fire and radiators. Heat is lost through the walls, windows and roof of the house.

Heating our buildings

Heating a building takes a lot of energy. This is expensive, and a lot of the heat is wasted because it is impossible to trap it all inside. What is more, energy use in our homes accounts for about 30% of the production of carbon dioxide in the UK. Carbon dioxide and other greenhouse gases contribute to global warming, so it is important to reduce the amount we produce. Knowing how **thermal energy** (heat) can be transferred from one place to another helps us to decrease the amount that is wasted.

Fossil fuels will not last forever, so buildings of the future will have to use less energy or more renewable sources of energy. Some modern buildings are already being designed for energy efficiency.

Buildings of the future

The Centre for Alternative Technology in Wales shows how we can keep buildings warm and bright without burning fossil fuels and producing carbon dioxide.

Their Information Centre was built mainly from local materials, so there was no need to transport bricks and wood over long distances. The inner walls are made from compacted earth. Unlike cement, this doesn't produce carbon dioxide when it is made. It also holds a lot of heat, so once it has warmed up it stays warm for a long time. The walls are insulated with wool and then an outer layer of wood, which helps to keep the heat in.

▲ The Information Centre at the Centre for Alternative Technology.

▲ A solar heating panel.

The building is heated using solar panels. Water flows through pipes in the panels. The Sun's rays heat up the pipes, and the thermal energy is transferred through the walls of the pipes into the water. The hot water is then pumped under the floor of the building. In the summer, the solar heating panels generate enough hot water to supply all the buildings at the Technology Centre. In the winter, when there is less sun and more heating is required, the water for the heating system is warmed using a boiler. The boiler burns wood chips from a local forest rather than fossil fuels.

The Information Centre building does not need much electric lighting because the roof contains skylights. These let in more light than standard windows. The computers do not need much electricity either. They use touch-screen LCD monitors, so there is no need for a keyboard or a mouse. LCD screens use far less energy than conventional computer monitors.

▲ A touch-screen LCD monitor.

Think about what you will find out in this section

How is thermal energy transferred from one place to another?	How can we conserve energy in our homes?
What factors affect the rate at which thermal energy is transferred?	How can we become more cost-effective in our use of energy?
What is meant by the efficient use of energy?	

Conduction

If you touch the metal part of a hot kettle, you may burn your hand. Thermal energy has been transferred through the metal from the hot water inside to your hand.

Even in solids, the particles (atoms or molecules) are never perfectly still. Although they stay in fixed positions and do not change places, they are vibrating. The more thermal energy you give them, the more energetically they vibrate.

The particles in the metal next to the hot water start to vibrate more vigorously. They pass this extra vibration to their neighbours, which in turn pass it on. This is called **conduction**. In metals and some other materials, the arrangement of the particles makes it easy for them to transfer energy to each other. These materials are described as good conductors. Materials that are poor conductors are described as good **insulators**. Some of the best solid insulators are plastics.

handle

Question
a Look at the photograph of the kettle. Why is the handle made of plastic?

Liquids are worse conductors than solids because their particles are moving from place to place. They do not have fixed neighbours to transfer their energy to. Gases are even worse conductors. Not only are their particles moving about, but they are spread far apart from each other. The particles in a gas don't often touch each other, so they can't easily pass on vibrations.

How well does it conduct?

A group of students investigated thermal energy conduction in four metals. They took rods made of brass, stainless steel, copper and aluminium, and put a blob of wax at one end of each rod. They heated the other end of the rod in a flame and measured how long it took for the wax to start melting. Here are their results.

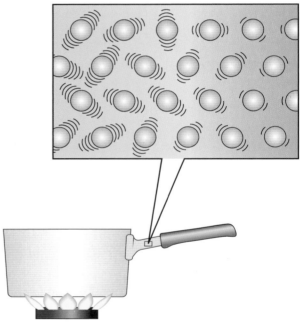

▲ The particles closest to the heat source vibrate as they heat up. They pass this extra vibration to their neighbours, which in turn pass it on until the metal part of the saucepan handle becomes hot.

Questions
b How does this experiment demonstrate conduction?
c Rank the metals from the best to the worst heat conductor.
d Some saucepans are made of steel, but have a copper bottom. Why is this?

Metal	Time for wax to start melting (s)
brass	58
stainless steel	103
copper	14
aluminium	29

Convection in gases

Air is a mixture of gases. When it is warmed, the particles gain energy and vibrate more. This makes them spread out further. Because the particles are further apart, warm air is less dense. Less dense substances float on denser substances, so the warm air rises and cooler air sinks to take its place. This flow of air is called **convection**. It creates a circulating convection current.

Convection currents occur naturally in the atmosphere. Some parts of the ground heat up more than others, so the air above these areas rises. Glider pilots and birds such as hawks use the currents, called thermals, to spiral upwards before gliding along.

Question

e How does convection carry the smoke from a fire up the chimney?

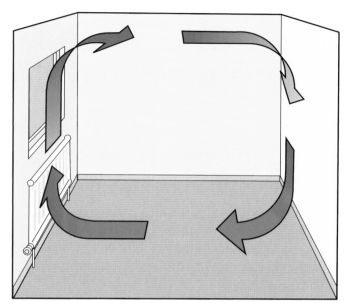

▲ A room is warmed by convection.

Convection in liquids

Convection also takes place in liquids. Just as in gases, the particles move around and spread out more when the liquid is heated, so the liquid becomes less dense. This is seen in some domestic hot water systems.

The boiler downstairs heats the water. The warm water is less dense, so it rises up into the hot water tank. Cooler, denser water falls to take its place.

Questions

f Why is the outlet for the hot water taps put at the top of the hot water tank rather than at the bottom?

g An electric immersion heater is also fitted in the hot water tank so that water can be heated in the summer without having the boiler working. At which position in the tank, X, Y or Z, would it be best to place the heater? Explain the reason for your choice.

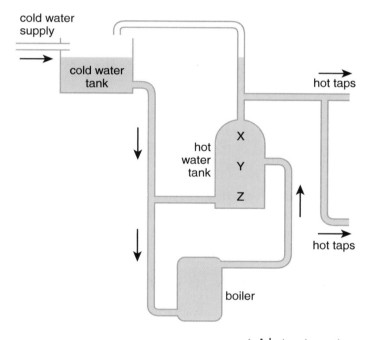

▲ A hot water system.

Convection is efficient when particles can flow freely, as they can in air or water. Thick, syrupy liquids do not transfer thermal energy so well by convection. Convection does not happen at all in solids.

Question

h Explain why convection can take place in gases and liquids but not in solids.

Key points

- In conduction and convection, thermal energy is transferred by particles.
- In conduction, the thermal energy moves from place to place but the particles do not. In convection, the particles move.
- Some materials transfer thermal energy faster than others.

The radiator in the sky

Thermal energy from the Sun reaches us across 150 million kilometres of empty space. There are no particles in space to transfer thermal energy, so the Sun's energy cannot be arriving by conduction or convection – both require particles.

The thermal energy is transferred by thermal **radiation**. Thermal radiation is actually **infra red** radiation, a type of **electromagnetic wave**. Electromagnetic waves, which include visible light as well as thermal radiation, can travel through a vacuum.

Electromagnetic waves don't *need* a vacuum in order to travel. After all, light and thermal radiation from the Sun travel through the Earth's atmosphere, which is full of gas particles. But the particles are not transferring the energy. They simply let it through, as a window pane lets light through.

Absorbing and emitting radiation

When you sit in the sun, you **absorb** (take in) some of the thermal energy that the Sun **emits** (gives out). However, it is not just very hot objects like the Sun that emit thermal radiation, and not just cooler objects like your body that absorb it. Your body radiates (emits) thermal energy too.

In fact, every object is emitting thermal radiation all the time. The hotter an object is, the more energy it radiates – but even an ice cube emits some thermal radiation. Every object is also absorbing thermal radiation all the time.

If an object is cooler than its surroundings, it absorbs faster than it emits, so it gains energy and warms up. If an object is warmer than its surroundings, it emits faster than it absorbs, so it loses energy and cools down.

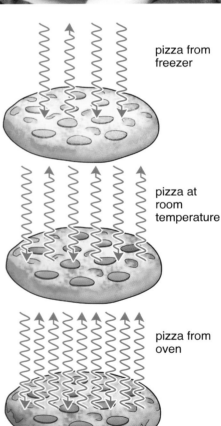

pizza from freezer

pizza at room temperature

pizza from oven

▲ All objects emit and absorb radiation. Hot objects emit radiation at a faster rate than they absorb radiation. The reverse is true for cold objects.

> ### Questions
>
> **a** Give an example of an object in a house that emits radiation faster than it absorbs it.
> **b** How could you change the surroundings of the same object to make it absorb radiation faster than it emits it?
> **c** What can you say about the rate of absorption and emission of thermal radiation for an object whose temperature is not changing?

Surfaces, radiation and reflection

Objects only emit and absorb thermal radiation at their surfaces. Some surfaces are good absorbers. When radiation hits them, most of it is absorbed. The rest bounces off – it is reflected. Other surfaces are bad absorbers. When radiation hits them, most of it is reflected and only a little is absorbed.

A group of students investigated how well different surfaces absorb radiation. They prepared three jars containing cold water. The first was painted black, the second dull white and the third shiny white. The students left the jars in the sunshine and measured the temperature of the water every minute.

Questions

> **d** How can you tell how good each jar is at absorbing thermal radiation?
> **e** Which jar is the best absorber? The worst?

Dark surfaces absorb radiation better than light ones. Light surfaces reflect radiation instead. Shiny surfaces are even better at reflecting radiation, and worse at absorbing it.

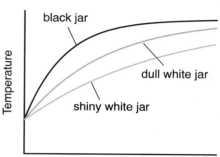

The students repeated the experiment, but this time they filled the jars with hot water and measured the temperature as the water cooled down. The graph shows their results.

Question

> **f** Which jar is the best emitter of thermal radiation? The worst?

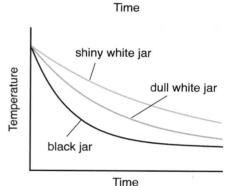

Dark surfaces emit radiation better than light ones, just as they absorb it better. Bright, shiny surfaces are the worst emitters, just as they are the worst absorbers.

More radiation in the sky

Sometimes the choice of surface for an object is crucial. This is especially true in situations where there is not much conduction or convection, so that thermal radiation is the most significant method of thermal energy transfer.

◀ The Space Shuttle Discovery.

When the Space Shuttle re-enters the Earth's atmosphere, the front and underside get red hot because of friction with the air. It is important to lose thermal energy quickly from these areas. The other parts of the shuttle do not get so hot on re-entry, but can get very hot from radiation from the Sun when in orbit.

Question

> **g** How do (i) the black tiles on the front and underside of the shuttle and (ii) the white tiles on the rest of the shuttle help prevent it from overheating?

Key points

- Thermal radiation transfers energy by electromagnetic waves without the need for particles.
- Dark surfaces are good absorbers and emitters of thermal energy.
- Light or shiny surfaces are poor absorbers and emitters.
- The radiation that is not absorbed by a surface is reflected.

Fins … and ears

This cooling unit from a computer is designed to transfer the thermal energy generated by the electronic components to the surroundings.

The base of the unit is a wide piece of metal in contact with the computer.

Questions

a How does the base of the cooling unit transfer thermal energy away from the computer?

b How does the large size of the base help it to transfer thermal energy?

Attached to the base are many slats of metal called fins. The fins have a large surface exposed to the air, and the gaps between the fins allow the air to circulate.

Question

c How do the large surface of the fins and the gaps between them help them to transfer thermal energy by radiation and convection?

The desert fox lives in hot climates, where overheating can be a problem. The Arctic fox lives in cold climates, where it is important to conserve thermal energy. The desert fox has huge ears while the Arctic fox has small, furry ears.

▲ The fennec or desert fox.

Question

d How do the ears of each species help it to survive?

Size, shape and energy transfer

The size and shape of an object have an important effect on its ability to transfer thermal energy.

Conduction relies on particles passing vibration to their neighbours. A large object conducts energy faster than a small one made from the same material, because it has more particles. Conduction requires particles that are in contact, so a shape with gaps slows down conduction.

Objects emit thermal radiation from their surfaces only, so objects with a large surface area radiate thermal energy better than those with a small surface area.

▲ The Arctic fox.

Convection requires the flow of gas or liquid. Shapes that allow gas or liquid to flow freely will be better at transferring thermal energy by convection than shapes that restrict the flow of gas or liquid.

e Two cups of tea are on a table. Someone puts a small teaspoon in one cup and a much larger tablespoon in the other. Which cup will cool down more quickly? Why?

f Are gloves or mittens better at keeping your hands warm? Why?

g How does a saucepan lid help to keep the food inside warm after cooking?

Cool and colder, warm and hotter

Two students made themselves hot drinks using boiling water. The drinks were soon cool enough to drink, but they remained warm for a long time. The students concluded that their drinks had cooled down rapidly to start with, but had cooled more slowly later on. They decided to investigate.

They put some boiling water into a beaker and measured the temperature every 2 minutes as the water cooled down. The table and graph show their results.

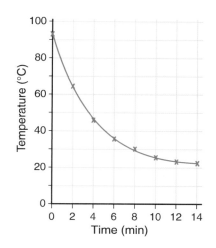

Time (min)	0	2	4	6	8	10	12	14
Temperature (°C)	93.6	64.6	47.1	36.4	30.0	26.0	23.7	22.2

h By how much did the temperature fall between 0 and 2 minutes? Between 12 and 14 minutes?

i Were the students correct in thinking that their drinks cooled more quickly to start with?

Thermal energy flows from hotter objects to colder objects. A hot drink in a room transfers thermal energy to the room. That's why the drink cools down. The room transfers thermal energy to an ice cream. That's why the ice cream warms up.

The rate of thermal energy transfer depends on the **temperature difference** between the two objects. The larger the temperature difference, the faster thermal energy is transferred. A very hot drink has a much higher temperature than the room, so it loses thermal energy fast. A warm drink has only a slightly higher temperature than the room, so it loses thermal energy slowly.

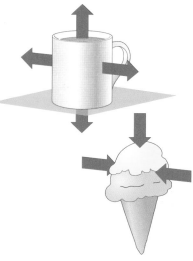

j Describe and explain the shape of the graph from the students' experiment.

k Two cartons of milk are taken from the refrigerator at 4 °C. One is left in the room at 20 °C. The other is put in the freezer at −18 °C. (i) In which direction is thermal energy transferred in each case? (ii) For which carton is thermal energy transferred at a faster rate? Explain your answers.

Key points

- The size and shape of an object affect the rate at which it transfers thermal energy.
- The bigger the temperature difference between an object and its surroundings, the faster the rate of thermal energy transfer.

Evaluating heat transfer

There are times when you want to transfer thermal energy effectively, and times when you want to reduce thermal energy transfer. Stopping thermal energy transfer may be a matter of convenience – like keeping your hot drink hot. It may be a matter of saving money – insulating a house, for example. Or it may be a matter of life and death, as it is for a firefighter who has to enter a burning building.

We cannot see thermal energy being transferred. But we need to ensure that thermal energy goes where we want it, and stays there. We can use our understanding of thermal energy transfer to design methods for reducing heat loss.

Keep it warm, keep it cool

An everyday example of a device designed to stop thermal energy transfer is the vacuum flask.

The flask has a double wall made of thin layers of glass coated with shiny metal. Between the layers of glass is a vacuum. The glass flask rests on small polystyrene blocks inside a protective outer flask. The opening at the top of the flask is narrow.

narrow opening

thin glass walls silvered inside

vacuum

outer flask

small polystyrene blocks

Questions

a Explain how each feature of the vacuum flask helps to prevent thermal energy transfer. Which methods of thermal energy transfer are reduced?

b Imagine that one layer of glass cracked and the space between the glass walls filled up with liquid. Would the flask be less or more effective? Why?

c How would the thermal properties of the flask be affected if its walls were made of ordinary glass without the shiny coating?

Choosing the right materials

Most houses today are built with cavity walls. These are double walls with a gap between them. In the simplest cavity walls, the gap contains air.

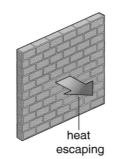

heat escaping

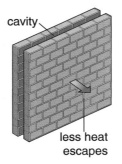

cavity

less heat escapes

Question

d Why does a cavity wall stop thermal energy transfer better than a solid wall?

The problem is that as the air in the cavity warms up, it starts to rise and convection currents carry the thermal energy away. To prevent this problem, the cavity can be filled with liquid foam. When the foam turns solid it traps thousands of tiny air bubbles in it and prevents the formation of convection currents. New houses usually have better cavity walls with a panel of fibreglass or other insulating material put into the wall as it is being built.

Question

e *Why does fibreglass in a cavity wall stop thermal energy loss better than air, even though it is a better conductor than air?*

We can measure the rate of thermal energy transfer through a wall or other building component. The rate is expressed as a U value. The lower the U value, the better the window is at stopping energy transfer. The table shows typical U values for cavity walls. (The U value is given in units of $W/m^2/K$.)

Cavity width (mm)	Thickness of insulation (mm)		
	0	50	100
100	0.60	0.52	0.44
150	0.42	0.37	0.32
200	0.26	0.25	0.24

Questions

f *Which has the greater effect on reducing thermal energy transfer, cavity width or insulation thickness?*

g *There is more than one method for measuring U values, and different methods give different values. How does this affect your interpretation of the table?*

h *The mean annual temperature is about 10°C in London and about 27°C in Singapore. A comfortable indoor temperature is around 20°C. Suggest how the concerns of house designers may differ in the two cities.*

Braving the flames

Firefighters work in environments where the temperature and the thermal radiation can be extreme.

A typical uniform is made of fabric woven from insulating plastic fibres. The lining contains a moisture barrier, which allows perspiration to escape but does not let in water from fire hoses. The barrier helps to keep the firefighter's inner clothing dry, trapping layers of air around the skin. Without the barrier, a film of water could develop between the uniform and the skin.

For some applications, firefighters wear an aluminised outer uniform. This is made from metal-coated fibres, producing a shiny metallic finish.

Questions

i *How do these features of the uniform help to reduce thermal energy transfer? When might aluminised fabric be used?*

j *How might you measure the effectiveness of a fabric at preventing thermal energy transfer?*

Key points

- It is possible to predict how thermal energy will be transferred into and out of objects.
- Equipment can be designed to reduce thermal energy transfer.

Transforming energy

Energy comes in many forms: thermal, chemical, kinetic, potential and so on. A lot of the devices we use – lights, motors, batteries – are designed to **transform** one form of energy into another. Others are designed to **transfer** energy from one place to another.

It is impossible to create or destroy energy, so the only way of getting the energy we want is by transferring or transforming it. For example, if we want electrical energy in our home, we can transfer it from a power station or we can use a generator to transform another form of energy into electrical energy.

No device is perfect. Whenever we transform energy or transfer it from place to place, some is wasted. We can never transform all the energy we have into the form we want.

Useful energy and wasted energy

A light bulb is intended to transform electrical energy into light energy, but it also produces a lot of thermal energy. The form we want – light – is **useful energy**. The form we do not want – heat – is **wasted energy**.

Which energy we call 'useful' and which we call 'wasted' depends on what we want. The thermal energy produced by an electric heater is useful, but the thermal energy produced by a light bulb is wasted because it is not the form that we want.

▲ A battery transforms chemical energy into electrical energy.

▼ Don't touch – it's hot!

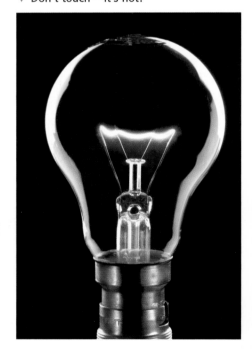

Question

a Name a device that produces sound as useful energy, and another device that produces sound as wasted energy.

Different devices carry out different energy transformations, and produce different energy wastages.

Device	Form of input energy	Useful form of output energy	Main forms of wasted energy
light bulb	electrical	light	thermal
solar electric cell		electrical	thermal
electric fan			
dynamo			
coal furnace			

Question

b Copy and complete the table above.

Wastage at every step

Many devices transform energy in several steps. Each step usefully transforms only part of the energy it starts with. Some energy is wasted at each transformation, so by the end of the whole process we have often lost a large proportion of the energy we began with.

For example, in a diesel-electric train, fuel is pumped into cylinders, where it is burned. The resulting explosion moves a piston back and forth. The movement is used to rotate a generator, making electricity. The electricity flows to an electric motor on each axle, where it is used to turn the wheels.

At each stage, some energy is wasted. The exploding diesel produces unwanted thermal energy as well as kinetic energy. When electricity is carried in wires, the wires heat up. By the end of the process, only about 30% of the chemical energy in the fuel has been used to move the train. The rest is wasted.

Spreading out

Chemical energy in fuel is concentrated in a small space. The fuel is easy to move and easy to use for energy transformations.

On the other hand, the thermal energy generated in a locomotive is spread out over many of the moving parts of the train. As time goes on, it spreads further as it is transferred to the surroundings. The same is true of energy wasted as noise.

Questions

c List the energy transfers and transformations that take place in a diesel-electric train, starting with the chemical energy of the fuel.

d Name one form of energy wastage in a diesel-electric train apart from thermal energy.

  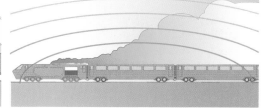

▲ Energy spreads out each time it is transformed.

The more spread out energy is, the harder it is to capture and use for more transformations. Once noise and thermal energy have spread into the surroundings, they are very difficult to use any more.

Even the energy that is usefully transformed into kinetic energy eventually spreads out. The train has to work against friction in its moving parts and from the air and the track, generating thermal energy. Eventually, all the energy is transferred to the surroundings as thermal energy, and the surroundings get warmer.

Question

e A fire burns coal to warm a room.
  (i) What form of energy goes into the fire, and what forms come out?
  (ii) When the fire has burnt out, why isn't the energy useful any more?

Key points

- Energy cannot be created or destroyed.
- Whenever energy is transformed or transferred so we can use it, some energy is wasted.

Making the best of our energy

Energy does not come for free. Most forms of energy cost money. There are also other costs. A lot of our energy comes from fossil fuels. Burning fossil fuels releases carbon dioxide into the atmosphere. Many people think that this contributes to global warming. Other pollutants are released too.

Some sources of energy are scarce or only found in certain countries, which can lead to conflicts as people fight over limited resources. So we want to make the best of the energy we use.

What is efficiency?

We know that whenever energy is transformed, only some of it is usefully transformed while the rest is wasted. We need to describe how much is usefully transformed and how much is wasted. **Efficiency** measures the proportion of the input energy that actually changes into the form we want. The more **efficient** a device is, the more of the input energy it transforms usefully, and the less it wastes.

For example, about 30% of the chemical energy in diesel fuel is usefully transformed into the kinetic energy of a diesel-electric train. We say the train has an efficiency of 30%.

The electric motor in a fan is more efficient than a light bulb. The bulb is intended to transform electrical energy into light, but it usefully transforms only about 5% of the electrical energy input and wastes the other 95%, mostly as thermal energy. The motor is intended to transform electrical energy into kinetic energy. It usefully transforms about 80% of the electrical energy supplied to it and wastes about 20%.

Calculating efficiency

▲ Disputes over energy resources can lead to conflict.

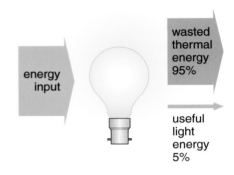

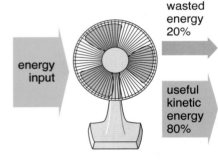

> **Questions**
>
> **a** How can an understanding of energy efficiency help designers of machines?
> **b** Does an electric fan motor get hotter or less hot than an ordinary tungsten bulb when they are switched on? Explain your answer in terms of efficiency.

Efficiency is calculated by dividing the useful output energy by the total input energy.

Here are some figures for a solar electric cell. The energy is measured in joules (J).

Total light energy supplied (J)	100
Amount of electrical energy given out (J)	15
Other forms of energy given out (J)	85

The useful output in this case is the electrical energy. Everything else is wasted energy, so we ignore it.

$$\text{efficiency} = \frac{\text{useful output energy}}{\text{total input energy}} = \frac{15\,J}{100\,J} = 0.15$$

If a device could usefully transform all the energy we supplied, the useful output would be the same as the input, so efficiency would be 1. But in fact, all devices waste some energy. The useful output is always less than the input, and efficiency is always less than 1.

Efficiency is often given as a percentage. To calculate efficiency as a percentage, multiply efficiency by 100.

percentage efficiency = 0.15 × 100 = 15%

Which devices are the most efficient?

Different devices have different efficiencies (even if they are intended to carry out the same energy transformation). The greater the percentage efficiency, the more efficient the device is. The table shows the useful output and the wasted output when 500 J of energy are supplied to various devices.

▼ You can often find out how efficient different products are, before you buy.

Questions

c 1000 J of chemical energy are supplied to a domestic gas boiler. It produces 800 J of thermal energy. What are (i) its efficiency; (ii) its percentage efficiency?
d If a device could usefully transform all the input energy and waste none, what would be its percentage efficiency?

Device	Intended energy transformation	Useful energy output (J)	Wasted energy output (J)	Efficiency (%)
halogen lamp	electrical → light	60	440	12
energy-efficient light bulb		125	375	
coal-fired power station	chemical → electrical	175		35
combined-cycle power station			225	55
domestic oil boiler		325		
domestic gas boiler			75	
bicycle dynamo				35
large electricity generator				95

Questions

e How many joules in total must (useful output) + (wasted output) add up to for each device in the table above? Why?
f Copy and complete the table.
g Which is the most efficient device in the whole table? The least efficient?
h Suggest reasons why somebody might use a less efficient device when a more efficient device exists for carrying out the same energy transformation.

Key point

● Efficiency measures the proportion of input energy that is usefully transformed.

It pays to save energy

Wasted energy costs money. The less energy you waste, the more money you save.

AQALec   **ELECTRICITY BILL**
1 January to 31 December

Running ordinary bulb for 1 hour per day.................... £2.40
Running energy-efficient bulb for 1 hour per day.................. £0.60

▲ Part of an annual electricity bill.

Questions

a How much would you save in annual running costs by switching from an ordinary bulb to an energy-efficient bulb, if the light is used for (i) 1 hour per day; (ii) 12 hours per day?

b A large industrial plant uses 10 000 bulbs, which are switched on 24 hours per day. How much would they save in annual running costs by switching to energy-efficient bulbs?

Effectiveness and cost-effectiveness

A method that is good at reducing energy consumption is **effective**. Insulating an uninsulated loft is very effective, because it saves a lot of energy. Adding more insulation if your loft is already thickly insulated is less effective, because it does not give much extra benefit.

Energy-saving measures save money, but they may also cost money. If you want to insulate the loft, you need to buy insulation.

If the savings make up for the cost, we say the measure is **cost-effective**. Insulating a loft costs around £150, and saves around £50 per year in heating costs. After one year, the measure is not cost-effective. You have spent £150 but saved only £50 – an overall loss of £100. However, after five years, the measure is cost-effective. You have spent £150, but saved £250 – an overall saving of £100.

SUPA STORES

1 Ordinary light bulb   £0.60
1 Energy-efficient bulb   £6.00

Questions

c How much more does an energy-efficient bulb cost than an ordinary bulb?

d How long does it take for switching bulbs to become cost-effective if the bulbs are used for (i) 1 hour per day; (ii) 6 hours per day?

e Energy-efficient bulbs last about ten times as long as ordinary bulbs. How does this affect the costs and savings of switching to energy-efficient bulbs from ordinary bulbs?

Getting about for less

One important way of reducing energy consumption is to choose energy-saving forms of transport. There are various ways to evaluate forms of transport. One method is to look at how much fuel each uses in travelling 1 kilometre.

From this chart, it looks as if the car is by far the best in terms of conserving energy. But the comparison is not really fair. A car might carry 3 people; a bus 30; and an aeroplane 300. The car uses so little fuel because it takes only a few people.

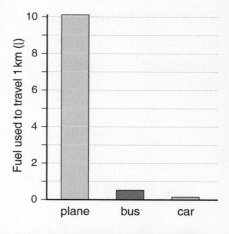

Question

f Explain in your own words why the difference in passenger numbers makes the comparison unfair.

A fairer way of comparing modes of transport is to look at how much energy each one uses to transport *one person* by a distance of *1 kilometre*. Imagine that somebody drives 1 kilometre in a car containing four people. The car uses up 6 million joules of energy. Since there were four passengers, the car used 1.5 million joules per passenger to go 1 kilometre.

Scientists disagree about what figures to use in these calculations. What if people typically drive with only two people in the car instead of four? The car will still use up about 6 million joules to go 1 kilometre. But now it is using 3 million joules per person, rather than 1.5 million. Before we can use the figures, we need to decide which numbers give a more realistic picture of an average journey.

▲ A dangerous way to save energy.

Mode of transport	urban bus	train	car	tram	aeroplane
Energy use (MJ/passenger-km)	1.2	0.8	2.6	0.9	2.7

Questions

g Rank the modes of transport from the best to the worst at saving energy.
h We do not really know how many people a bus, train, car or tram carries on an average journey. How will this affect the reliability of the figures?

Key point

● By analysing costs and savings, we can evaluate the effectiveness and cost-effectiveness of different methods for reducing energy consumption.

2 Making and using electricity

Electrical devices produce light, heat, sound and other forms of energy at the flick of a switch. We rely on electricity because it is so convenient and can be used for so many purposes. But some of the energy sources we use to make electricity are running out.

The day the lights went out

SHANGHAI, CHINA – SUMMER 2004

Air conditioning units are working flat out in the hot summer. The electricity supply is at breaking point. The Government has ordered some businesses to shut during the day and work at night when the temperature is cooler. And all unnecessary lighting is to be switched off – inlcuding the coloured lighting signs that symbolise success and wealth in Shanghai.

Relying on electricity

Without electricity, we would have no electric lights, television or internet. Our factories would grind to a halt. In the developed world, we depend on electricity. This means that we also depend on the fuels and other energy sources used to make it.

But two billion people in the world have no access to electricity. Imagine how different it would be living without electrical power. How would you manage without a refrigerator or a telephone?

◀ A school in Kenya without electricity.

Fuels to generate electricity

Coal, gas and oil contain chemical energy. When they are burned, it is transformed into thermal energy. This energy can be used in power stations to boil water, making steam for the turbines to generate electricity.

Fossil fuels will not last for ever. If we go on using them up at the present rate, scientists predict that the world could run out of oil in about 40 years, gas in about 60 and coal in about 200. But these predictions are uncertain. More reserves may be discovered, so fossil fuels may last longer than we think. But as countries develop, they will start using more fuel, so fossil fuels may run out sooner than we think.

The burning of fossil fuels also causes pollution and releases greenhouse gases which many scientists think contribute to global warming.

We cannot simply stop using electricity. So it is important to look for other energy sources that are more environmentally friendly and that will not run out.

▲ A satellite photograph of air pollution over China caused by burning fossil fuels.

Other sources of electricity

The natural world contains immense reserves of energy that will last as long as we can imagine. The Sun provides heat and light. Winds blow, and waves and tides rise and fall. These energy sources can be harnessed to produce electricity cleanly.

Sources of energy that will last for a very long time, or that can be replaced, are called **renewable** energy sources.

At present, only about 3% of the electricity in the UK comes from renewables. But the Government wants to increase that figure to 10% by 2010, and 15% by 2015.

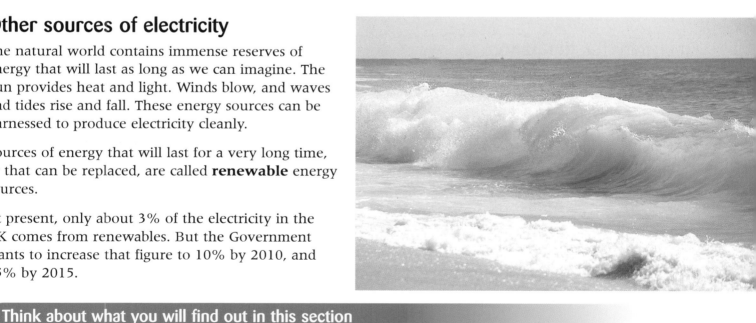

Think about what you will find out in this section

What is meant by power?	How should we generate the electricity we need?
Why is electrical energy so useful?	How can we make more use of renewable resources?
How do we calculate the cost of paying for electricity?	

Why are electrical devices so useful?

Electrical devices transform electrical energy into whatever form we want quickly and easily. Many different electrical devices exist to make many different forms of energy. For example, we can transform electricity into thermal energy. A kettle, an iron and a toaster all do this.

Question

a Name four forms of energy that can be produced from electricity. For each form of energy, name two electrical devices that can produce it.

Electricity is also a useful form of energy because it can easily be transferred across large distances. If you want to transfer chemical energy across the country, you have to move large amounts of fuel by road or rail. But you can transfer electrical energy over long distances without moving a large amount of material.

Question

b Give two reasons why electricity is such a convenient form of energy.

Electricity for the nation

A network of wires transfers electricity from the **power stations**, where it is made, to the people who use it. This network, the **National Grid**, links power stations with factories, houses and other users all over the country. The electricity it supplies is called mains electricity.

Demand for electricity is different at different times of the day and the year. Much more electricity is used at six o'clock on a winter's evening than at three o'clock on a summer's morning. The National Grid is designed to cope with this changing demand. It is also designed to provide a constant and reliable supply even if part of the grid fails.

Whenever electricity flows through a wire, the wire warms up. Some energy is wasted as thermal energy. We can reduce the amount of energy wasted by reducing the electrical current in the wire.

▲ Transferring chemical energy means moving a lot of material.

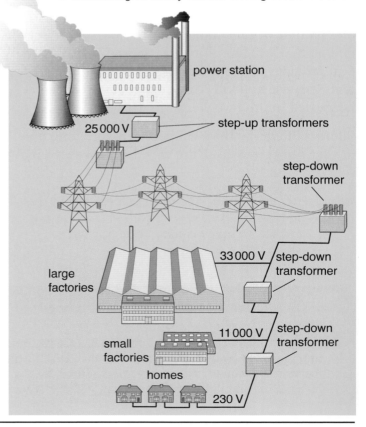

▲ Transferring electricity without moving a lot of material.

The higher the voltage at which the electricity is transferred, the lower the current. In the National Grid, the electricity is carried at a very high voltage – up to 415 000 V. This means that the current is low, which reduces energy loss.

Electricity is generated in power stations at about 25 000 V. In the home, it is used at only 230 V, because high voltages are too dangerous. The voltage is changed using devices called transformers. A **step-up transformer** between the power station and the grid raises the voltage. A **step-down transformer** between the grid and the home lowers the voltage.

Energy and power

Different devices transform energy at different rates. The greater the rate, the higher the **power** of the device. A device with higher power transforms more joules (J) of energy per second than a device with lower power. A large earth borer and a small hand drill both transform electricity into kinetic energy. But the earth borer transforms more energy per second and has a higher power.

The power is measured in watts (W) or kilowatts (kW). A kilowatt is 1000 watts. A hand drill might be rated at 500 W. An industrial earth borer might be rated at 15 kW. The higher the wattage, the greater the power. Many electrical devices carry labels showing their power rating.

Question

e Which has a higher power: a 1000 W iron or a 1.2 kW toaster?

The amount of energy transformed does not depend only on the power of the device. It also depends on how long the device is switched on. A 1000 W heater switched on for 1 hour transforms as much energy as a 100 W light bulb switched on for 10 hours, because the heater has ten times the power. A 2 kW oven would transform the same amount of energy in half an hour.

Question

f How many hours would a 60 W light bulb take to transform as much energy as a 1.2 kW water heater transforms in an hour?

Questions

c Why is electricity transferred through the grid at very high voltage but used in houses at much lower voltage?

d How does the voltage at which electricity is transferred affect the efficiency of the transfer?

▲ This device has a power of 2000 W.

Key points

- Electricity is a very convenient form of energy.
- It is transferred all over the country using the National Grid.
- The power rating of a device is the rate at which it transforms energy.
- The amount of electrical energy transformed depends on how long the device is turned on for and the rate at which it transforms energy.

The right tools for the job

Both these devices carry out the same energy transformation. But they have different uses.

The tubular heater on the right is rated at 60 W. It is designed to keep greenhouses and workshops above freezing temperature in the winter. It does not give off enough thermal energy to make a room really warm. The bar heater below is rated at 3 kW. It is too powerful for a greenhouse. It would use up expensive electricity and make the greenhouse too hot for many plants. But it can heat a large room.

Questions

a What energy transformation do both devices carry out?

b Compare and contrast the advantages and disadvantages of each device.

c What factors would you consider when choosing between electric heaters of different powers?

How much energy?

The bar heater transfers energy from the mains at a faster rate than the tubular heater. If both are switched on for the same length of time, the bar heater transfers more energy. And the longer each device is switched on, the more energy it transfers.

We can calculate how much energy a device transfers if we know its power and how long it is switched on.

energy transferred = power × time

If we measure power in kilowatts and time in hours, then the energy is measured in kilowatt-hours (kWh). For example, if a 3 kW electric heater is switched on for 4 hours, then:

$$\text{energy transferred (kWh)} = \text{power (kW)} \times \text{time (h)}$$
$$= 3\,\text{kW} \times 4\,\text{h}$$
$$= 12\,\text{kWh}$$

You may wonder why we do not measure the energy in joules (J). The reason is that a joule is a very small unit of energy. 12 kWh is over 43 million joules! It is inconvenient to use such large numbers, so we choose kWh instead.

Don't forget that, in order to calculate energy in kWh, the power must be measured in kW and the time in hours. If you are given a power in watts or a time in minutes, you must convert them.

Device	Power	Time used	Energy transferred from mains (kWh)
electric heater	2 kW	3 hours	
electric kettle	1.5 kW		6
water heater		2 hours	6
electric lawnmower	800 W	1½ hours	
hand drill	600 W	20 minutes	

Question

d Copy and complete the table, giving all energies in kWh.

Paying for electricity

Electricity companies charge us for each kWh of energy we use. They measure the number of kWh we have used by reading the electricity meter.

total cost = number of kWh used × cost per kWh

For example, if we use 300 kWh and each kWh costs 6p, then

total cost = 300 kWh × 6p/kWh
= 1800p or £18.00

On electricity bills, a kWh of energy is called a 'unit' of electricity.

AQALec   ELECTRICITY BILL

Previous reading	Current reading	Units used	Cost per unit	Total cost
45100	45500	400	7 pence	£28.00

▲ An electricity meter showing a reading of 11483.09 kWh.

Questions

e Electricity companies often charge less for electricity consumed at night than for electricity consumed during the day. Suggest a reason for this.

f A 1.5 kW tumble drier is used for 4 hours per week. If electricity costs 7p per unit, what is the weekly cost?

g How could you use an electricity meter and a clock to measure the power of an electrical appliance?

1 June 2005

1 September 2005

▲ Meter readings taken 3 months apart.

h The next bill arrives on 1 December 2005. Would you expect the number of units used to be similar to the number on the previous bill? Explain your answer.

Key points

- Different devices are suitable for different applications.
- The amount of energy transformed by a device, and its cost, can be calculated.

Turbines and generators

The device that makes electricity in a power station is called a **generator**. In order to make electricity, the generator must be turned. This is done by linking it to a **turbine**. A turbine is a bit like a ship's propeller. In most power stations, the turbine is turned by a blast of steam blowing onto the blades.

Fossil fuels

To make steam you have to boil water. Many power stations do this by burning coal, gas or oil. These fuels were formed tens of millions of years ago from the remains of living things. So they are called **fossil fuels**. Fossil fuels take millions of years to form, but we are using them up much faster than this.

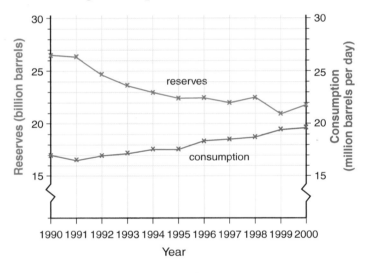

▲ Oil reserves and consumption in the USA, 1990–2000.

Questions

a What were the approximate US oil reserves in 1990? In 2000?

b What was the percentage decrease in reserves between 1990 and 2000?

c Estimate when US oil reserves will run out if no more oil is discovered.

d Describe how US oil consumption changed between 1990 and 2000 and suggest reasons for this change.

e Suggest reasons why it is difficult to estimate the whole world's oil reserves.

Choking the planet

Burning fossil fuels releases carbon dioxide into the atmosphere. Many scientists think that this contributes to global warming. Burning fossil fuels also releases smoke and poisonous gases. Some of the gases dissolve in rainwater forming acid rain, which can damage plants and buildings.

Smog is a harmful mixture of acidic fog and smoke that comes from burning fossil fuels. In 1952, during a severe smog in London, 4700 people died in one week. The average death rate in London at that time was about 2000 per week.

▲ Smog in Los Angeles, USA, caused by burning fossil fuels.

Gas is the cleanest fossil fuel. It causes least pollution when it is burned. And it can be distributed through pipes. But it is difficult to store as it takes up a lot of space. It can also be dangerous, because a spark can make it explode.

Coal and oil are easier to store. But they have other disadvantages. They do not burn as cleanly as gas. Coal cannot flow through pipes, so it must be transported by rail or road. Oil is very messy and causes severe pollution if it leaks.

Energy without burning

Radioactive elements like uranium and plutonium are unstable. Their atoms can be made to split. This process of splitting is called **nuclear fission**. It generates thermal energy. Nuclear power stations use the energy to heat water. This is another way of making steam to turn turbines.

Nuclear fuel is a very concentrated source of energy. You can get a lot of energy from very little fuel, using a relatively small power station that does not take up a huge land area. Nuclear fuel does not release polluting gases into the air. But there is a big disadvantage. The waste from nuclear power stations is radioactive.

Radioactive material damages living things. So it is important to store it safely until the radioactivity decays. The problem is that this will take thousands of years. It is very costly to maintain good safety procedures while a nuclear power station is being built, while it is used, and for thousands of years afterwards. Many scientists doubt whether anything can be stored safely for that long without leaking. People are also worried about what would happen if terrorists managed to steal the material.

There have been several accidents at nuclear power stations. The worst happened at Chernobyl, Ukraine, in 1986. Many people have died as a result of the accident, and scientists estimate that thousands more will die of the long-term effects.

The reactor at Chernobyl was old-fashioned and there was not enough money to maintain it. Safety procedures were not followed properly. Some people think that a disaster like Chernobyl could never happen again because reactor design and safety procedures have improved. Others think that nuclear power will always be risky.

Question

f Give an advantage and a disadvantage for each of (i) coal; (ii) oil; (iii) gas.

▲ The destroyed nuclear reactor at Chernobyl.

Questions

g Describe and explain some advantages and disadvantages of nuclear power.
h Why are people worried about terrorist attacks on nuclear power stations?

Key points

- Electricity can be produced from fossil fuels or nuclear fission.
- Each method has advantages and disadvantages. Fossil fuels cause pollution and will run out. Nuclear power can be dangerous.

Spinning in the wind

We can use the wind to turn a turbine. When the wind blows, the blades spin.

Small wind turbines are used to generate electricity for remote houses, farms and campsites, where there is no mains supply. They can also be attached to boats to generate electricity on the move.

A large wind turbine can have blades 50 metres long and generate enough electricity for over 1000 homes. Turbines are often arranged in groups called wind farms. In 2003, the Government announced a new round of wind farm projects, mostly off the coast. If built, these farms would provide enough electricity for 4 million homes.

Wind farms do not release harmful substances. There is plenty of wind in the UK, especially offshore. The energy source is free and will not run out. And when a wind farm reaches the end of its life, it can be dismantled without much harm to the environment.

But there are disadvantages to wind turbines. If there is not enough wind, they do not work. Too much, and they have to be shut down so they are not damaged. Some people think the turbines spoil the landscape. Offshore wind farms can affect shipping, and may harm sea birds. And spinning turbines are noisy.

Energy from moving water

Waves and tides carry a great deal of energy, which can be transformed into electricity.

The world's first commercial wave power generator opened in Scotland in 2000. In this generator, the bobbing of the waves pushes air in and out of a chamber. The rushing air drives a turbine. The unit is in a low building on the shore so that it does not spoil the view. Other designs for harnessing wave power include floating machines moored to the sea bed several kilometres off the coast.

▲ Erecting a wind turbine off the coast of Kent.

Question

a Some wind farms are on dry land, while others are off the coast. Suggest advantages and disadvantages for each location.

▼ A wave power generator on the island of Islay, Scotland.

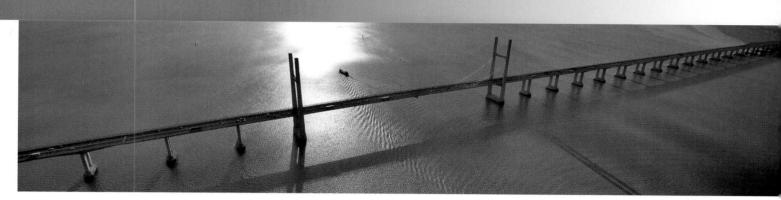

The tide rises and falls twice a day. The water can be stopped by building a dam or 'barrage'. Barrages can be built across bays or across tidal estuaries. At high tide, water builds up outside the barrage trying to get in. At low tide, water is trapped behind the barrage trying to get out. If a gate is opened in the barrage, the water flows through, turning a turbine. The greater the difference in water level between high and low tides, the more energy is available.

Wave and tide power are renewable and free. But to use them, we must build large, expensive dams and power stations on the seashore or on river estuaries. Stopping the tide spoils wildlife habitats. Barrages prevent ships from passing. And it is hard to build structures that will resist the sea's harsh waves and salty water for many years.

Harnessing a river

Hydroelectric power plants also use the energy of flowing water. In most hydroelectric schemes, a dam is built across a river. This traps a huge lake of water uphill. When the dam is opened, the water rushes downhill and turns a turbine.

Large hydroelectric plants can generate a great deal of electricity. But they can be very controversial. The Chinese government is constructing a hydroelectric dam at Three Gorges on the Yangtze river. The scheme will produce as much electricity as 10 000 large wind turbines. But the lake of trapped water will submerge over 600 square kilometres of countryside and 100 towns. Millions of plants and animals will die, and over a million people will have to be resettled.

▼ A diagram of a hydroelectric plant.

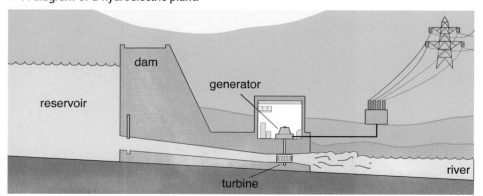

▲ If a tidal barrage is ever built in the UK, it might be here, across the Severn estuary.

Question

b What form of energy does the water have when it is trapped behind the barrage?

Question

c Explain why neither the wind nor the tides can generate a constant, even supply of electricity.

Question

d Give some advantages and disadvantages of wind, wave, tidal and hydroelectric schemes.

Key points

- Wind and moving water are renewable sources of energy.
- They are less polluting than fossil fuels, but have other disadvantages. Winds and tides cannot provide a constant electricity supply. Hydroelectric schemes flood large areas.

Energy from the Sun

Silicon generates electricity when light falls on it. Materials like this can be used to make **solar electric cells**, also called photovoltaic cells.

Small cells are used to power some watches, calculators and other devices. These devices do not need batteries. The solar cell is portable and will work wherever there is light.

There is another way of producing electricity from the Sun. The Sun's heat can be concentrated with mirrors and used to boil water, making steam to drive a turbine. But when people talk about solar electric cells, they mean cells that generate electricity directly from sunlight.

▲ A solar-powered radio.

Rich and poor

Solar cells can be set up wherever electricity is needed, so they can provide electricity in places with no national grid. They have no turbines or other moving parts, so they are silent and need very little maintenance. They go on working for decades. And the energy they use is free. For all these reasons, solar cells are useful in developing countries.

The Danish Technological Institute has developed refrigerators and coolers that run purely on solar electricity. They are being tested in developing countries. A single cooler can hold enough vaccines for 50 000 people.

One problem with solar cells is that they are expensive. This is a problem for developing countries. One of the world's largest solar power plants is in Germany, a wealthy country. Its three sites cover a total of 25 hectares (an area equivalent to nearly 60 football pitches). The plant generates enough electricity for a few thousand homes. But the project cost £35 million. A wind farm costing this much could supply ten times as many homes.

▲ A solar-powered vaccine cooler and refrigerator.

▶ Large solar power plants will produce clean energy for once polluted areas of Germany.

Another disadvantage of solar cells is that they need light to work. They cannot generate electricity at night. And they work best in countries with much more sun than Germany.

Questions

a *The power station in Germany generates 10080 kW of power. Each solar panel generates 175 W. How many panels are used in total?*

b *The power station gets about 1500 hours of sunshine per year. Some parts of California get 2500 hours per year. (i) By what percentage is the amount of sunshine in California greater than in Germany? (ii) What power could the power station supply if it were in California?*

c *Many people predict that solar cells will become less expensive as they get more popular. Why do you think this is?*

Energy from the Earth

The centre of the Earth is very hot. Scientists estimate that the temperature is around 6000 °C – similar to the surface of the Sun.

As you get further from the centre, the temperature gets lower. The outer skin of the Earth, the crust, is not usually very hot until you go down many kilometres. But in volcanic areas, the crust is thin. In some areas, the molten rock underneath heats the crust to 300–400 °C just a few kilometres below the surface.

Sometimes rainwater seeps into the hot rocks and becomes trapped. By drilling a deep hole, we can release steam under high pressure. If no water is trapped, we can pump water in. It turns into steam and comes to the surface again. The steam can be used to drive a turbine.

Energy from the Earth's heat is called **geothermal** energy. It will not run out. And geothermal power plants do not take up much land compared with other kinds of power plant.

The first geothermal electricity plant in the world was built just over a hundred years ago in Italy. It produces 10% of the world's geothermal electricity – enough for about a million homes.

But there are not very many places in the world with suitable rocks close to the surface. It is expensive drilling several kilometres into the ground. And the steam sometimes carries harmful substances such as sulfur up with it.

▲ The geothermal power plant at Larderello, Italy.

Question

d *What might be the risks of building a power plant in a volcanic area?*

Key points

- Solar electric cells generate electricity directly from light. But they are expensive, and do not work in the dark.
- The Earth's heat can be harnessed to make geothermal electricity. But only a few places in the world are suitable.

Making choices

Energy sources for generating electricity have different advantages and disadvantages. A choice that is good for one place may not be suitable for another.

Science can give us facts about cost, pollution and so on. But science can't make decisions for us. We have to decide the best energy source for each situation. There is no one right answer.

Building power stations

The table shows some building costs for different types of power station in the UK or Europe.

The solar park looks the cheapest. But it also produces the least power. To make the comparison fair, we must think about how much power each station will provide as well as how much it costs. The power output is given in megawatts (MW). 1 MW = 1000 kW = 1 000 000 W.

	Type of power station					
	Gas	Coal	Nuclear	Hydro	Wind	Solar
building cost (£ millions)	300	560	1500	140	51	35
amount of power generated (MW)	750	700	1000	100	60	10
building cost per MW (£ millions)	0.4					

Questions

a List the power stations in order of building cost per MW, starting with the cheapest.

b Onshore wind farms and solar parks can be built in a few months. A gas or coal power station takes many years to build. Is it worth paying extra to get electricity quickly?

Running power stations

Once the power station is built, we have to buy fuel, keep the machinery working, pay the workers, and so on. We also have to dismantle the station safely at the end of its life.

Scientists can calculate the cost of producing 1 kWh of electricity from each source. The calculations take account of all the building and running costs for the different power stations. To maintain the machinery it is sometimes necessary to shut it down. The start-up time afterwards varies for different types of power stations and this contributes to running costs. Nuclear power has the longest start-up time and gas-fired power the shortest.

But the costs are hard to predict. Nobody knows how much fossil fuels will cost in the future, or how much it costs to store nuclear waste safely for thousands of years. Different scientists use different numbers, so they get different results. The chart shows a range of estimates. The shading indicates the lowest and highest estimates.

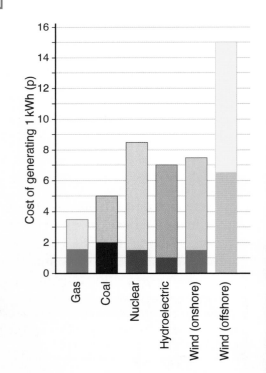

Questions

c How certain are scientists about the costs of generating electricity from different sources? Explain your answer.

d The higher estimates for gas and coal include an extra cost because they produce carbon dioxide. Is this fair? Can we decide how much money pollution is worth?

e The higher estimates for nuclear power include an extra cost because of the risk of something going wrong. Is this fair? Can we know how much risk there is or how much an accident would cost?

Supplying electricity

People need electricity all the time. But we can't rely on every energy source to provide a constant supply. A wind farm works efficiently only 30% of the time, while the best nuclear power stations can work 90% of the time. Nuclear power has greater **reliability**.

Question

f The higher estimates for wind power in the chart include the cost of generating electricity from an alternative source when there is not enough wind. Is this fair?

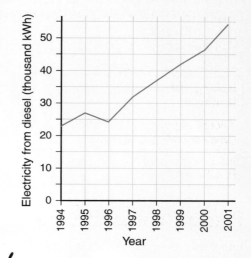

We also need to think about where the electricity is needed. The raw materials must be transported to the power station, and the electricity must be transferred to users.

Dominica is a small Caribbean island. It has some hydroelectric schemes, but they cannot produce enough electricity for everyone. The rest comes from diesel, a fossil fuel that must be imported.

As the country develops, people need more electricity. More diesel has to be imported. Between 1994 and 2001, the amount of electricity generated from diesel went up from 23 000 kWh to 54 000 kWh. In the same period, the price of electricity rose by over 10%.

The island would like to use more local renewable sources of energy. But at the moment, it is too expensive to install new wind and solar power stations, and the diesel power station already exists.

Question

g How do you think Dominica should generate its electricity?

Key points

● Energy sources for making electricity have different advantages and disadvantages.
● To choose between them, we have to think about many factors including the cost of electricity, the reliability of the energy source and the environmental impact.

1 Match the words **A**, **B**, **C** and **D** with the spaces **1–4** in the sentences.

    A conduct   **B** transfer
    C cool down   **D** emit

Metals ____**1**____ thermal energy better than plastics because of the way their particles are arranged. But unpainted metals do not ____**2**____ thermal radiation well because of their shiny surfaces.

Metal and plastic objects can both ____**3**____ thermal energy to the air by convection as long as there is a free flow of air. When objects lose thermal energy by any method, they ____**4**____.

2 A group of students investigated the absorption of thermal radiation by different surfaces using two copper cubes of the same size. One was painted dull white and the other was painted shiny black.

The diagram shows how the experiment was set up.

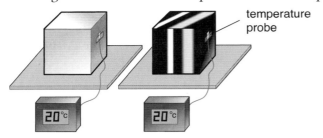

temperature probe

The cubes were left on cork mats in the sunlight. They were positioned so that they received the same amount of radiation. Each cube had a temperature probe attached to its surface. The probes allowed the students to measure the temperature of the cubes.

The students measured each cube's temperature every 2 minutes. The table shows some of the results.

Dull white		Shiny black	
Time (min)	Temp. (°C)	Time (min)	Temp. (°C)
0	20.0	0	20.0
2	23.0	2	24.0
4	24.8	4	26.0
6	26.0	6	27.4
8	27.0	8	28.5
10	27.8	10	29.3
12	28.5	12	30.0
14	29.0	14	30.6
16	29.5	16	31.1

a Would you expect a white or a black surface to be a better absorber? *(1 mark)*

b Would you expect a dull or a shiny surface to be a better absorber? *(1 mark)*

c Use your answers to parts **a** and **b** to explain why the results of this experiment were hard to predict. *(1 mark)*

d Which surface was the better absorber? *(1 mark)*

e Give **two** variables that have been controlled in this experiment. *(2 marks)*

f After the experiment, the cubes were taken indoors and left on a table, still on their cork mats. Predict which cube cooled down more quickly. Explain your answer. *(2 marks)*

3 The diagram shows a heat sink from the back of a computer. The heat sink is designed to transfer thermal energy from the computer to the surroundings.

The heat sink is made of metal. The base is in contact with the computer. The fins have a large surface area in contact with the air. The whole computer, including the heat sink, is enclosed in a plastic casing.

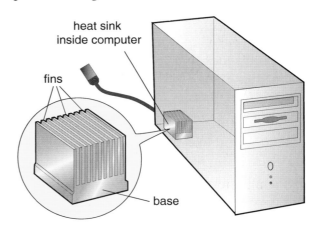

heat sink inside computer

fins

base

a By which method is thermal energy transferred from the computer to the heat sink base? *(1 mark)*

b The heat sink base is one of the heaviest parts of the computer. A lighter base would make the computer easier to carry. But the manufacturer says that a base with a larger mass transfers thermal energy faster. Is this correct? Explain your answer. *(2 marks)*

c i Which method of thermal energy transfer needs air to flow freely around the fins? *(1 mark)*

ii Explain why the computer's plastic casing makes the heat sink less good at transferring thermal energy. *(1 mark)*

d The computer has a fan to blow air over the heat sink fins. Explain how this helps the heat sink to transfer thermal energy to the surroundings. *(1 mark)*

4 The diagram shows the energy input into a device and the useful and wasted energy outputs.

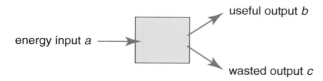

The efficiency of the device is
- **A** *b*/*a*
- **B** *c*/*a*
- **C** *b*/*c*
- **D** (*b* + *c*)/*a*

5 Complete the sentence by using the correct words from the box.

useful	transformed	hotter	destroyed
	efficient	spread out	wasted

When energy is _____ or transferred, only some of the output is in the form that we want. The rest is _____. When we use energy, it becomes increasingly _____ but it is never _____.

6 A company producing pre-packed meals wants to reduce energy consumption at one of its factories. The company asks an energy efficiency consultant to suggest some ways of reducing energy consumption. The table shows the methods suggested by the consultant.

Energy-saving method	Cost (£)	Annual saving (£)
Run extractor fan at lower speed.	0	4 000
Replace light bulbs with energy-efficient bulbs.	8 000	10 000
Buy new energy-efficient refrigerators.	21 000	3 000
Buy device to extract wasted heat from factory machinery and use it to warm the factory.	11 000	3 000

a Which method is most effective at reducing energy consumption? *(1 mark)*

b Which method is cost-effective soonest? *(1 mark)*

c The factory decides to use all the suggested methods.
i What is the total cost? *(1 mark)*
ii What is the total annual saving? *(1 mark)*
iii How long does the combination of methods take to become cost-effective? *(1 mark)*

d The factory's annual energy bill before the energy-saving measures were taken was £160 000. What is the percentage decrease in the annual energy bill after the energy-saving measures have been taken? *(2 marks)*

7 Which one of the sentences **A**, **B**, **C** and **D** is a correct definition of power?
A The total amount of energy transformed by a device.
B The amount of energy usefully transformed by a device.
C The rate at which energy is transformed by a device.
D The proportion of the energy input that is usefully transformed by a device.

8 Two light bulbs were compared. The results are shown in the table.

	Bulb 1	Bulb 2
Cost (£)	4	35
Power (W)	100	2 000
Efficiency (%)	15	4
Running cost per hour (p)	1	20

a What is the main form of energy wastage for most light bulbs? *(1 mark)*

b Give **two** advantages of bulb 1. *(2 marks)*

c Suggest a situation for which bulb 2 would be suitable, but bulb 1 would not. *(1 mark)*

9 The passage below gives some information about refrigerators.

> A refrigerator works by transferring thermal energy from the inside to the outside using a 'heat pump'. The pump does not run all the time.
>
> As the pump runs, the inside of the refrigerator cools down. When the inside has reached the correct temperature, the pump stops.
>
> Because the inside of the refrigerator is cooler than the surroundings, thermal energy flows back in through the walls. The insulation in the walls slows this down.
>
> The energy flowing into the refrigerator gradually warms it up. When the temperature rises above a certain level, the pump comes back on.

Use information from the passage to help you to answer these questions.

a Explain in your own words what happens when the inside of the refrigerator is cold and the pump stops. *(1 mark)*

b Because of the way the refrigerator works, the pump is not running most of the time. Explain why the pump would have to run more of the time if the insulation were removed. *(1 mark)*

c A refrigerator pump has a power rating of 200 W. The refrigerator transfers 0.5 kWh of electricity from the mains per day. Calculate how long the pump is running each day. *(2 marks)*

10 The electricity meter in a house shows a reading of 12 900. No electrical device is switched on, so the meter reading is not changing.

A 1.5 kW electric fan is plugged in and switched on. After 4 hours, another meter reading is taken.

a The meter reading at the end of 4 hours is
  A 12904   **B** 18900
  C 12906   **D** 13260

b If the electricity used by the fan in 4 hours costs 90p, the cost of one unit of electricity is
  A 0.015p   **B** 22.5p
  C 15p   **D** 135p

c A kilowatt-hour (kWh) is a unit of
  A energy   **B** power
  C rate   **D** efficiency.

11 Some students are discussing the advantages of different energy sources for generating electricity. They make the following statements:

1 Fossil fuels are found everywhere in the world.

2 Nuclear fuel produces no harmful waste.

3 The tides can provide a constant, steady supply of electricity.

4 Solar cells can store light to make electricity at night.

Which of the statements are correct?
  A 2 and 4   **B** 2 only
  C 1, 3 and 4   **D** none of them

12 Why are only a few places in the world suitable for building geothermal power plants?
A Because in most places it is too dangerous to dig deep holes.
B Because most places are not close enough to active volcanoes.
C Because in most places there is no water underground.
D Because in most places the hot rocks are too far from the surface.

13 The diagram shows some parts of a hydroelectric power station.

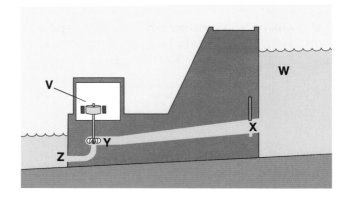

a In this hydroelectric plant:

   i At which point does the water have the most gravitational potential energy?

                     (1 mark)

   ii At which point does the water turn the turbine? *(1 mark)*

b What is the device labelled **V**? *(1 mark)*

c This power plant uses a renewable source of energy. Explain what that means. *(1 mark)*

d Give **one** disadvantage of hydroelectric power generation. *(1 mark)*

14 The graph shows the estimated reserves of gas in the UK between 1995 and 2003.

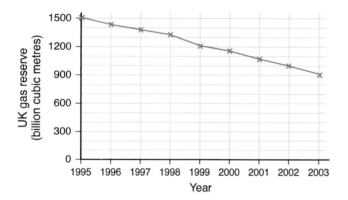

a Write down the estimated reserves in

   i 1995 *(1 mark)*

   ii 1999 *(1 mark)*

   iii 2003 *(1 mark)*

b Calculate the mean annual decrease in reserves between 1995 and 2003. *(2 marks)*

c If the reserves continue to decrease at the same rate, how long will it take for them to be used up? *(2 marks)*

d Suggest **one** reason why the estimates of reserves might not be accurate. *(1 mark)*

15 Turbogen Electrical Company wants to build a power station in the countryside near Anytown. Some local people are in favour of the plan, but others are against it.

The passage below is part of a newspaper article discussing the plan.

> The proposal has split the community. The National Association for Bird Protection is opposed to the plan. 'Birds will fly into the turbines and be killed,' said the head of the local branch.
>
> But some environmental groups are in favour. The local council recently dropped plans for a coal-fired power station. 'That would have been a disaster,' said an environmental protestor. 'The new plans are a big improvement.'
>
> Meanwhile, the company that wants to build the power station denies that many birds will be killed. The head of research at Turbogen says that the turbines will have less impact on birds than a coal-fired power station. 'Coal pollution is bad for birds,' she said. 'Our power station will release no harmful gases.'

Use information from the passage to help you to answer these questions.

a What type of power station is the article discussing? *(1 mark)*

b Give **two** advantages of this energy source for generating electricity. *(2 marks)*

c Suggest **one** reason why environmental groups might prefer this type of power station to a coal-fired station. *(1 mark)*

d Write down **one** issue that the National Association for Bird Protection and the electricity company disagree about. *(1 mark)*

e Suggest how they could investigate this issue to find out the facts. *(2 marks)*

We are all used to the idea of particles carrying energy – we can see lumps of matter and they hurt if they hit us! Waves can also carry energy and many of them are invisible. We can't see them, but they can still do us harm if they hit us.

▲ Personal stereo and hairdryer, or something more sinister?

X-ray vision

The photograph above is not the usual one that you might expect to see of your holiday suitcase – it was taken using X-rays. This sort of technology helps us to see things that we wouldn't normally be able to.

We all know that we get light energy from the Sun. Light energy travels to us as a wave and we 'see' it with our eyes. There are all sorts of other waves, similar to light, that we cannot 'see' in the same way – but we can put them to good use provided we can control the dangers they present. They can help us to communicate, and to find out what things are like inside, where we can't see.

X-rays are a kind of wave that can penetrate some solid materials. We can put suitcases through an X-ray machine at an airport, but we can't put people through – the X-rays would be too dangerous. Instead, we walk through a gate that contains a metal detector. These use another kind of wave, but the problem is that they can only detect metal, not plastic and other non-metallic materials.

A NEW WAY OF DETECTING TERRORISTS

In 2004 scientists started developing a new way of detecting explosives hidden under people's clothing.

Using wavelengths between microwaves and infra red, these devices can detect plastic explosives that normal metal detectors can't. They work by analysing the different ways in which plastics and other materials reflect and absorb the waves. They will not be used to produce an image of the person on a screen, because it would appear that the person had no clothes on! Instead they will be used to trigger an alarm if anything suspicious is detected. However, it may actually be an advantage not to have an operator who has to continually watch a screen.

Terahertz technology

Terahertz waves – or T-waves as they are known – could have many uses. They are less harmful to the body than X-rays. They may be used to detect skin cancer: the waves only penetrate the top few millimetres of skin, and this is where the skin cancers grow. They could also be used as a safer alternative to X-rays for checking teeth.

Think about what you will find out in this section

What are electromagnetic waves?	How can electromagnetic waves be used?
What are the dangers of electromagnetic waves?	Are mobile phones dangerous to use?
Is it dangerous to live close to a TV transmitter?	Is it dangerous to sunbathe?
Why shouldn't I have too many X-rays taken?	

Making waves

Waves are a way of getting energy from one place to another.

The stone carries energy as it travels. When it hits the water, the energy makes the water molecules move up and down. The energy travels to the shore but neither the water nor the boat does.

▲ You can't bring the boat to the shore by making waves close to it.

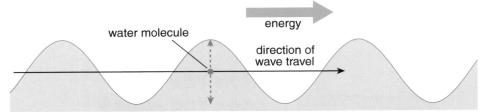

▲ The energy travels horizontally but the water molecules only bob up and down.

Some water waves carry much more energy

The film *The Perfect Storm* was based on a true story of a fishing boat that was caught in a terrific storm in the Atlantic. Fierce winds had whipped up the sea into waves 30 metres tall. In September 2005, hurricane Katrina caused waves 10 metres high on Lake Pontchartrain, causing devastating flooding in nearby New Orleans.

Other giant waves at sea, called tsunamis, are created by earthquakes under the sea floor, or by landslides falling into the sea. One of the worst tsunamis ever recorded occurred just off the coast of Sumatra in December 2004. The energy of this wave, travelling at up to 1000 km/h, reached as far as South America – nearly halfway round the world from its starting point.

Waves like these at sea are easy to detect: we can see them, hear them and even feel them.

▲ The energy carried by these huge waves is enormous.

> ### Question
>
> **a** Where did the energy in the waves in the photo come from originally?

But there are some waves that are harder to detect, even though they are all around us. These waves are caused by changes in an electric field, and they are called electromagnetic waves.

Tuning in

When you select channels on your radio or TV, you are choosing the wavelength or the frequency of the radio signal you want to receive. Your radio will pick up only the waves that are exactly the frequency you have chosen. But what do we mean by frequency and wavelength? You can picture these more easily by looking again at a wave in water.

A wave is made up of one unit, called a **cycle**, repeated over and over again.

The **frequency** of a wave means how many of these cycles pass a given point every second. A frequency of 1 cycle per second is called 1 hertz (Hz).

The **wavelength** is the distance from any point on the cycle to the same point on the next cycle.

The **amplitude** of the wave is the height of a crest or the depth of a trough. The greater the amplitude the greater the amount of energy that the wave carries.

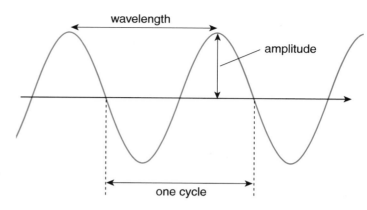

Questions

b How many cycles are shown in the diagram?
c If it takes 2 seconds for one of these cycles to pass you, what is the frequency of the wave?

Same but different

We see different colours because light is made up of a range of wavelengths and frequencies.

Outside the visible **spectrum** there are many other kinds of radiation. For example, a thermometer with a blackened bulb, placed just outside the red light in the photo on the right, would register a rise in temperature. This is because of infra red radiation that we cannot detect with our eyes.

This whole family of waves is called the **electromagnetic (EM) spectrum**. They all have different wavelengths and frequencies, but travel at the same speed in a vacuum (3×10^8 m/s or 300 million m/s).

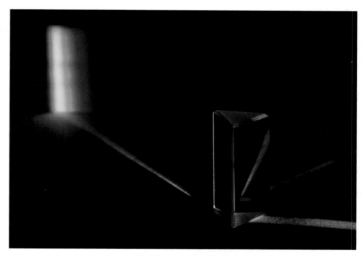

▲ When white light is shone through a prism it splits into a spectrum of different colours.

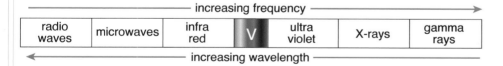

increasing frequency

| radio waves | microwaves | infra red | V | ultra violet | X-rays | gamma rays |

increasing wavelength

In practice, there is no sharp division between the different parts of the spectrum – but for convenience they are often divided into these seven sections.

Key points

- Waves carry energy.
- Electromagnetic waves are caused by disturbances in an electric field.
- All EM waves travel at the same speed in a vacuum.
- Electromagnetic waves have different wavelengths and frequencies.

Question

d What is the name of the very narrow band in the middle of the spectrum, labelled V in the diagram?

The wave formula

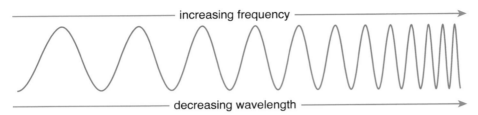

increasing frequency →

decreasing wavelength →

▲ As the frequency of a wave changes, so does the wavelength.

You can see from the diagram that as the frequency gets higher, the wavelength gets smaller. These two measurements are related by the formula:

$$\text{wave speed} = \text{frequency} \times \text{wavelength}$$
$$\text{(metres/second)} \quad \text{(hertz)} \quad \text{(metres)}$$

Examples

Example 1

A water wave has a wavelength of 50 metres and a frequency of 0.2 Hz. What is its speed?

Use the formula:

$$\text{wave speed} = \text{frequency} \times \text{wavelength}$$
$$= 0.2 \text{ Hz} \times 50 \text{ m}$$
$$= 10 \text{ m/s}$$

For the Higher tier exam, you will need to transform formulae – this means making a different term the subject of the equation.

Example 2

A radio wave has a wavelength of 80 m. What is its frequency?

First, make frequency the subject of the equation:

$$\text{frequency} = \frac{\text{wave speed}}{\text{wavelength}}$$

Then put in the numbers, remembering that all electromagnetic waves travel at a speed of 300 million m/s.

$$\text{frequency} = \frac{300\,000\,000}{80} \text{ Hz}$$
$$= 3\,750\,000 \text{ Hz}$$
$$= 3.75 \text{ MHz}$$

(1 megahertz (MHz) = 1 000 000 Hz)

▲ As the waves reach shallower water they slow down. The frequency stays the same so this means that the wavelength decreases.

Questions

a A radio wave has a frequency of 200 000 Hz and a wavelength of 1500 m. What is the speed of the wave?

b Some microwaves have a frequency of 10^{10} Hz. Using wave speed = 300 000 000 m/s, find their wavelength in cm.

Which wave?

We have seen that waves in the EM spectrum have different wavelengths and frequencies. They are produced in different ways and have different properties. Because of their properties they have different uses and dangers.

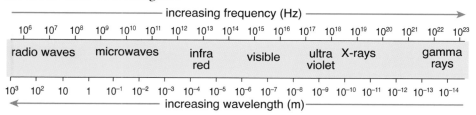

Radio waves have the longest wavelength, ranging from about a metre to several kilometres. Approximately one million infra red waves could fit into one radio wave, and approximately one million gamma waves could fit into one infra red wave.

Questions

c Which wave has: (i) the lowest frequency; (ii) the smallest wavelength?
d Suggest a value for the wavelength of visible light.
e Suggest a value for the frequency of microwaves.

Generally the higher the frequency of a wave, the more energy it carries and the more dangerous it is likely to be.

Questions

f Which two types of EM wave are likely to be most dangerous?
g Some cancer treatments use wave energy to kill cancer cells. Which type of wave might be used for this?

In the 1930s, workmen fixing a powerful radio transmitter noticed that a hot dog they had left close to the transmitter became hot.

Questions

h Which type of wave do you think was responsible for heating up the hot dog?
i What does this tell you about low frequency EM waves?

Key points

- All EM waves travel at the same speed in a vacuum (300 million m/s).
- Electromagnetic waves obey the wave formula:
  wave speed = frequency × wavelength
- The uses and dangers of electromagnetic waves depend on their wavelengths and frequencies.

What happens to the energy of a wave?

All electromagnetic waves carry energy. The height of a wave (its amplitude) is a measure of how much energy it carries. Also, the higher frequency waves usually carry more energy.

Electromagnetic waves can carry this energy through empty space (a vacuum). But when the wave hits a material, something happens to all this energy. The wave can be **reflected**, **absorbed** or **transmitted**, or a combination of these.

> **Question**
>
> **a** Look back to the diagram of the electromagnetic spectrum on page 201. Which type of wave carries the most energy?

Reflection

This means that the wave bounces off in a different direction.

The photograph shows a solar furnace. These are often used in tropical countries, for example in Africa, where they can provide a cheap supply of thermal energy. Small versions can be used for cooking, larger ones for industrial use.

> **Question**
>
> **b** Suggest one reason why solar furnaces are not much used in the UK.

▲ Infra red radiation from the Sun is reflected to a focus in this concave mirror.

Absorption

This means that the energy will go into warming up the material and will not get through. The energy carried by the wave will be absorbed by the particles in the material, making them vibrate more vigorously. In this experiment to carry out photosynthesis, the light is shone through a beaker of water. The water transmits the light but absorbs the infra red.

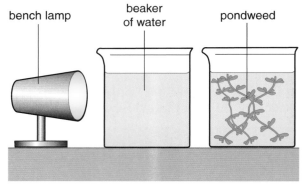

bench lamp   beaker of water   pondweed

▲ The water in the first beaker absorbs thermal energy and so stops the water containing the pondweed from warming up.

Water molecules are good at absorbing microwave energy. When you cook food in a microwave oven, the energy from the microwaves makes the water molecules vibrate more vigorously, so raising the temperature. The heat generated in the surface of the food (the top 3 cm) is then conducted through to the inside.

If you want to prove that it is the water that is heated, dry an ice cube and put it in the microwave. Switch on, and you will find that the ice does not melt!

Radio receiver aerials absorb the energy from radio waves. The radio waves produce a tiny alternating current in the aerial. The radio receiver and speaker then turn this into sound that you can hear.

Transmission

This hand-held global positioning system uses signals from satellites orbiting high above the Earth. Even though the waves carry only about one billionth of the power of a mobile phone signal, they can still get through the cloud cover.

Light waves can travel through glass and water, and some X-rays can get through soft tissue but not bone. Different materials transmit different EM waves. For example, glass is excellent at transmitting light and that is why it is used in windows.

Some materials, like glass, will reflect, absorb and transmit EM radiation.

Sometimes when glass reflects light, it causes glare. Some special types of glass can reduce this.

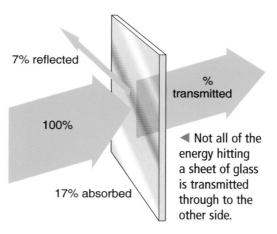

7% reflected

100%

% transmitted

◄ Not all of the energy hitting a sheet of glass is transmitted through to the other side.

17% absorbed

▲ Radio signals from satellites can get through cloud.

Question

c *What percentage of light is transmitted through this piece of glass?*

Different types of glass can have different characteristics.

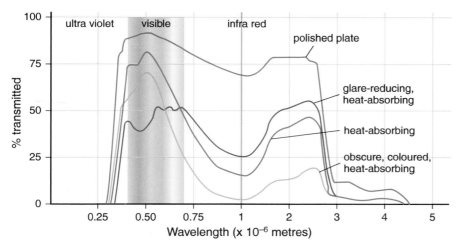

▲ The transmission characteristics of four different types of glass. (Adapted from Canadian Building Digest, No. 60.)

Questions

d *Which type of glass is best at allowing visible light to be transmitted?*
e *Which type of glass would you fit in your windows if you wanted to keep the inside of your house cool in the summer?*

Key points

- Waves can be reflected, absorbed or transmitted.
- Different materials are good at reflecting, absorbing or transmitting different wavelengths.
- When radiation is absorbed, the energy makes the substance hotter, and may create an alternating electric current of the same frequency as the radiation itself.

Radio waves

Radio waves have the longest wavelength of all the electromagnetic waves. They include waves for television as well as radio.

◀ These aerials at Droitwich are used to transmit BBC Radio 4 on long wave.

Question

a Radio 4 broadcasts on a frequency of 198 kHz. Use the wave formula to calculate the wavelength (Remember that all EM waves travel at a speed of 300 million m/s.)

Microwaves

TETRA is a new communications system for the police and other emergency services. The system is similar to that used for mobile phones, but uses microwaves at a frequency of 400 MHz.

▶ These aerials transmit microwaves for a system called TETRA.

Question

b What wavelength does TETRA use?

Microwaves are useful for communications because they can pass easily through the atmosphere. Long-wavelength microwaves are also used for radar.

Microwaves are sent out from the dish. When they hit an object such as an aeroplane, they bounce back. The time taken between sending out the waves and detecting their return is used to work out the position and distance of the object.

Question

c A radar system is used to detect an aircraft. The time taken between the radar pulse being sent out and its return is 10 microseconds. (1 microsecond = $\frac{1}{1\,000\,000}$ of a second.) How far away was the aircraft?

▲ A typical radar dish.

Microwaves and mobile phones

Here is a news item about mobile phones

Mobile phone firms have been accused of withholding information about radiation levels from handsets. Some models emit much more than others, but most people do not know this. It is very difficult to find out which phones are safest, unless this information is clearly printed on the phones.

In 2000, the Stewart Report warned that children should strictly limit their use of mobiles. Children's skulls are thinner than adults' and their cells are still developing. It warned that there might be effects that cause illnesses, such as brain tumours, 20 years later. The report said that '... it is not possible to say categorically that there are not health effects'. But what has come out from the industry is that mobile phones are safe.

The Mobile Operators Association said, 'All mobile phones sold in the UK comply with international health and safety exposure guidelines set by independent scientific experts.'

How do we communicate?

Most types of EM waves can be used for communication, but visible light, infra red, microwaves and radio waves tend to be used the most.

Question

i Which end of the EM spectrum is used most for communications – long wavelength or short wavelength?

In order to carry information waves need to be altered in a meaningful way, and the simplest way to do this is to turn the signal on and off.

Digital and analogue signals

The lighthouse is an example of a **digital signal**. A digital signal is one that makes sudden jumps between on and off. An **analogue signal** can vary continuously between off and a maximum. For example, you could send a message by turning a dimmer switch up and down to vary the brightness of a lamp.

Digital signals are less likely to be affected by interference. An electronic circuit samples the signal many times per second and if the signal has drifted, the circuit sets it back to the correct value. This is because digital signals are interpreted as being either on or off – if the signal increases or decreases very slightly, this is still interpreted as being 'on'. With an analogue signal, this slight variation would become amplified and result in distortion.

Questions

d Give one example of a way in which radiation from mobile phones could damage health.
e Why do scientists believe that children might be at more risk than adults?
f Why are scientists concerned about possible dangers, even though there is no evidence at present that they are harmful?
g Why do you think that mobile phone operators are keen to deny the scientists' warnings?
h Some people think that it might be safer if children send text messages rather than speaking on the phone. What do you think is the reason for this?

▲ This lighthouse sends out three flashes of light every 5 seconds.

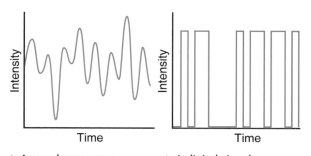

▲ An analogue wave.   ▲ A digital signal.

Key points

- Microwaves and radio are widely used in communications.
- Communication signals can be analogue or digital.
- Digital signals tend to be higher quality, and can be processed by computers.

Visible light

This is what enables us to see – the eye is a detector of **visible light**. We also use light for taking pictures with cameras, for operating photocell detectors and for generating electricity with photovoltaic cells.

Photographic film is coated with chemicals. When exposed to light, these chemicals turn black. The stronger the light, the blacker the film becomes.

Darkrooms were often illuminated with red light. This is because some black-and-white films are insensitive to red light, and so a light of this colour could safely be switched on when developing the film. Modern films have a much wider response spectrum, and some can even detect infra red light.

Photocells are often used when small amounts of electricity are needed and there is no mains supply easily available. A photocell converts light energy into electricity.

▲ The electricity needed to operate this parking meter is provided by a photocell.

Ultra violet waves

Certain substances fluoresce (or glow) under **ultra violet** (UV) light. For example, some washing powders contain an ingredient that makes clothes look 'whiter-than-white' when seen in sunlight. You can use a special pen to write your postcode on your valuable possessions – you can't see it in normal light, but it shows up under ultra violet.

Crime scene investigators can use UV to reveal hidden blood, fingerprints, fibres, and bruises on living and dead bodies.

Ultra violet light can affect living things. Scientists have carried out experiments to find out the effect of ultra violet light on fungi. They used two different species of fungi, and measured the length of the germ tube to find the effect on growth.

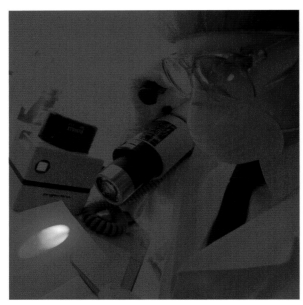

▲ Blood stains will appear to glow in the light from this UV lamp.

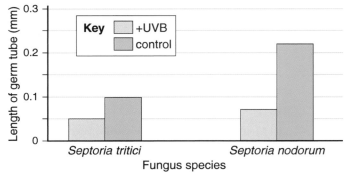

▲ The bar charts show how ultra violet light can affect the growth of fungi. The control experiment measures the growth of the same fungus, in the same conditions, except without exposure to ultra violet.

Questions

a What effect does ultra violet light (UVB) have on the growth of these fungi?

b What is the purpose of a control experiment?

c Why do you think that the scientists used two different species of fungi, rather than just one?

d What could the scientists have done to make the results more reliable?

e What do you think is the use of research like this?

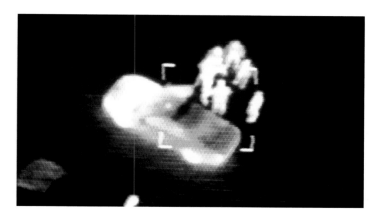

Infra red radiation

This is sometimes called heat radiation because hot objects emit more **infra red radiation** than cold objects. Infra red (IR) radiation is used for sensors for burglar alarms, remote controls for televisions and cars, and infra red photography. The police often use thermal imaging cameras at night to detect criminals who are trying to escape.

◄ This photo was taken from a police helicopter at night to locate a bank robber.

Question

f Why does the image of the men appear white when the surroundings appear dark?

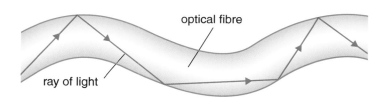

optical fibre

ray of light

Fibre optics

Laser light or infra red can be sent along optical fibres made of glass. These fibre optics can channel the light over long distances and round corners with very little loss of energy.

Fibre optics have many applications. They can be used to look into small spaces and round corners. For example doctors can use them to inspect the inside of your stomach, or plumbers can use them to inspect the insides of pipes.

◄ This surgeon is using an endoscope to examine the inside of the patient's body.

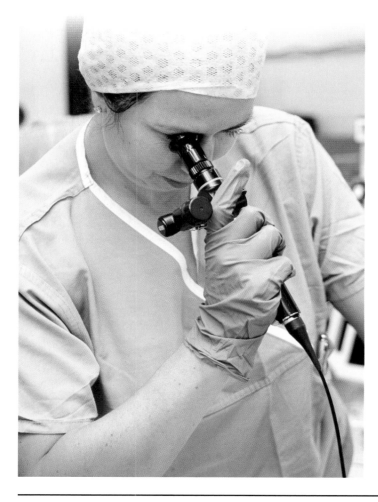

Optical fibres are also used in communications. A fibre optic can carry many thousand of times the information in the form of light signals than a copper cable can carry in the form of electrical signals. There are transatlantic underwater fibre optic cables between Europe and America that carry telephone messages.

Key points

- UV rays can be harmful to living cells.
- UV can cause fluorescence.
- Visible light and IR can be used to send signals along optical fibres.

X-rays

Doctors often use **X-rays** to help in diagnosing different conditions. X-rays can penetrate soft tissue quite easily, but are absorbed by more dense materials such as bone and metal. They are also used at airport security to look inside luggage.

X-rays generally have a longer wavelength than gamma rays. As with all electromagnetic waves, over-exposure to X-rays can cause cell damage and mutations (changes). This is why radiographers stand behind a protective lead shield when they take an X-ray (lead is good at absorbing X-rays). They may also wear badges that check how much radiation they have been exposed to.

This type of badge is designed to detect any radiation that has been received by the wearer. Underneath the bottom section is a piece of photographic film, wrapped in black paper. Different types of radiation will be absorbed or transmitted through the different layers of plastic and metal.

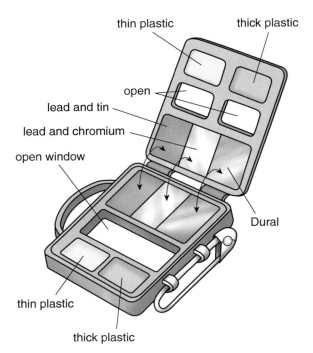

▲ The diagram shows a badge worn by radiographers.

X-rays cause nearly 1000 deaths per year in the UK

Scientists have some evidence that using X-rays to diagnose patients' illnesses could actually result in more cancers being produced.

Research has shown that just over 0.5% of the total cancer risk may be attributed to X-ray examinations carried out in hospitals.

It is recommended that unnecessary X-rays should be avoided, but doctors say that the benefits of X-rays still outweigh the risks.

Gamma rays

Gamma rays have the shortest wavelength, the highest frequency and carry the most energy. They are produced by some radioactive substances and by stars.

Because of the high amount of energy they carry, they can kill cells. This makes them very dangerous, but the effect can be put to good use to kill cancer cells.

Questions

a Why is the photographic film wrapped in paper?
b How will the badge show the amount of radiation that the wearer has received?

Questions

c In what way could X-rays cause cancer?
d What sort of evidence do you think that the scientists needed to collect in order to come to these conclusions?
e What are the benefits of using X-rays for diagnosis rather than other methods?

They can also be used to irradiate food to stop it from going bad. The high energy in the gamma rays will kill organisms, such as bacteria, that cause food to decay. However, it is not suitable for all foods, as it can lead to a change of texture or taste. One of the big success stories of irradiated food is strawberries. These are notoriously difficult to preserve in any other way – for example, freezing them reduces them to a mushy pulp because the ice crystals formed inside rupture the cells.

Ingredients: A blend of Thyme; Sage; Origanum and Marjoram (irradiated).

Ideal to complement the flavour of pizza, tomato, meat, chicken and fish dishes.

Recipe Suggestion: BUTTERMILK HERB BREAD: Preheat

▲ This label from a jar of Choice Mixed Herbs says that the herbs have been irradiated.

Question

f The table on the right shows how much radiation each kind of fruit can withstand, and how much is needed to kill the mould (kGy is short for kilogray, the unit used to measure the amount of radiation).
Which type of fruit could most successfully be preserved by gamma irradiation? Give a reason for your choice.

Type of fruit	Amount of radiation before damage (kGy)*
apricots	0.5
cherries	0.7
peaches	0.5
raspberries	1.0
strawberries	4.0

*Amount of radiation needed to kill mould: 2 kGy.

Gamma radiation can also be used for checking for cracks in cast metals or checking that welds in steel pipes have been made correctly. Because of its high energy, gamma radiation is very penetrating. This means that it can pass through thick metals that other types of radiation could not. When the radiation meets a crack, the waves change speed and are partially reflected, and these changes can be detected. Gamma radiation needs several centimetres of lead or several metres of concrete to absorb it: this is why shielding for gamma radiation has to be very thick.

Question

g The table on the right shows the amount of gamma radiation received from a certain source through various thickness of lead shielding.
(i) Plot a graph of these results.
(ii) What is the effect of doubling the thickness of the lead shielding?

Thickness of lead (cm)	Radiation transmitted (Bq)*
1	1000
2	500
3	375
4	250
5	180

*Bq (Becquerel) is a measure of the radioactivity.

Key points

- The hazards of EM waves depend on the type of wave and the dose received.
- Gamma rays and X-rays have high frequency and short wavelength.
- Because gamma rays and X-rays are very penetrating, they are used for diagnostic purposes and for killing cancer cells and bacteria.
- People who work with gamma rays and X-rays need to take special precautions.

▲ Gamma rays can be used to detect faults in a pipeline.

Science and advertising

Here are two recent cuttings from newspapers.

EMPRO✝ECT

Why wait for scientists to prove that
mobile phones are dangerous?

Buy **EMPRO✝ECT** now!

Emprotect is a small lapel badge that
contains special crystals that provide
biofeedback resonance to
protect your brain cells.

For only £100 you can protect yourself today!

MOBILE PHONE DANGER

Which?, the magazine of the independent Consumers'
Association, recently tested several radiation shields
for mobile phones. They found that these shields
offered little or no protection.

◀ Cutting A.   ▲ Cutting B.

Question

a One of these cuttings may be biased.
(i) Explain what is meant by biased.
(ii) Which of the two cuttings do you think is likely to be
biased?
(iii) Explain why you think that one of the cuttings may
be biased.

Very low frequency waves

Whenever an alternating current (a.c.) goes through
a wire, it produces an alternating electromagnetic
field. This in turn produces electromagnetic waves.

The frequency of the a.c. mains is 50 Hz. This
means that near overhead power lines there will be
electromagnetic waves of frequency 50 Hz.

Question

b (i) Use the wave formula to calculate the wavelength of
electromagnetic waves whose frequency is 50 Hz.
(ii) In which part of the EM spectrum do these waves
belong?

At present, no one is absolutely sure if these waves
have any effect on our bodies. However, some
people who live very close to National Grid lines are
worried that there may be some long-term effects.

▲ Power lines often run very close to houses.

Here are two different newspaper articles about the effects that living very close to overhead power lines might have.

Some newspapers often carry stories like this that tend to pick out one or two 'headline' points, and do not always tell the full story.

Power cables cause cancer

A suspicion that overhead power lines might contribute to an increased incidence of breast cancer has led Norwegian scientists to carry out new research. They found that women who lived close to power lines were 1.5 times more likely to develop breast cancer when compared with those who did not live near to power lines.

Question

c Before you could have any confidence in the results of the 'research' quoted above, you would need to know a lot more about how the investigation was carried out. For each of the points below, say why you would need this data:

(i) period of time for which the data was collected

(ii) number of women included in the data

(iii) distances from power lines of the women's homes

(iv) ages of the women who contracted breast cancer.

No danger from overhead power lines

Recent studies in Australia have found no evidence of a link between cancer and power lines. No increases in the incidence of cancer were detected in mice after prolonged exposure to the type of fields emitted by power lines.

Question

d What questions would you ask the scientists who carried out the research described above, in order to decide whether their conclusion was valid?

This is an example of a case where science has yet to find out the truth. There is much conflicting evidence and many different opinions. You need to consider the evidence carefully, thinking about how it was obtained, and don't believe everything that you read in the newspapers!

Key points

- It is possible to collect data that can be analysed in order to provide evidence for scientific theories.
- It is necessary to distinguish between opinion based on valid and reliable evidence and opinion based on non-scientific ideas.

Radioactivity

Radioactivity occurs naturally all the time. We are all exposed to low levels of radiation every day. This is called background radiation. It is important to study radioactivity so that we can find out what causes it, what effects it might have, and how we can reduce any harmful effects.

Radiation from rocks

Some of the **background radiation** comes from rocks in the Earth's crust. Radon is a radioactive gas that is released from rocks that contain traces of uranium-238. These occur in many parts of the UK, particularly Cornwall. The uranium changes first into radium and then into radon. The radon itself can then break down, releasing radiation. If this gets into the lungs it can cause cancer. The gas can build up beneath floorboards in houses.

Radon accounts for about half of the radioactivity received on average by each person in the UK. Normally these doses are very tiny and pose no threat, but in cases where the gas builds up in a house it can cause a problem. Fortunately the problem is easy to tackle. A pump can be fitted to vent the gas safely into the atmosphere.

Cosmic radiation

A lot of radiation comes from space; this is called cosmic radiation. Most of it gets filtered out by the atmosphere, but some of it gets through and adds to the background radiation. Airline pilots and cabin crew spend a lot of time at 30 000 feet where the atmosphere is thinner, and so are exposed to a lot more cosmic radiation.

Everyday sources of radiation

Some of the background radiation comes from manufactured sources, such as nuclear power stations, X-ray machines and luminous watches. Most of us have a smoke alarm fitted in our homes. The most common type contains a weak radioactive source.

The pie chart below shows the percentage of background radiation that comes from different sources.

▲ Where radon gas is a problem, householders can buy a kit to test for it.

▲ This pump has been fitted to the side of a house to pump radon gas out from beneath the floor.

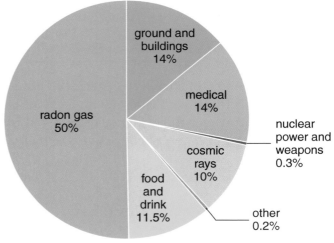

ground and buildings 14%

medical 14%

radon gas 50%

nuclear power and weapons 0.3%

cosmic rays 10%

food and drink 11.5%

other 0.2%

▲ Most of the radiation we receive comes from natural sources.

Risks and dangers

In spite of the relatively small amount of background radiation that comes from nuclear power stations, people are still very concerned about its use.

In 1986 there was a terrible accident at the Chernobyl nuclear power station, near Kiev in the Ukraine. While testing one of the reactors, a number of safety measures were ignored and a chain reaction became out of control. This caused an enormous explosion that blew off the reactor's steel and concrete lid. Thirty people were killed instantly and over 100 000 had to be evacuated from within a 20-mile radius of the reactor. Radioactive fallout was carried by winds to many neighbouring countries with disastrous ecological results. People living in the area were monitored to find out if their health had suffered in any way.

Nuclear power stations have some advantages compared with those that burn fossil fuel. For example, they produce less carbon dioxide. Carbon dioxide is a greenhouse gas, and so the less that we can put into the atmosphere the better.

▲ Decontaminating buildings after the Chernobyl disaster.

▼ Amount of carbon dioxide produced for each GWh of electricity from different fuels.

Amount of fuel needed to produce 1 GWh of electricity	Amount of carbon dioxide produced (tonnes)
400 tonnes of coal	850
300 tonnes of oil	800
150 tonnes of gas	400
0.003 tonnes of uranium	1

Think about what you will find out in this section

What are atoms made from?	Why do some atoms split up into pieces?
What are the different kinds of radioactivity?	What is meant by half-life?
How can we use radioactivity?	What are the dangers of radioactivity?
How can we protect ourselves from radioactivity?	

Storing up waste

British radioactive waste stockpile still growing

Britain has over 1000 m³ of high-level nuclear waste. This is enough to completely fill 20 average school science labs. For lower-level waste, there is 300 times as much. The waste is stored at more than 20 different sites around the country, and some of it will be radioactive for more than 200 000 years. As more nuclear power stations are shut down and taken out of service, this amount will rise – perhaps by as much as 50 times over the next 10 or 20 years. This represents a potential danger to the public and the Government is being urged to come up with a plan for dealing with this.

Rates of decay

Plutonium is a **radioactive** substance present in some nuclear waste. The plutonium atom is unstable – this means that it splits up to make a new nucleus, and at the same time gives out some radioactivity. We call this process **radioactive decay**.

The decay takes place at different rates, depending on the substance. Some substances take thousands of years to decay completely, but others take only fractions of a second.

Radioactive decay is unpredictable – we can never know for sure when a particular atom will decay, but we can estimate when half the atoms in a particular sample will have decayed. This is called the **half-life**.

Another way of defining half-life is to say that it is the time taken for the count rate to fall to half of its current value. The count rate is a measure of how radioactive a substance is. Count rate can be measured by a Geiger counter, a device that gives a click or records a number every time it detects some radiation.

Question

c What is the background count shown on the graph on the right?

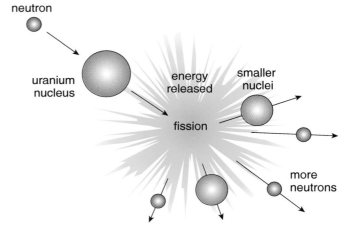

▲ Fission of a uranium atom.

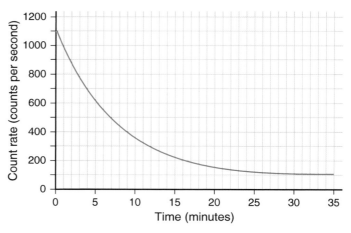

▲ The graph shows how the rate of decay for a radioactive material changes with time.

To find the half-life, we must first deduct the background count, then find the time interval for the activity to fall to half its initial value.

The graph on the right shows the same decay, but with the background count removed.

Question

d What is the half-life of the material shown in this graph?

This next graph shows the rate of decay for three different substances.

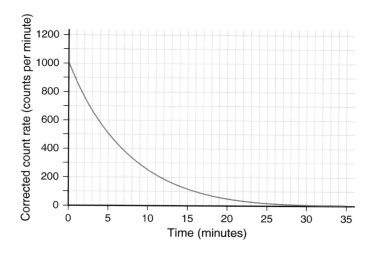

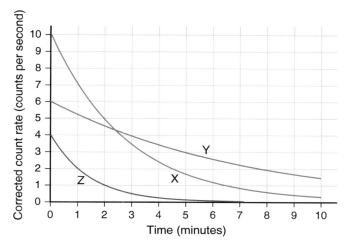

Remember that it doesn't matter how many atoms are present to start with – for any one substance, it always takes the same length of time for half of them to decay.

Atoms decay spontaneously – no matter what happens to them. Things such as temperature or pressure or chemical reactions do not affect the rate of decay.

We have to use the term 'half-life' because radioactive substances do not decay at a steady rate. The rate of decay is most rapid at the start when there are lots of atoms available for decay. The rate of decay gets slower and slower as time goes on. The rate of decay is proportional to the number of 'decayable' atoms present.

Look at the gradient of each decay curve. This tells you about the rate of decay – the gradient is much steeper at the start and gradually gets shallower.

Questions

e Which substance has the longest half-life?
f Which substance had the highest activity to start with?

Question

g Phosphorus-32 has a half-life of 14.7 days. If you started with 12 grams of this substance, how much would you have left after 58.8 days?

Key points

- Some nuclei are unstable, and give out radiation. These substances are said to be radioactive.
- Some substances give out radiation all the time, whatever is done to them.
- The half-life of a substance is the time it takes for half the atoms in a sample to decay.
- A half-life may be fractions of a second or thousands of years, depending on the substance.

Looking inside the atom

Scientists have developed a model of the atom as being rather like a miniature solar system, with a central nucleus orbited by electrons. But this is only a model to help us visualise an atom. If we could actually see an atom, it would probably not look like this.

▶ This is an atom of helium. The nucleus in the middle has two protons and two neutrons. Orbiting the nucleus are two electrons.

Atoms are very small, about 10^{-10} metres across (that's 0.000 000 000 1 metres).

Atoms that have the same number of **protons** but different numbers of **neutrons** are called **isotopes**.

Usually there are about the same number of neutrons in the nucleus as there are protons. Atoms that have more than the normal number of neutrons have nuclei that are unstable. These nuclei can break down into smaller pieces to release radioactivity. These materials are radioactive isotopes. They break down spontaneously without any encouragement. Some other isotopes can emit radioactivity if they are encouraged to do so. For example, some nuclei can be split if they have neutrons fired into them.

Uranium, for example, has two commonly occurring isotopes. One isotope of uranium has 143 neutrons and 92 protons. Another has 146 neutrons and 92 protons.

You can see that both isotopes have the same number of protons. You can also see that they have a different number of neutrons.

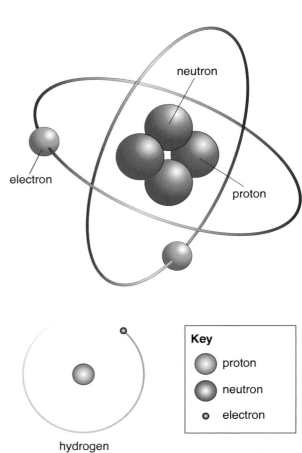

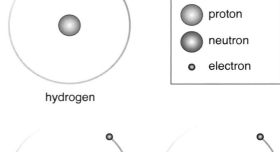

hydrogen

Key

○ proton

○ neutron

∘ electron

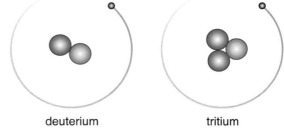

deuterium   tritium

▲ Three isotopes of hydrogen.

Questions

a How many more neutrons are there in the second isotope compared with the first isotope?

b Which one of these two isotopes of uranium is likely to be radioactive?

▲ A typical smoke detector.

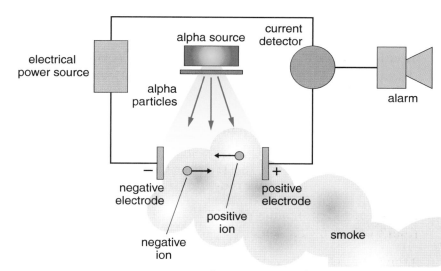

▲ The main parts inside a smoke detector.

Americium-241 is a radioactive metal. The americium gives off a type of radioactivity called **alpha particles**. A tiny amount of the metal is placed in a smoke detector. A 9 V battery is also needed to power a monitoring circuit. The alpha particles bombard the molecules of the air and help them to create a tiny electric current. If there is a fire, smoke particles get inside the detector and stop the electric current. As soon as the current falls, the monitoring circuit turns on an alarm.

Three types of radioactivity

Americium-241 gives out alpha particles, but there are two other types of radioactive decay: beta and gamma. (The names come from the first three letters of the Greek alphabet.) Different substances are chosen for different uses depending on the type of radioactivity they emit.

Many radioactive substances have medical applications. Thallium-201 can be used to diagnose heart disease. Thallium-201 is injected into the blood and binds strongly to heart muscle. The patient is then asked to exercise, which increases the blood flow. If an artery is constricted, some parts of the heart may not receive sufficient blood. Those parts will not take up as much thallium and therefore will show up as a dark spot on an image.

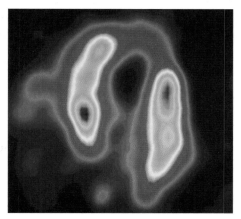

▲ This photo shows a heart scan.

Questions

All thallium atoms have 81 protons in the nucleus.
c How many neutrons are in the nucleus of the thallium-201 isotope?
d Some thallium atoms have only 100 neutrons. Choose the name of this type of thallium from the list below:
   A thallium-21   **B** thallium-8   **C** thallium-100   **D** thallium-181
e There are many different isotopes of thallium. Three of them are shown below:
   (i) thallium-180   (ii) thallium-200   (iii) thallium-205
   For each one, write down the number of protons and the number of neutrons in the nucleus.

Key points

- All atoms are made up of a small central nucleus surrounded by electrons.
- The nucleus of an atom is made up of neutrons and protons.

Becquerel discovers radioactivity

Henri Becquerel, a French scientist, was the person who first discovered radioactivity over 100 years ago. He had some uranium salts in a drawer in his desk, together with some photographic film. When the film was developed, it was fogged, although it had been tightly wrapped in light-proof paper. When Becquerel investigated this he found that some invisible radiation was able to get through the paper from the uranium salts.

Alpha, beta or gamma?

There are three types of radioactivity – alpha, beta and gamma.

Alpha particles consist of two neutrons and two protons (the same as a helium nucleus). They are absorbed in the air within a few centimetres and can be stopped completely by a thin sheet of paper. Although not very penetrating, alpha particles cause a large amount of **ionisation**. This is the process of making ions. Ions are atoms that have lost or gained electrons and so are electrically charged. Ionising radiation is very dangerous to living tissue.

Beta particles are more penetrating but can be stopped by thick cardboard or a thin metal sheet. They consist of electrons that have come from the break-up of the nucleus. They generally cause less ionisation than alpha particles. They are also deflected by electric and magnetic fields.

Gamma rays can travel easily through concrete walls or several centimetres of lead shield. They are electromagnetic waves, not particles, and are generally less ionising than alpha or beta. They are not deflected by electric or magnetic fields.

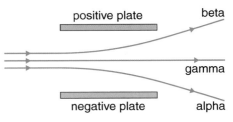

▲ The three different types of radiation have different properties, and behave differently when passing though electric or magnetic fields.

> **Question**
>
> **a** *The radioactive source in a domestic smoke detector emits alpha radiation. Why is this considered safe to use, even though alpha is the most ionising of the three types of radiation?*

Remember that whatever type of radioactivity you are dealing with, the best form of protection is to put as much distance between you and the source as possible. Partly this is because alpha and beta particles lose energy when they collide with molecules in the air. Partly it is because when any type of radiation spreads out, there will be less energy concentrated at any one point.

Radioactivity can be used to control the thickness of aluminium foil produced by machines.

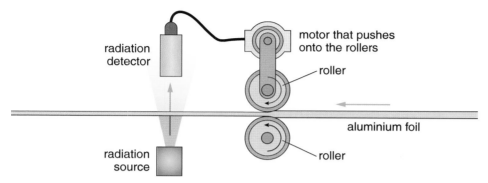

Radiation from the source passes through the foil to the detector. The thicker the foil, the less radiation gets through. The thinner the foil, the more radiation gets through. The detector senses this and sends signals to the motors to put more or less pressure on the rollers. If the foil is too thick, the rollers will push harder on the foil to make it thinner.

Gamma radiation can be used to sterilise medical equipment. Items such as artificial hip joints, surgical gowns and dressings are placed in sealed packets and passed beneath the source so that they are exposed to radiation. The radiation sterilises the materials by killing the bacteria.

Question

b Explain which source you would choose for this machine: alpha, beta or gamma.

Questions

c Why it is important that the gamma source for this type of application should have a long half-life?

d Irradiation is also used to sterilise food and cosmetics. Why do you think this is a better method than sterilising by boiling?

e Imagine that you are a vet investigating a health problem of an expensive racehorse. You need to inject a radioactive tracer, and can choose between polonium-210 (alpha) and cobalt-60 (gamma). Explain which you would choose and why.

Radioactive dating

Carbon has two isotopes – carbon-12 and carbon-14. Most of the carbon in the carbon dioxide in the air is carbon-12. A small fraction is the radioactive isotope carbon-14. Plants absorb carbon dioxide for photosynthesis, and so take in both isotopes of carbon. While the plant is still alive, the ratio of the two isotopes remains constant. Once the plant dies, the carbon-14 isotope decays, and so as time goes on there is less of it. By measuring the ratio of carbon-12 to carbon-14, scientists can estimate how long ago the plant was alive.

Question

f Carbon-14 has a half-life of 5730 years. Why is carbon dating not suitable for finding the age of the skeleton of a person who died about 100 years ago?

Key points

- The three type of radiation are alpha particles, beta particles and gamma rays.
- Alpha particles are very ionising, but not very penetrating.
- Beta particles produce less ionisation, but are more penetrating than alpha particles.
- Gamma rays are very penetrating. They can only be stopped by several centimetres of lead or several metres of concrete.

How dangerous is radioactivity?

All radioactivity is potentially dangerous, but how dangerous it is depends on:

- the type of radiation (alpha, beta or gamma)
- the intensity (strength) of the radiation.

Gamma radiation

At low intensities gamma radiation can damage cells, but at high intensities it kills cells. Gamma radiation can be used to kill cancer cells by focusing a beam of gamma rays onto them.

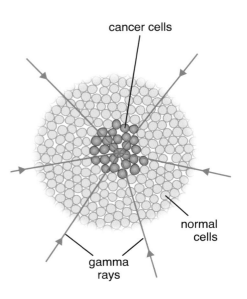

▲ The intensity is greatest at about 5 mm below the surface. The normal cells receive a much lower dose.

> **Question**
>
> **a** *Explain why the normal cells receive a lower dose than the cancer cell.*

X-rays

X-rays are very helpful in showing doctors what is going on inside our bodies, but they have to be used with care. Too much exposure increases the risk of cancer. The table below shows how the level of risk is related to exposure.

Type of X-ray	Equivalent period of background radiation	Extra lifetime risk of cancer in addition to the 1 in 3 chance we all have of getting cancer
chest or teeth X-ray	a few days	less than 1 in 1 000 000
head X-ray	a few weeks	between 1 in 1 000 000 and 1 in 100 000
breast (mammography)	a few months to a year	between 1 in 100 000 and 1 in 10 000
stomach (barium meal)	a few years	between 1 in 10 000 and 1 in 1 000

To put the risks into perspective, a 4-hour plane flight carries about the same extra risk as a chest X-ray.

> **Questions**
>
> **b** *Which type of X-ray carries the smallest extra risk?*
> **c** *The types of X-ray treatments that carry the highest extra risk are normally only carried out on people who are seriously ill. What do you think is the reason for this?*
> **d** *Why are pregnant women advised not to have a stomach X-ray?*

Hiroshima

We now know quite a lot about the short-term effects that radiation has on our bodies, but we don't yet know much about the long-term effects.

On 6 August 1945 an atomic bomb was dropped on the Japanese city of Hiroshima. Many thousands of people died instantly, and thousands more were affected by the radiation. Sixty years later, scientists are still studying the effects that the radiation has had on the survivors and their descendants.

Professor Henji Kamiya of Hiroshima University said, 'This is the only place in the world where we can research the long-term effects of radiation on the human body.' This research has helped scientists to produce guidelines for safe exposure to radiation. These guidelines have helped to protect thousands of workers in the nuclear industry.

Professor Kamiya says that when people were exposed to the radiation, it damaged their genes. In many cases, their genes repaired themselves and these people survived. But in some cases, the repair was not complete and now, 60 years later, these people have a higher risk of developing cancer. The greatest risk is to those who were young children when they were exposed to the radiation.

Dealing with waste

The more that we use nuclear fuels and radioactive materials, the more radioactive waste builds up. Some of this can remain a danger for thousands of years. Society must decide how to deal with the waste.

Suggested method	Advantage	Disadvantage
Put it on a spaceship and fire it into the Sun.		
Put it into thick metal tanks.		
Bury it at the bottom of a disused coalmine.		
Vitrification – that is turning it into a glass-like material.		

Nobody has yet come up with the perfect solution. What has to be done is to consider carefully the advantages and disadvantages of using such materials, and then try to make a rational decision based upon the best scientific evidence available.

Key point

● It is important to evaluate the benefits, drawbacks and risks of scientific and technological developments. Decisions about science and technology are likely to have social, economic and environmental effects, and may raise ethical issues.

Ever since the dawn of civilisation, people have gazed into space and wondered how the Universe is put together and how it all started. In modern times, we have begun to find some of the answers to these questions.

How did our Universe begin?

In the twentieth century there were two main theories put forward to explain the origin of the Universe. One, produced by Professor Fred Hoyle, was called the 'steady state' theory. This said that although matter seemed to be disappearing, it was continually being replaced.

The other theory was the 'big bang' theory. This stated that all the matter in the Universe was originally at one point. A tremendous explosion occurred, and ever since the material has been travelling outwards.

Modern scientific instruments have allowed us to work out the structure of our solar system with its nine planets revolving around the Sun. We now know that our Sun is just one of millions of stars that make up our galaxy (the Milky Way); and that there are millions of such galaxies in the Universe.

When you look at the stars, you are actually looking back in time. Even at the incredibly fast speed that light travels, it takes about 8 minutes to reach us from the Sun, and about 4 years to reach us from the next nearest star. Light from some of the stars has taken many millions of years to reach us.

But the big questions are – how did it all start and how is it changing now?

▲ The Crab Nebula is the remnant of a huge explosion called a supernova. Although this happened over 6000 years ago, it was not seen on Earth until 1054. At that time it was bright enough to be seen in the daytime, as bright as 400 million Suns.

▶ The Earth from space.

▲ Photo of CS31082-001 taken by the Hubble telescope.

Scientists think that the Universe is about 15 billion (15 000 000 000) years old. One way that they have arrived at this figure is by studying an ancient star, coded CS31082-001.

By analysing the light from this ancient star, scientists have found traces of thorium-232. By comparing the amount of thorium detected with present-day amounts, the age of the Universe can be estimated. Thorium-232 has a half-life of about 14 billion years. Scientists have been able to confirm these results by also analysing the amount of uranium-238, which has a half-life of about 4.5 billion years.

By studying the light and other types of radiation from distant galaxies, we can work out what the Universe must have been like at the very beginning. It may have started as a primordial 'soup' of incredibly dense material and energy.

▲ Special telescopes, such as the Hubble telescope, have been launched into space to collect information that would be impossible to collect on Earth.

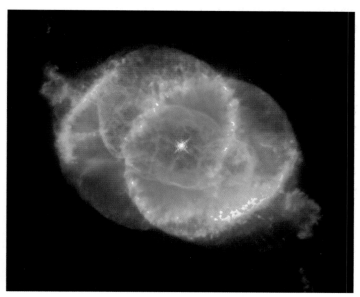

▲ Photos taken from space are clearer – the radiation does not have to travel through the dust and gases in the Earth's atmosphere.

Think about what you will find out in this section

How do scientists use telescopes of different sorts to observe the Universe?	How can electromagnetic waves be used to study the Universe?
What is the red-shift and why is it important?	What sort of radiation do stars give out?
Is the Universe expanding?	How do we know the age of the Universe?

The first telescopes

Ancient peoples observed the skies using their eyes only. They were able to predict the movements of comets and other celestial bodies, but there was a limit to the amount they could see until the development of telescopes in the last few hundred years. The first telescopes were those using the visible part of the electromagnetic spectrum – in other words, light.

In the seventeenth century, Galileo used a refracting telescope to observe four of Jupiter's moons. This enabled him to confirm an earlier theory of Copernicus, which stated that the Earth and other planets revolved around the Sun.

A refracting telescope uses lenses to focus the light into an image. One of the problems with lenses is that, as the light passes through them, some of it is absorbed. Also, unless the lenses are shaped perfectly, they can make the image distorted. This prompted Sir Isaac Newton, a few years after Galileo, to develop a new kind of telescope called a reflecting telescope. This used a concave mirror in addition to a lens to focus light into an image.

▲ A refracting telescope.

Question

a Why do reflecting telescopes give better images than refracting telescopes?

Modern telescopes

The problem with all telescopes sited on the Earth is that the atmosphere tends to get in the way and reduces the amount of radiation reaching the telescope. That is why in 1990 NASA launched the Hubble telescope. This telescope was mounted on a satellite orbiting the Earth above the atmosphere.

Optical telescopes on Earth cannot be used during the day, as there is too much light from the Sun. Cloud cover can also affect their images.

▲ The Mount Palomar reflecting telescopes.

Not all telescopes use visible light to investigate the Universe. This is because stars (including the Sun) give off radiation throughout the entire electromagnetic spectrum. Hubble, for example, can detect ultra violet and infra red radiation, as well as visible light.

X-ray and gamma ray telescopes have also been built. One of the big advantages of these is that X-rays and gamma rays have very short wavelengths. This means that the images can provide greater detail.

In November 2004 'Swift' was launched. This is a satellite fitted with three different types of telescope: gamma, X-ray and UV/optical. Its mission is to explore the origins of the Universe by detecting gamma ray bursts.

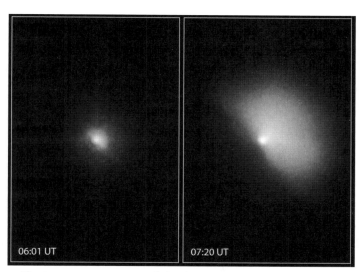

▲ The Deep Impact spacecraft fired a massive projectile straight into a comet to find out what it was made of. This picture of the impact was taken with the Hubble telescope.

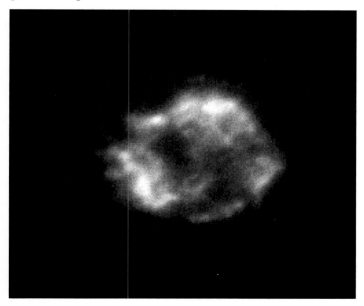

▲ The explosion of a massive star about 13 billion years ago.

This photograph shows the most distant object we have yet seen in the Universe.

The red-shift

Astronomers discovered that the Universe appears to be expanding. They used the idea of **red-shift** in developing this theory.

You might have noticed that the siren of an emergency vehicle changes in pitch as it passes you – it seems to be higher when coming towards you, and lower pitched when moving away. A change in pitch results from a change in frequency, and the effect applies to all sorts of waves, electromagnetic as well as sound waves.

Remember that the frequency of a wave means how many cycles reach you every second. With sound waves, the higher the frequency the higher the pitch.

If you are standing still in front of a source of waves, then the frequency with which the waves reach you is constant. If it's a sound, the pitch stays the same; if it's a light source, the colour stays the same.

If the source of the waves is coming towards you, then the cycles reach you sooner than they would otherwise. In other words, the frequency appears to have increased. This means that a sound wave would have a higher pitch or a light source would appear to be more blue.

If the source of the waves is moving away from you, then the waves reach you later. In other words, the frequency appears to have decreased. This means that a sound wave would have a lower pitch or a light source would appear to be more red.

You can easily notice the effect with sound, but you do not normally notice the effect with light. This is because light waves have such a small wavelength that the source of light has to be moving very fast for it to be noticeable. But it is this effect on the light from stars that astronomers refer to as the red-shift.

stationary
source

▲ The waves reach you at a constant frequency.

source moving
towards observer

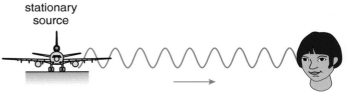

▲ The frequency seems higher if the wave source is coming towards you.

source moving
away from observer

▲ The frequency seems lower if the wave source is moving away from you.

Question

a How would the wavelength appear to change if the wave source was moving away from you?

The first diagram shows the spectrum of light from the Sun – our closest star. Various elements present in the Sun cause the black lines in it.

▶ Spectrum formed by the Sun.

The second diagram shows the spectrum for a much more distant star. Notice how the black spectral lines have been shifted to the right (red end) of the spectrum.

▶ Spectrum formed by a distant star.

Astronomers have concluded that the stars are therefore moving away from us. They have also found out that the further away the stars are from us, the faster they seem to be moving.

Questions

b The table on the right shows the names of three stars and their distances from us.
Which star would you expect to show: (i) the smallest red-shift; (ii) the largest red-shift? Explain your choices.

c The exploding star detected by the Swift satellite in 2005 had the largest amount of red-shift yet detected. What does this tell you about this star?

Name of star	Distance from Earth in light years
Alpha Centauri	4.27
Deneb	1600
Sirius	8.64

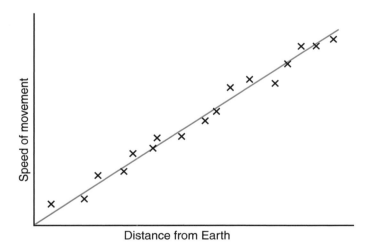

Distance from Earth

Question

d The graph shows the speed at which stars are moving away from us, plotted against distance. What does this graph tell you about how these two quantities are related?

Key points

● If a wave source is moving, a stationary observer will observe a change in wavelength and frequency.
● This effect causes a red-shift in light from distant galaxies.
● The further away a galaxy is, the bigger the red-shift.

The great debate

Throughout the nineteenth century a great debate raged concerning nebulae – are they collections of stars outside our galaxy (the Milky Way) or clouds of matter inside it?

In the 1890s Henrietta Leavitt made a study of some stars that vary in brightness over a short period of time. She called these **variable stars**. The most famous is called Delta Cephei. This star reaches maximum brightness in about one day and then takes a further four days to reduce to its minimum brightness. Since then many variable stars have been discovered, and they are now known as Cepheid variables.

Henrietta Leavitt found that the frequency of the variation of brightness was related to how bright the star was. In the 1920s Edwin Hubble was able to use this to work out the distance to a Cepheid variable in the Andromeda nebula. He found that it was about nine times further away than the diameter of our galaxy.

Cepheid variables are now used like 'yardsticks' to measure distances in the Universe.

▲ Henrietta Leavitt.

Is the Universe changing?

In the twentieth century, astronomers became occupied with questions about the origins of the Universe. Two main theories emerged that dealt with how the Universe might be changing – the steady state theory and the big bang theory.

The big bang

Einstein's theory of relativity had predicted that the Universe should be expanding, and in 1912 an American scientist called Vesto Slipher noticed a red-shift in the spectra of light from many galaxies. A red-shift would mean that these galaxies are moving away from us. Later, Edwin Hubble was able to compare the amount of red-shift with the distance he had measured to some of these galaxies, and was able to show that the further away a galaxy was, the faster it appeared to be moving.

This led other scientists to develop what became known as the **big bang theory**. If the Universe is expanding, there must have been some time at which all the matter in the Universe was compressed into a single point (some scientists reckon it was about the size of a pea). This incredibly dense and incredibly small lump of matter exploded, and the Universe has been expanding ever since. By measuring the distance away of a galaxy, and knowing the speed it is moving, we can work out how long it has been moving for. According to this theory, the Universe is about 14 billion years old.

▲ Edwin Hubble.

Question

a What two pieces of information do we need to work out how long a galaxy has been moving for?

The steady state theory

Other scientists did not like the idea that the Universe had been created at some point in time – they believed that it must have always existed. Sir Fred Hoyle developed the **steady state theory**, which states that as the Universe expands and the galaxies get further apart, new galaxies are being formed. This would keep the density of the Universe constant, or in a steady state.

Which theory is correct?

A good scientific theory should be able to make predictions. We can then look for some evidence to see if these predictions are correct.

- The big bang theory states that the Universe was once tiny, with a lot of energy packed into it. As the matter and energy spread out, the temperature would have dropped and we should be able to detect the radiation from the early beginnings of the Universe. In 1965 this was detected, and is now known as **cosmic microwave background radiation**.

- The other prediction of the big bang theory is that, in the first couple of minutes after the big bang, conditions would be just right to produce hydrogen and helium in the ratio of about 4 to 1. This is exactly what we find today when we look at the spectra of the most distant stars. Light from these stars has been travelling for the longest time, and so they tell us what conditions were like when these stars were first made.

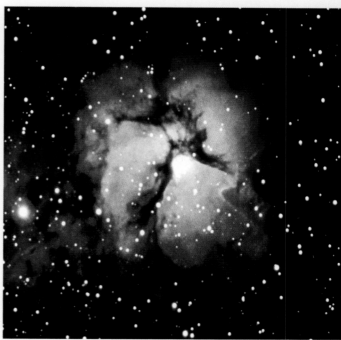

▲ Stars are forming in the red and blue glowing gases of the Lagoon Nebula.

Question

b Do you think that scientists have now proved that the big bang theory is correct? Explain your answer.

What created the Universe in the first place?

This is one of those questions that science will probably never be able to answer.

Not all questions can be answered by scientists. Scientists observe and collect data and often construct models to describe the things they have seen. Their ideas may be developed into a hypothesis or a theory, but remember – no amount of evidence can *prove* that a theory is correct. Tomorrow, somebody may discover a single piece of evidence that proves that it is wrong.

Key points

- Uncertainties in scientific knowledge and ideas change over time.
- There are some questions that science cannot currently answer and some that science cannot address.

1 The diagram shows a water wave.

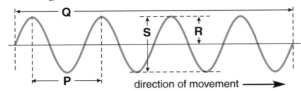

a Which letter on the diagram shows
   i the wavelength? *(1 mark)*
   ii the amplitude? *(1 mark)*

b What is it that travels in the direction labelled 'direction of movement'? *(1 mark)*

c Copy the drawing of the wave and underneath sketch another wave that has a higher frequency than the one shown. *(1 mark)*

2 The table below shows some data for three different kinds of electromagnetic wave.

Type of wave	Frequency	Wavelength
radio	100 MHz	
microwave		1 cm
light		5×10^{-7} m

a At what speed do all electromagnetic waves travel in a vacuum? *(1 mark)*

b Copy the table and use the wave formula to complete the empty boxes. *(3 marks)*

c If these waves are directed towards a sheet of glass, not all of the energy of the waves will pass through.
   i Which word could be used to refer to the energy that passes through?
      A translated   **B** transmitted
      C transmuted   **D** transported
   ii State **two** things that could happen to the energy that does not pass through the glass. *(2 marks)*

3 Terahertz waves can be used at airports to scan travellers. The results will not be shown as an image on a screen, but will be used to trigger an alarm if anything dangerous is suspected.

a Suggest **one** advantage of being able to see the contents of the suitcase on a screen. *(1 mark)*

b Suggest **one** advantage of not needing an operator to continually watch a screen. *(1 mark)*

4

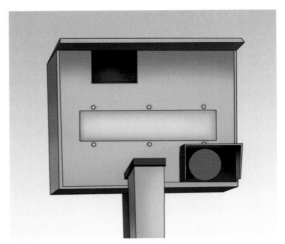

▲ This device uses radar to measure the speed of cars.

The camera inside the box takes two pictures of a car a short distance apart when triggered by the radar mechanism inside. The radar mechanism uses microwaves of wavelength 0.000 125 m. What is their frequency?
   A 2.4×10^{12} Hz
   B 3.75×10^4 Hz
   C 3×10^8 Hz
   D 1.25×10^4 Hz

5

▲ These X-ray machines were common in shoe shops in the 1950s.

In the 1950s, most shoe shops had X-ray machines for checking that children's shoes fitted properly. The child, the shop assistant and the parent could all look into the machine to see the child's foot inside the shoe.

a Explain how the X-rays were able to show whether the shoes fitted properly. *(2 marks)*

b Why would the machine not have worked if it had used light rays instead of X-rays? *(1 mark)*

c Why do you think that these machines are no longer used? *(1 mark)*

d X-ray machines are still used in hospitals, but under controlled conditions.

   i State **one** precaution that is taken to ensure that the X-ray machine operator does not suffer from over-exposure to X-rays. *(1 mark)*

   ii State **one** precaution that is taken to ensure that the patient does not suffer from over-exposure to X-rays. *(1 mark)*

6 Radon is a radioactive gas. It has a half-life of 4 days and it emits alpha particles when it decays.

a Why does the fact that radon is a gas make it particularly dangerous?

   A When breathed in, alpha particles will get inside the lungs.

   B Unlike other radioactivity, it will be impossible to see.

   C Because it is a gas, it has very low density.

   D Radioactive gases have much longer half-lives than liquids or solids.

b What is an alpha particle?

   A an electron

   B a proton

   C two protons and two neutrons

   D two protons and two electrons

c What is meant by the term half-life?

   A Half the time an atom exists before it decays.

   B Half the time that it takes for all the atoms to decay.

   C The time it takes for an atom to half decay.

   D The time it takes for half of the atoms to decay.

d A sample of radon contains 120 000 atoms. How many might you expect to remain after 12 days?

   A 10 000   **B** 15 000

   C 30 000   **D** 40 000

7 A scientist measured the decay of a sample of barium-143 for a period of 1 minute.

The following results were obtained.

Time in seconds	0	10	20	30	40	50	60
Count rate (counts per second)	4000	2225	1025	700	400	250	130

a Plot the data onto a sheet of graph paper. Remember to choose a suitable scale and to label the axes. *(3 marks)*

b Draw a best-fit line on your graph. *(1 mark)*

c Use your graph to calculate the half-life of barium-143. Show your workings on your graph. *(2 marks)*

8 Carbon-14 has a half-life of 5 700 years. In living animals, the proportion of carbon-14 in their bones remains constant as it is continually being replaced. When the animal dies, the carbon-14 continues to decay but is no longer replaced. The proportion of carbon-14 therefore gets less.

A living human was found to have 96 units of carbon-14 in one of the leg bones. An identical bone from an ancient burial site was found to have 6 units.

a Estimate the age of the ancient bone. Show how you obtained your answer. *(2 marks)*

b Why would this method not be suitable for determining the age of a skeleton from the last century? *(1 mark)*

9 The diagram shows two sources emitting radiation.

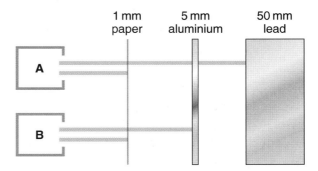

What **two** types of radiation are emitted by

a source A? *(1 mark)*

b source B? *(1 mark)*

10 The diagram shows part of a system used in a factory to check whether plastic bottles have been fully filled. The radioactive source contains a beta emitter. The sensor detects the amount of radiation received and sends a signal to the control unit.

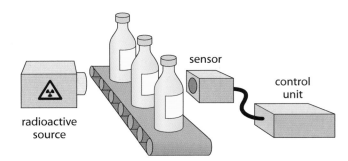

a Explain how you think the system would work. *(2 marks)*

b Explain why you think the source contains a beta emitter rather than an alpha or a gamma emitter. *(3 marks)*

c Why would this system not work for checking whether metal cans had been properly filled? *(1 mark)*

11

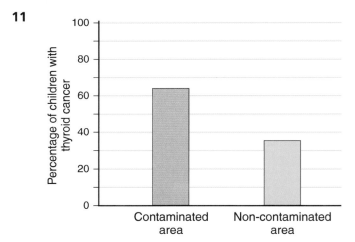

▲ The bar chart shows the percentage of children who developed thyroid cancer in the years following the explosion at Chernobyl.

a Does this data **prove** that the increased incidence of thyroid cancer was caused by the Chernobyl disaster, or does it simply suggest a **link** between the two?
Explain you answer. *(1 mark)*

b The explosion at Chernobyl was reported as causing 'disastrous ecological results'. Suggest what these might be, other than the effect on people's health. *(1 mark)*

c Why are people who live near to or work at nuclear power stations more at risk than those who live or work further away? *(1 mark)*

d Other than accidents, what other dangers are associated with nuclear power stations? *(1 mark)*

12 Scientists have found traces of thorium-232 in an ancient star. This has helped them to estimate the age of the Universe as about 15 billion years, and they have confirmed this by analysis of uranium-238 in the same star. Thorium-232 has a half-life of about 14 billion years, and uranium-238 has a half-life of about 4.5 billion years.

a If the scientists conclusions are correct, about how much of the original amount of thorium would be left in this star now? *(1 mark)*

b Why is it important for the scientists to carry out a second investigation using uranium instead of thorium? *(1 mark)*

c Why is the estimate of the age of the Universe likely to be more accurate using data from uranium rather than thorium? *(1 mark)*

13 Astronomers have for many years been trying to discover the origins and development of the Universe.

a What were the **two** main theories that were proposed during the twentieth century to explain the origins of the Universe? *(2 marks)*

b Discovery of the red-shift was important in helping to decide which of these two theories was the most likely explanation.
i What is meant by the term 'red-shift'? *(2 marks)*
ii What does the red-shift tell us about distant stars? *(1 mark)*
iii Which of the two theories does the red-shift evidence support? *(1 mark)*
iv According to this theory, what is the approximate age of the Universe? *(1 mark)*

14 Read this article about radon gas, and then answer the questions that follow.

The Dangers of Radon Gas

from our Science Correspondent

Many people, in different parts of the UK, are becoming increasingly worried about the effects of radon gas. The gas, which is invisible and odourless, is produced by the radioactive decay of materials naturally occurring in certain rocks. The gas rises through cracks and faults in the Earth's crusts and can collect in spaces under floors or even in attics. This is more of a problem in modern houses that are well insulated and draught proofed.

Radon is part of the background radiation and accounts for about half of all the radiation that we receive. Normally, the level of radiation that we receive from this is very small and causes no problem. When the gas becomes trapped in our homes, the levels can becomes dangerously high. It has been estimated that radon in our homes is responsible for about 1000 cancer deaths each year. This represents about 1% of all cancer deaths per year.

Householders can help themselves in many ways, but the first thing to do is to have your house checked to find out if you have dangerously high levels of radon gas.

a Give **one** reason why people should be worried about the effects of radon gas.

(1 mark)

b Suggest **one** reason why some parts of the UK have a major problem with radon gas while other parts of the UK are not affected.

(1 mark)

c Explain how the radon gas is able to collect in spaces under the floor or in attics. *(2 marks)*

d Why is the accumulation of radon gas more of a problem in modern houses than it is in older houses? *(1 mark)*

e What is meant by the term 'background radiation'? *(1 mark)*

f Radon accounts for about half of the background radiation. Suggest **one** source of the remaining half. *(1 mark)*

g Why is radon gas more dangerous when it becomes trapped in our homes? *(1 mark)*

h Suggest **one** way in which radioactivity in the home could be detected. *(1 mark)*

i Suggest **one** way in which a householder could reduce the dangers from radon gas.

(1 mark)

Glossary

absorb To take in radiation.

absorbed A wave loses energy when travelling through a material; this energy is absorbed by the material.

acid rain Rain that has been acidified by pollutants such as sulfur dioxide.

adaptations A feature or features that make a structure or organism more suitable for its function.

addicted Dependent on a drug.

addition polymerisation Polymerisation that occurs when alkene monomers are made to combine by opening their double bond; no other chemicals are involved in the main reaction.

alkane A hydrocarbon which only has single C–C or C–H bonds, e.g. ethane C_2H_6.

alkene A hydrocarbon with one (or more) C=C double bonds, e.g. ethene C_2H_4.

alloy Carefully blended metal mixture with specific properties.

alpha particle Two protons and two neutrons – the same as a helium nucleus.

amplitude The height of a wave; its maximum disturbance.

analogue signal An analogue signal has a shape which corresponds to the shape of the signal being carried; as opposed to a digital signal.

antibiotics Chemicals produced by microbes, used to destroy bacteria in the body.

antibodies Substances produced when white blood cells detect the presence of a particular antigen.

antitoxins Substances produced by white blood cells to neutralise poisons produced by microbes.

arthritis A painful inflammation of the joints.

asexual reproduction Reproduction that does not involve the formation of gametes.

atom The smallest part of an element that still has the properties of that element.

background radiation We are exposed to background radiation all the time, from radioactive substances around us and from cosmic rays.

bacteria A type of microbe; some bacteria are useful, while others cause disease.

balanced diet A diet made up of a variety of different foods to provide the energy and all the nutrients needed to stay healthy.

beta particle An electron emitted from the nucleus of an atom during radioactive decay.

big bang theory The theory that the Universe was created in a huge explosion.

biodegradable Something that can be broken down easily by natural, biological processes.

biodiesel A renewable fuel made from vegetable oil that can be used in place of diesel.

carbon monoxide Poisonous gas produced by incomplete combustion of carbon compounds.

carcinogens Substances that produce cancer.

cartilage A smooth tissue that covers the ends of bones at joints and so allows easy movement.

cement A powder which sets hard when mixed with water. It is made by heating limestone with clay.

central nervous system The brain and spinal cord.

characteristics Distinguishing features.

chemical bonds Bonds that form between atoms during chemical reactions that hold molecules and other compounds together.

cholesterol A fatty substance made in the liver.

chromatography A way to separate different dyes.

chromosomes Long threads containing many genes which are found in the nucleus of a cell.

clinical trial Set of tests on people that provide data on the effectiveness of a drug.

clones Genetically identical organisms.

concrete A building material made by mixing cement, sand and gravel with water; it sets to become a very hard 'artificial rock'.

conduction Transfer of thermal energy by transfer of vibration from particles to their neighbours.

conductor A substance that is good at conducting thermal energy.

continental drift The exceedingly slow movement of the continents across the surface of the Earth.

contraceptive pill A pill containing hormones that prevent an egg being released.

convection Transfer of thermal energy in a gas or liquid by the movement of particles from place to place. Hotter, less dense regions float; cooler, denser regions sink.

convection current The circulating currents that form in a gas or liquid (including molten rock) when they are heated.

correlation A mutual relationship of interdependence between two or more variables.

cosmic microwave background radiation Radiation from the early beginnings of the Universe.

cost-effective A measure is cost-effective if it saves more money than it costs.

cracking The process by which long-chain hydrocarbons are broken up into shorter and more useful hydrocarbons.

crust The thin, hard and brittle outer layer of the Earth.

cycle A series of processes that always occur in the same order.

deficiency The lack of a substance in the diet.

diabetes Disorder where the pancreas fails to control glucose concentration.

digital signal A digital signal carries information in the form of a string of on and off pulses; as opposed to an analogue signal.

effective A measure is effective if it has a big effect. An energy-saving measure is more effective the more money it saves.

effector An organ or cell that brings about a response to a stimulus.

efficiency The proportion of the energy supplied to a device that is transformed usefully rather than wasted.

efficient The higher the efficiency of a device, the more efficient it is.

egg The female sex cell (gamete).

electrolysis The tearing apart of a molten (or dissolved) ionic compound using electricity.

electromagnetic (EM) spectrum All types of electromagnetic radiation, arranged in order according to their wavelengths and frequencies.

electromagnetic wave A form of energy that is transferred as fast-moving waves. Electromagnetic waves include light and thermal radiation and can travel through a vacuum.

electron A small particle with tiny mass and a single negative charge.

embryo transplants Transferring embryos from one organism and implanting them into another uterus (womb).

emit To give out radiation.

emulsifier A chemical that helps to stop an emulsion from separating.

emulsion A mixture of tiny droplets of oil in water (or water in oil).

epidemic When a disease spreads rapidly across a country.

ethanol The 'alcohol' in alcoholic drinks made by fermenting sugar. It may also be used as a fuel.

faeces Waste matter remaining after food has been digested, which is discharged from the body.

fossil Preserved remains of plants and animals that have not decayed.

fossil fuel A fuel such as coal, oil or gas, formed over millions of years from the remains of living things.

fossil record Evidence for evolution obtained from the remains of plants and animals.

fractional distillation A form of distillation where only a partial separation of the liquids in a mixture is obtained.

fractions The different liquids produced from a complex mixture such as crude oil by fractional distillation.

frequency The number of waves per second; measured in hertz (Hz).

gametes Specialised sex cells involved in sexual reproduction in plants and animals.

gamma rays The part of the electromagnetic spectrum of waves that have the shortest wavelength and highest energy.

gel A material with a grid-like structure that can trap water.

generator A device that produces electricity when it spins. Power stations contain generators.

genes Part of a chromosome which controls an inherited characteristic.

genetic modification Modification of the genetic material of an organism (also called genetic engineering).

geothermal Using steam heated by hot underground rocks to make electricity.

glands Small organs controlling bodily functions by chemical means.

global dimming Sunlight reaching the Earth is weakened due to atmospheric pollution.

global warming Increased proportions of greenhouse gases such as carbon dioxide are causing the average temperature at the surface of the Earth to rise.

GM crops Genetically modified crops. These are crop plants that have had new genes added from another species.

greenhouse effect Gases such as carbon dioxide help to trap heat energy in the atmosphere.

greenhouse gas Gases such as carbon dioxide that help to trap heat energy in the atmosphere.

half-life The average time taken for half the atoms in a sample of a radioactive substance to decay.

HDLs High-density lipoproteins which carry cholesterol.

herbicides Chemicals used to kill weeds.

high blood pressure A higher than average value of pressure in arteries; associated with an increased risk of heart attacks and strokes.

hormones A chemical, produced by one part of an organism, that controls a process in another part of the organism.

hydrocarbon Compounds made of carbon and hydrogen atoms only.

hydroelectric Using water flowing down a hill to make electricity.

hydrogels Strong gels that can be used for contact lenses.

hydrogenation A chemical reaction where a hydrogen molecule joins with another compound, e.g. the hydrogenation of an unsaturated oil to make saturated fat.

hydrolysis A chemical reaction where a water molecule joins with another compound, e.g. the hydrolysis of ethene to make ethanol.

immune Protected against disease by the production of antibodies.

immunisation Injecting or swallowing vaccines to develop immunity.

immunised Given a vaccine containing dead or inactive pathogens, which stimulates the immune system to produce antibodies and memory cells.

immunity Protected against disease by the production of antibodies.

impulses Form in which information is transmitted by nerve cells.

infra red A type of electromagnetic radiation that transfers thermal energy; it has wavelengths just longer than visible light.

infra red radiation Energy spreading out from a hot object in the form of electromagnetic waves.

ingest Take food into the body.

inherited Characteristic transmitted from parents to offspring via gametes (eggs and sperm).

inherited characteristics Features that are passed from parents to their offspring by gametes (eggs and sperm).

insecticide Chemical used to kill insects.

insulator A substance that is bad at conducting thermal energy.

in vitro **fertilisation (IVF)** Fertilisation of an egg outside the body of a female by the addition of sperm, as a means of producing an embryo.

ionisation An ionised atom or molecule is electrically charged because it has lost or gained electrons.

ions Charged particles.

isotope Atoms of an element come in different forms, depending on the number of neutrons they have in their nuclei.

Kyoto treaty A treaty established in 1997, under the United Nations, which requires its signatories to reduce emissions of all greenhouse gases.

lattice The regular arrangement of particles, e.g. in a crystal.

LDLs Low-density lipoproteins which carry cholesterol.

lipoprotein Proteins that are combined with fats or other lipids.

malnourished Suffering from inadequate nutrition.

mantle The middle, soft, rocky layer of the Earth which can move very slowly.

menstrual cycle The monthly cycle of changes in a woman's reproductive system, controlled by hormones.

metabolic rate A measure of the energy used by an animal in a given time period.

microorganism An organism so small it can only be seen through a microscope.

microwaves Part of the electromagnetic spectrum of waves that have wavelengths from about 10 cm to $\frac{1}{10}$ of a millimetre.

monomer The small molecules that are joined up to form a polymer.

mortar A paste made from slaked lime and water that was once used to stick bricks together.

motor neurone Nerve cell that carries information to an effector organ, such as a skeletal muscle.

MRSA A type of bacteria resistant to antibiotics (methicillin resistant *Staphylococcus aureus*).

mutation A natural change in a gene which may result in different characteristics.

National Grid The system of power stations, cables and transformers that transfer electricity all over the country.

nerves Bundle of nerve cells.

neurones A cell specialised to transmit electrical nerve impulses and so carry information from one part of the body to another.

neutron A subatomic particle with no electric charge and a relative mass of 1.

noble gas A gas from Group 0 of the periodic table, e.g. helium, argon, neon.

non-renewable Once used it cannot be replaced.

nuclear fission The splitting of radioactive atoms. Nuclear fission releases energy.

nucleus The central part of the atom containing the proton(s) and, for all except hydrogen, the neutrons; it contains most of the mass of the atom.

obese Very fat or very overweight.

ore A natural compound of a metal from which the metal can be extracted.

oxidation Reaction with oxygen, e.g. iron is oxidised when iron oxide forms during rusting. Oxidation may also be defined as the loss of electrons.

painkillers Drug that reduces pain.

pandemic A pandemic disease is one which is spread rapidly across many countries.

penicillin Antibiotic produced by the mould *Penicillium*.

pesticides Chemicals that kill pests such as insects.

plate tectonics Theory used to explain continental drift.

polymerisation The chemical process that joins monomers together to make a polymer.

polymers Very long-chained molecules made by joining lots of small molecules together.

power The rate at which energy is transformed.

power station A factory for producing electricity.

proton A subatomic particle with a single positive charge and a relative mass of 1.

quicklime Calcium oxide (CaO), a strong alkali formed by heating limestone.

radiation Energy spreading out as waves from a source (e.g. infra red or light energy), or carried by particles (e.g. from a radioactive substance). Radiation in the form of electromagnetic waves can transfer energy through a vacuum.

radio waves Part of the electromagnetic spectrum of waves that have the longest wavelength.

radioactive A radioactive material contains some atoms whose nuclei are unstable; these may spontaneously break down, giving out radiation.

radioactive decay When a radioactive atom decays, it emits radiation and becomes a different type of atom.

receptors Organs or cells that are sensitive to external stimuli.

recycle To re-use materials over and over again.

red-shift The change in wavelength of light from a distant star; it looks redder because it is receding.

reduction The removal of oxygen from a compound, e.g. iron oxide is reduced to iron.

reflected When a wave bounces off a surface it is reflected.

reflex action Rapid involuntary response to a particular stimulus.

relay neurone A neurone that carries information from a sensory nerve cell to a motor nerve cell.

reliability The proportion of the time that a device is working. Some types of power station have greater reliability than others because they can work more of the time.

renewable An energy source that will not run out.

resistance A bacterium that has antibiotic resistance can't be destroyed by the action of antibiotics.

respiration A series of reactions in which living organisms release energy from food.

saturated A carbon-chain molecule that only has single bonds between the carbon atoms.

sense organs Organs of the body which are sensitive to external stimuli.

sensory neurone A nerve cell which carries information to the brain or spinal cord.

sexual reproduction Biological process of reproduction involving the combination of genetic material from two parents.

slaked lime Calcium hydroxide ($Ca(OH)_2$), made by adding water to quicklime.

solar electric cell A device that converts light directly into electricity.

species A class of things having some characteristics in common and are able to breed together.

spectrum A series of waves, arranged in order according to their wavelengths and frequencies.

sperm The male sex cell (gamete).

statins Drugs which act to reduce levels of cholesterol in the blood.

steady state theory A theory of the structure of the Universe that states that matter is continually being replaced as it spreads out.

step-down transformer A device that changes a high voltage into a lower one.

step-up transformer A device that changes a low voltage into a higher one.

symptoms Effects of a disease on the body, such as high temperature and runny nose.

synapse A junction of two nerve cells.

tectonic plates Massive sections of the Earth's crust that gradually move around the Earth's surface, transporting the continents.

temperature difference The difference in temperature between one object and another.

thermal decomposition Breaking down a chemical compound by heating.

thermal energy A form of energy; heat. The hotter an object, the more thermal energy it has.

tissue culture A cloning technique which grows groups of cells into new plants.

toxins Poison produced by microbes.

transfer To move energy from place to place.

transform To change energy from one form to another.

transition metals Metals such as iron and copper, found in the central block of the periodic table.

transmitted When waves are able to pass through a material they are transmitted.

tsunami A large wave generated by an undersea earthquake.

turbine A device that is designed to turn in order to spin a generator.

ultra violet Part of the electromagnetic spectrum of waves that have wavelengths that are just shorter than those of visible light.

unsaturated A carbon-chain molecule that has at least one double bond between its carbon atoms.

useful energy The energy output from a device that is in the form we want.

vaccination Injecting or swallowing vaccines to develop immunity (also called immunisation).

vaccine Preparation made from dead or inactive pathogens, which can be injected or swallowed so that white blood cells make antibodies to destroy live pathogens of the same type.

variable stars Stars that vary in brightness over a short period of time, either because of changes in the physical properties of the star or because of external occurrences like eclipses.

viruses Types of microbes that cause disease; examples of such diseases are measles and the common cold.

visible light A very narrow band in the middle of the electromagnetic spectrum that enables us to see.

wasted energy The energy output from a device that is in a form we do not want.

water table The level below which the ground is saturated with water.

wavelength The length of a single wave, measured from one wave crest to the next.

withdrawal symptoms Symptoms in a person with drug dependence that occur when they stop taking the drug or reduce the dosage.

X-rays Part of the electromagnetic spectrum of waves that have very short wavelengths, similar to the diameter of atoms.

Index

mountains
  building 146, 147
  under the sea 145
mouth-watering reflex 7
MRSA (methicillin-resistant
  Staphylococcus aureus) 36
muscles 2, 7

Naples, Vesuvius 150
National Grid 180
natural climate change 157
natural resources conservation 74
natural selection 62
neon 153
nerves 6
nervous system 2, 6–7
  alcohol 23
neurones 6, 7
neutrons 216
new drugs 26–7
new species 62–3
Newton, Sir Isaac 224
NHS, drug treatment 22
nickel 99
nicotine 22, 25
nicotine replacement therapy
  (NRT) 24
nitrogen oxide 70
noble gases 152
North Sea oil 107
NRT *see* nicotine replacement
  therapy
nuclear fission 185
nucleus (atoms) 84

obesity 14
oestrogen 8
oil 106–21
  edible 136–7
  electricity 179
  energy 136
  health 137
  olive 134
  plants 134–43
  uses 122–33

oilseed crops 134–5
oldest mother 10
olive oil 134
omega oils 137
ores 94
organisms, evolving 60
origin of the Universe 222
overweight *see* obesity
oxidation 95

painkillers 32, 33
paint 140–1
pandemic flu 31
pathogens 30, 31
payment, electricity 183
penguins 47
penicillin 32
The Perfect Storm (film) 198
periodic table 85
pesticides 69
pet cloning 55
photocells 206
photographic film 206
photovoltaic cells *see* solar electric
  cells
the pill 9
placebos 27
plants
  cuttings 54
  defence mechanisms 49
  oil 134–43
plastics
  future applications 131
  packaging 132
  plastic age 132–3
  products 122–3
  recycling 132
  waste disposal 133
plate tectonics 145
plutonium, decay 214
polar bears 47
politics, oil use 107
pollution, air 70–1
poly(ethene) *see* polythene
polymerisation 128

polymers 128, 129
poly(propene) *see* polypropylene
polypropylene 129
polytetrafluoroethene *see* PTFE
polythene 128
polyvinyl alcohol *see* PVA
Pompeii 150
population growth 68
power
  electricity 181
  stations 180, 190
power lines 210–11
predicting earthquakes 150–1
pregnancy 8–9
preservatives 139
prevention of disease 32–3
price, steel 97
processed food 138–9
protection against disease 34–5
protons 216
PTFE (polytetrafluoroethene) 131
pupils 7
PVA (polyvinyl alcohol) 130

quadrat 50
quarries 83
quicklime 87, 88

rabbits 49
radiation 166–7
  cosmic 212
  hazards 220–1
  health 208–9
  rocks 212
  sources 212
radio tuning 198
radio waves 204
radioactive dating 219
radioactive materials, electricity
  generation 185
radioactive waste 214, 221
radioactivity 212–21
randomised control trial 27
rape (oilseed crop) 134
raw materials 68